COMPUTER
APPLICATIONS
IN
HYDRAULIC
ENGINEERING

*Connecting Theory
to Practice*

Fifth Edition

HAESTAD
PRESS

Computer Applications in Hydraulic Engineering

Fifth Edition

This book is published by Haestad Methods, Inc. and is intended for academic purposes and educational needs.

Haestad Methods, Inc. Trademarks

The following are registered trademarks of Haestad Methods, Inc:
CADMAGIC, CIVILQUIZ, CULVERTMASTER, CYBERNET, FLOWMASTER, GRAPHICAL HEC-1, HAESTAD PRESS, JUMPSTART, PONDPACK, SEWERCAD, STORMCAD, WATERCAD, and WWW.HAESTADMETHODS.COM & Oval Design www.haestadmethods.com (logo).

The following are trademarks of Haestad Methods, Inc:

APEX, CD 2000, CIVILGEMS, CIVILNEXUS, COGOGEMS, DARWIN, E-DEMO, ENGINEERING WITHOUT BOUNDARIES, FIRECAD, FLEXTABLES, FLEXUNITS, GEM, GEMS, GES, HAESTAD METHODS, HAESTAD METHODS, INC., HEC-PACK, HECPACK FOR WINDOWS, HECGEMS, HMI, KNOWLEDGEBASE, MERGEFAX, METHOD AND SYSTEM FOR AUTOMATIC WATER DISTRIBUTION MODEL CALIBRATION, MUNICIPALGEMS, POND-2, PONDCAD, PONDGEMS, PONDGIS, PONDSAFE, PONDSAGE, PUMPGEMS, PUMPMASTER, PUMPNEXUS, RIVERCAD, ROADGEMS, SEWERATLAS, SEWERCAD, SEWERGEMS, SEWERGIS, SEWERNET, SEWEROBJECTS, SEWERSAFE, SEWERSAGE SEWERTALK, SITEGEMS, SKELEBRATION, SKELEBRATOR, SPRINKLERCAD, STORMATLAS, STORMGEMS, STORMGIS, STORMNET, STORMOBJECTS, STORMSAFE, STORMSAGE, STORMTALK, STREAMCAD, STREAMGEMS, SURVEYGEMS, TRANSGEMS, UTILITY GEMS, VIEW GEMS, WATER ATLAS, WATER GEMS, WATERGIS, WATER NET, WATER OBJECTS, WATER SAFE, WATERS AGE and WATER TALK.

The following are service marks of Haestad Methods, Inc:

CLIENTCARE, CORPORATECARE, HAESTAD METHODS, HAESTAD METHODS CLIENTCARE, HAESTAD METHODS MASTER MODELER AUTHORIZED WATER PROVIDER, HAESTAD SEVERITY INDEX, HMI CLIENTCARE, WSS, and WSSI.

The following are certification marks of Haestad Methods, Inc:

HAESTAD METHODS A+ MODELER AUTHORIZED WATER PROVIDER, HAESTAD METHODS CERTIFIED AUTHORIZED WATER PROVIDER, HAESTAD METHODS EXPERT MODELER AUTHORIZED WATER PROVIDER, and HAESTAD METHODS MASTER MODELER AUTHORIZED WATER PROVIDER,

Haestad Methods is a registered trade name of Haestad Methods, Inc.

All other brands, trademarks, company or product names belong to their respective holders.

Library of Congress Control Number: 2002108860

ISBN Number: 0-9714141-4-9

Contributing Authors

Haestad Methods Engineering Staff is an extremely diverse group of professionals from six continents with experience ranging from software development and engineering consulting, to public works and academia. This broad cross-section of expertise contributes to the development of the most comprehensive software and educational materials in the civil engineering industry. This book was truly a team effort and many at Haestad Methods contributed.

Thomas M. Walski, Ph.D., P.E. is Vice President of Engineering for Haestad Methods, and is registered as a professional engineer in Pennsylvania and Mississippi. He received his Master's Degree and Ph.D. in Environmental and Water Resources Engineering from Vanderbilt University. He has written a number of authoritative books and over 40 peer reviewed journal papers on the subject of water distribution modeling. Dr. Walski spent five years as an Associate Professor in the Environmental Engineering Program at Wilkes University, and has recently been named a Diplomate Environmental Engineer by the American Academy of Environmental Engineers.

Thomas E. Barnard, Ph.D., P.E. is a senior engineer with Haestad Methods. He has more than 20 years of experience in environmental engineering working as a consultant, researcher, educator, and author. He holds a B.S. in Civil Engineering from the University of Vermont, an M.S. in environmental engineering from Utah State University, and a Ph.D. in environmental engineering from Cornell University. His expertise includes water and wastewater treatment, hazardous waste management, surface water hydrology and water quality monitoring systems. Dr. Barnard's experience includes hydrologic and water quality modeling of a delta lake in Egypt. He is registered professional engineer in Pennsylvania.

S. Rocky Durrans, Ph.D., P.E. is currently an Associate Professor of Civil and Environmental Engineering at the University of Alabama, and is responsible for the hydrologic and hydraulic engineering programs. Prior to his academic career, Dr. Durrans spent many years in the consulting arena where he gained extensive experience in design of stormwater and major urban drainage systems. He is regarded as an authority on flood and rainfall analyses, and has many publications to his credit.

Michael E. Meadows, Ph.D., P.E. is an Associate Professor in the Department of Civil and Environmental Engineering at the University of South Carolina where he instructs undergraduate and graduate courses on hydraulics and hydrology. He has coauthored texts on stormwater modeling and has published numerous papers on improved methods for estimating stormwater discharge and evaluating drainage system performance. Dr. Meadows has also served as special consultant to SC DOT, USACE, USGS, EPA, and other state and municipal agencies in developing, evaluating, and applying water resource modeling methodologies.

Table of Contents

APPENDIX C COST MANAGEMENT   311

APPENDIX D GRAVITY FLOW DIVERSIONS   341

Revision History

During the development of each edition of *CAiHE,* we encourage feedback from the hundreds of universities that have adopted this textbook and accompanying software. We are interested in learning more about what professors and students want added to this publication and the way it is being utilized within civil engineering curricula.

In the **Second Edition,** we added tutorial example problems with step-by-step instructions for solving the problems using the included computer software. More problems to be solved by students using the software were added. In addition, updates were incorporated into the software on the CD-ROM.

In the **Third Edition,** we added two new chapters: one chapter on drainage inlet design, and the other on sanitary sewer design. These chapters included tutorials and problems. Also, a brief discussion of weirs and orifices as an application of the energy equation was added to Chapter 1. More problems were added to the existing chapters. The CD-ROM enclosed with this text contained new versions of FlowMaster and StormCAD, as well as a new product, SewerCAD. In addition, updates were incorporated into other software on the CD-ROM.

In the **Fourth Edition,** we added discussions on the use of hydrographs and hydrologic routing to the sanitary sewer modeling chapter (Chapter 6). An extended-period simulation problem was added to this chapter as well.

In this **Fifth Edition,** we have added a chapter on basic hydrology and a chapter on detention pond design, accompanied by the latest academic version of PondPack. Tutorials throughout the text have been updated and expanded per the latest software versions, and current updates have been incorporated into the software on the CD-ROM. In response to requests from professors, the capacity of the software on the CD-ROM has been increased so that students may work with more complicated problems.

The following table lists the software that accompanies each chapter.

Chapter	Accompanying Software
Chapter 1	FlowMaster
Chapter 2	*not required*
Chapter 3	StormCAD
Chapter 4	CulvertMaster
Chapter 5	PondPack
Chapter 6	WaterCAD
Chapter 7	SewerCAD

Contacting Haestad Methods

We welcome feedback regarding our products and services; we feel this is the best way for us to continue providing software, training, publications, and support that are tailored to the needs of professionals in the field of hydraulics and hydrology today.

Included with this book is a CD-ROM containing academic versions of our award-winning software, WaterCAD, SewerCAD, StormCAD, PondPack, CulvertMaster, and FlowMaster. They have been included to assist you with working the problems contained in this book, and to introduce you to the latest developments in computer-aided hydraulic and hydrologic modeling.

We hope that once you try the companion software packaged with *CAiHE,* you'll discover many ways in which it can enhance your work outside of this book. You can get more product and upgrade information on any of our software by calling our Sales department at +1-203-755-1666 or by visiting the Haestad Methods Web Site:

www.haestad.com/software

Haestad Methods also works to bring the global civil engineering community together with our Online Forums. Get in touch with fellow professionals worldwide and discuss the latest tips and tricks in hydraulic and hydrologic modeling. Post your engineering questions and share your unique modeling experiences with an audience of thousands of professionals. Participants from around the world include many industry-recognized experts and users like you. Get connected today by visiting:

www.haestad.com/forums

If you have any comments regarding this publication and/or any of Haestad Methods' products and services, please contact us at:

Haestad Methods
37 Brookside Road
Waterbury, CT 06708-1499 USA

Voice: +1-203-755-1666
Fax: +1-203-597-1488
Email: info@haestad.com
Internet: www.haestad.com

Foreword

Since 1979, Haestad Methods, Inc. has been developing hydrology and hydraulics software for civil engineers and providing textbooks, training, and technical support to tens of thousands of professional civil engineers, modelers, and universities.

Along the way, we have learned a lot about our clients and their professional and educational backgrounds. Now in its tenth year, our continuing education program offers courses for professionals who need to quickly get up-to-speed with various numerical methods and practices.

Why is this important?

Our experience has shown us a great deal about the areas where engineers are being trained, and it has also revealed a significant gap in this training—the link between hydraulic theory and practical computer applications.

Hundreds of textbooks exist that offer enormous detail in the areas of engineering history, equation derivations, and hand calculation methods. There are also hundreds of published theses and articles that deal with computer applications—unfortunately, most of these are highly research-oriented, and are usually tied to a specific case study or an unusual set of circumstances. Both of these publication types are very important to the civil engineering industry, but in the majority of cases, they fail to address the issues most commonly encountered by professionals in day-to-day practice.

This publication is intended as an introduction to the more common applications of water resources engineering software, and it demonstrates the types of situations that an engineer will most likely come across on a daily basis in the real world. It shows the true benefits of computer software: increased efficiency, better flexibility, and—most important—an increased ability to try different and better designs.

It is our hope that engineers, technicians, and students will find this book to be challenging, but also easy to understand and very practical. Combined with standard hydraulic references, we believe that this text provides many of the tools needed to successfully proceed with a career in the fields of hydrology and hydraulics.

Basic Hydraulic Principles

1.1 General Flow Characteristics

In hydraulics, as with any technical topic, a full understanding cannot come without first becoming familiar with basic terminology and governing principles. The basic concepts discussed in the following pages lay the foundation for the more complex analyses presented in later chapters.

Flow Conveyance

Water travels downhill from points of higher energy to points of lower energy (unless forced to do otherwise) until it reaches a point of equilibrium, such as an ocean. This tendency is facilitated by the presence of natural conveyance channels such as brooks, streams, and rivers. The water's journey may also be aided by man-made structures such as drainage swales, pipes, culverts, and canals. Hydraulic concepts can be applied equally to both man-made structures and natural features.

Area, Wetted Perimeter, and Hydraulic Radius

The term *area* refers to the cross-sectional area of flow within a channel. When a channel has a consistent cross-sectional shape, slope, and roughness, it is called a *prismatic* channel.

If the flow in a conveyance section is open to the atmosphere, such as in a culvert flowing partially full or in a river, it is said to be *open-channel flow* or *free-surface flow*. If a channel is flowing completely full, as with a water distribution pipe, it is said to be operating under *full-flow* conditions. *Pressure flow* is a special type of full flow in which forces on the fluid cause it to push against the top of the channel as well as the bottom and sides. These forces may result from, for example, the weight of a column of water in a backed-up sewer manhole or elevated storage tank.

A section's *wetted perimeter* is defined as the portion of the channel in contact with the flowing fluid. This definition is illustrated in Figure 1-1.

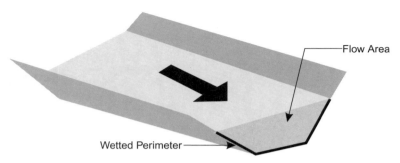

Figure 1-1: Flow Area and Wetted Perimeter

The **hydraulic radius** of a section is not a directly measurable characteristic, but it is used frequently during calculations. It is defined as the area divided by the wetted perimeter, and therefore has units of length.

The hydraulic radius can often be related directly to the geometric properties of the channel. For example, the hydraulic radius of a full circular pipe (such as a pressure pipe) can be directly computed as:

$$R = \frac{A}{P_w}$$

or

$$R_{circular} = \frac{\pi \cdot D^2/4}{\pi \cdot D} = \frac{D}{4}$$

where R = hydraulic radius (m, ft)
            A = cross-sectional area (m^2, ft^2)
           P_w = wetted perimeter (m, ft)
            D = pipe diameter (m, ft)

Velocity

As shown in Figure 1-2, the **velocity** of a section is not constant throughout the cross-sectional area. Instead, it varies with location. The velocity is zero where the fluid is in contact with the conduit wall.

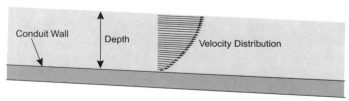

Figure 1-2: Velocity Distribution

The variation of flow velocity within a cross-section complicates the hydraulic analysis, so the engineer usually simplifies the situation by looking at the average (mean) velocity of the section for analysis purposes. This average velocity is defined as the total flow rate divided by the cross-sectional area, and is in units of length per time.

$$V = Q / A$$

where V =   average velocity (m/s, ft/s)
        Q =   flow rate (m³/s, ft³/s)
        A =   area (m², ft²)

Steady Flow

Speaking in terms of flow, the word *steady* indicates that a constant flow rate is assumed throughout an analysis. In other words, the flow velocity does not change with respect to time at a given location. For most hydraulic calculations, this assumption is reasonable. A minimal increase in model accuracy does not warrant the time and effort that would be required to perform an analysis with changing (*unsteady*) flows over time.

When analyzing tributary and river networks, storm sewers, and other collection systems in which it is desirable to vary the flow rate at different locations throughout the system, the network can often be broken into segments that can be analyzed separately under steady flow conditions.

Laminar Flow, Turbulent Flow, and Reynolds Number

Laminar flow is characterized by smooth, predictable *streamlines* (the paths of single fluid particles). An example of this type of flow is maple syrup being poured. In *turbulent* flow, the streamlines are erratic and unpredictable. Turbulent flow is characterized by the formation of eddies within the flow, resulting in continuous mixing throughout the section (see Figure 1-3).

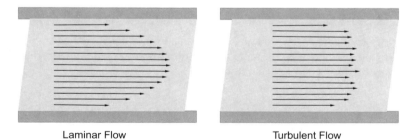

Laminar Flow   Turbulent Flow

Figure 1-3: Instantaneous Velocity Distributions for Laminar and Turbulent Flow

Eddies result in varying velocity directions as well as magnitudes (varying directions not depicted in Figure 1-3 for simplicity). At times, the eddies contribute to the velocity of a given particle in the direction of flow, and at other times detract from it. The result is that velocity distributions captured at different times will be quite different from one another, and will be far more chaotic than the velocity distribution of a laminar flow section.

By strict interpretation, the changing velocities in turbulent flow would cause it to be classified as unsteady flow. Over time, however, the average velocity at any given point within the section is essentially constant, so the flow is assumed to be steady.

The velocity at any given point within the turbulent section will be closer to the mean velocity of the entire section than with laminar flow conditions. Turbulent flow velocities are closer to the mean velocity because of the continuous mixing of flow, particularly the mixing of low-velocity flow near the channel walls with the higher-velocity flow toward the center.

To classify flow as either turbulent or laminar, an index called the **Reynolds number** is used. It is computed as follows:

$$Re = \frac{4VR}{v}$$

where Re = Reynolds number (unitless)
           V = average velocity (m/s, ft/s)
           R = hydraulic radius (m, ft)
           v = kinematic viscosity (m²/s, ft²/s)

If the Reynolds number is below 2,000, the flow is generally laminar. For flow in closed conduits, if the Reynolds number is above 4,000, the flow is generally turbulent. Between 2,000 and 4,000, the flow may be either laminar or turbulent, depending on how insulated the flow is from outside disturbances. In open channels, laminar flow occurs when the Reynolds number is less than 500 and turbulent flow occurs when it is above 2,000. Between 500 and 2,000, the flow is transitional.

Example 1-1: Flow Characteristics

A rectangular concrete channel is 3 m wide and 2 m high. The water in the channel is 1.5 m deep and is flowing at a rate of 30 m³/s. Determine the flow area, wetted perimeter, and hydraulic radius. Is the flow laminar or turbulent?

Solution

From the section's shape (rectangular), we can easily calculate the area as the rectangle's width multiplied by its depth. Note that the depth used should be the actual depth of flow, not the total height of the cross-section. The wetted perimeter can also be found easily through simple geometry.

$$A = 3.0 \text{ m} \times 1.5 \text{ m} = 4.5 \text{ m}^2$$

$$P_w = 3.0 \text{ m} + 2 \times 1.5 \text{ m} = 6.0 \text{ m}$$

$$R = A / P_w = 4.5 \text{ m}^2 / 6.0 \text{ m} = 0.75 \text{ m}$$

In order to determine whether the flow is likely to be laminar or turbulent, we must determine the Reynolds number. To do this, first find the velocity of the section and a value for the kinematic viscosity.

$$V = Q / A = 30 \text{ m}^3/\text{s} / 4.5 \text{ m}^2 = 6.67 \text{ m/s}$$

From fluids reference tables, we find that the kinematic viscosity for water at 20°C is 1.00×10^{-6} m^2/s. Substituting these values into the formula to compute the Reynolds number results in

$$Re = (4 \times 6.67 \text{ m/s} \times 0.75 \text{ m}) / (1.00 \times 10^{-6}) = 2 \times 10^7$$

This value is well above the Reynolds number minimum of 4,000 for turbulent flow.

1.2 Energy

The Energy Principle

The first law of thermodynamics states that for any given system, the change in energy (ΔE) is equal to the difference between the heat transferred to the system (Q) and the work done by the system on its surroundings (W) during a given time interval.

The energy referred to in this principle represents the total energy of the system, which is the sum of the potential energy, kinetic energy, and internal (molecular) forms of energy such as electrical and chemical energy. Although internal energy may be significant for thermodynamic analyses, it is commonly neglected in hydraulic analyses because of its relatively small magnitude.

In hydraulic applications, energy values are often converted into units of energy per unit weight, resulting in units of length. Using these length equivalents gives engineers a better "feel" for the resulting behavior of the system. When using these length equivalents, the engineer is expressing the energy of the system in terms of "head." The energy at any point within a hydraulic system is often expressed in three parts, as shown in Figure 1-4:

- Pressure head p/γ
- Elevation head z
- Velocity head $V^2/2g$

where p = pressure (N/m^2, lbs/ft^2)
           γ = specific weight (N/m^3, lbs/ft^3)
           z = elevation (m, ft)
           V = velocity (m/s, ft/s)

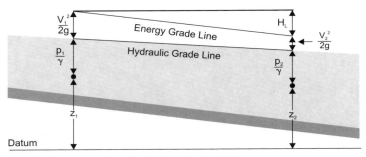

Longitudinal Section (Profile)

Figure 1-4: The Energy Principle

Note that a point on the water surface of an open channel will have a pressure head of zero, but will have a positive elevation head higher than that of a point selected at the bottom of the channel for the same station.

The Energy Equation

In addition to pressure head, elevation head, and velocity head, energy may be added to a system by a pump (for example), and removed from the system by friction or other disturbances. These changes in energy are referred to as ***head gains*** and ***head losses,*** respectively. Because energy is conserved, the energy across any two points in the system must balance. This concept is demonstrated by the energy equation:

$$\frac{p_1}{\gamma} + z_1 + \frac{V_1^2}{2g} + H_G = \frac{p_2}{\gamma} + z_2 + \frac{V_2^2}{2g} + H_L$$

where p = pressure (N/m^2, lb/ft^2)
  γ = specific weight of the fluid (N/m^3, lb/ft^3)
  z = elevation above a datum (m, ft)
  V = fluid velocity (m/s, ft/s)
  g = gravitational acceleration (m/s^2, ft/s^2)
  H_G = head gain, such as from a pump (m, ft)
  H_L = combined head loss (m, ft)

Hydraulic Grade

The ***hydraulic grade*** is the sum of the pressure head (p/γ) and elevation head (z). For open channel flow (in which the pressure head is zero), the hydraulic grade elevation is the same as the water surface elevation. For a pressure pipe, the hydraulic grade represents the height to which a water column would rise in a piezometer (a tube open to the atmosphere rising from the pipe). When the hydraulic grade is plotted as a profile along the length of the conveyance section, it is referred to as the ***hydraulic grade line,*** or HGL.

Energy Grade

The *energy grade* is the sum of the hydraulic grade and the velocity head ($V^2/2g$). This grade is the height to which a column of water would rise in a Pitot tube (an apparatus similar to a piezometer, but also accounting for fluid velocity). When plotted in profile, this parameter is often referred to as the *energy grade line,* or EGL. For a lake or reservoir in which the velocity is essentially zero, the EGL is equal to the HGL.

Energy Losses and Gains

Energy (or head) losses (H_L) in a system are due to a combination of several factors. The primary cause of energy loss is usually the internal friction between fluid particles traveling at different velocities. Secondary causes of energy loss are localized areas of increased turbulence and disruption of the streamlines, such as disruptions from valves and other fittings in a pressure pipe, or disruptions from a changing section shape in a river.

The rate at which energy is lost along a given length of channel is called the *friction slope,* and is usually presented as a unitless value or in units of length per length (ft/ft, m/m, etc.).

Energy is generally added to a system with a device such as a pump. Pumps are discussed in more detail in Chapter 6.

Example 1-2: Energy Principles

A 1,200-mm diameter transmission pipe carries 126 l/s from an elevated storage tank with a water surface elevation of 540 m. Two kilometers from the tank, at an elevation of 434 m, a pressure meter reads 586 kPa. If there are no pumps between the tank and the meter location, what is the rate of head loss in the pipe? (Note: 1 kPa = 1,000 N/m^2.)

Solution

Begin by simplifying the energy equation. Assume that the velocity within the tank is negligible, and that the pressure head at the tank can be discounted because it is open to the atmosphere. Rewriting the energy equation and entering the known values, we can solve for head loss. The velocity can be calculated using the flow rate and pipe diameter.

$$Q = 126 \text{ l/s} \times (1 \text{ l/s} / 10^3 \text{ m}^3/\text{sec}) = 0.126 \text{ m}^3/\text{s}$$

$$A = \pi \times (0.6 \text{ m})^2 = 1.13 \text{ m}^2$$

$$V = Q/A = 0.126 \text{ m}^3/\text{s} / 1.13 \text{ m}^2 = 0.11 \text{ m/s}$$

$$V^2/2g = (0.11 \text{ m/s})^2 / (2 \times 9.81 \text{ m/s}^2) = 0.0006 \text{ m (negligible)}$$

Neglecting the velocity simplifies the energy equation even further, and we can now solve for head loss as

$$H_L = 540 \text{ m} - 434 \text{ m} - (586,000 \text{ N/m}^2) / 9810 \text{ N/m}^3 = 46.27 \text{ m}$$

The rate of head loss (or friction slope) can now be computed as

Friction slope = 46.27 m / (2 × 1000 m) = 0.023 m/m, or 23 m/km

1.3 Orifices and Weirs

The energy equation serves as the foundation for calculating the flow through and over hydraulic structures based on the size of the opening associated with the structure and the difference in energy on either side of it. The flow exiting the structure can be calculated by solving the energy equation for velocity, V_2, and multiplying the resulting formula by the flow area and a coefficient to account for different hydraulic and physical variables. These variables include: head loss, the shape and nature of the opening, the contraction of the flow after it leaves the structure, and countless indefinable variables that are difficult to measure but produce quantifiable effects.

Two common devices for which equations are derived in this manner are weirs and orifices. They are important not only because of their widespread usage in the industry, but also because the equations that describe them serve as the foundation for mathematical descriptions of more complicated hydraulic devices such as drainage inlets and culverts.

Orifices

Orifices are regularly shaped, submerged openings through which flow is propelled by the difference in energy between the upstream and downstream sides of the opening. The stream of flow expelled from the orifice is called the *jet*. When the jet exits the orifice, adverse velocity components cause it to contract to a point after which the flow area remains relatively constant and the flow lines become parallel (see Figure 1-5). This point is called the *vena contracta*.

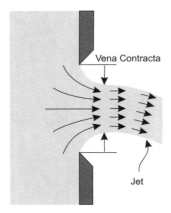

Figure 1-5: Cross-Sectional View of Typical Orifice Flow

Orifices and the orifice equations have the following applications:

- Regulating the flow out of detention ponds
- Regulating the flow through channels in the form of radial and sluice gates
- Approximating the interception capacity of submerged drainage inlets in sag (see Chapter 3)
- Approximating the flow allowed through a submerged culvert operating under inlet control (see Chapter 4)
- Measuring flow

Example 1-3: The Orifice Equation

For the structure in Figure 1-6, derive the orifice equation for an orifice of area A.

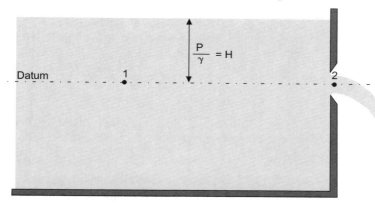

Figure 1-6: Orifice Example

Solution

First, start with the energy equation from Section 1.2:

$$\frac{p_1}{\gamma} + z_1 + \frac{V_1^2}{2g} + H_G = \frac{p_2}{\gamma} + z_2 + \frac{V_2^2}{2g} + H_L$$

List known variables and assumptions:

- The datum is at the centerline/centroid of the orifice
- $p_1/\gamma = H$
- Point 2 occurs at the vena contracta
- Elevation heads, z_1 and z_2, are equivalent
- The velocity in the tank at point 1 is negligible

- The jet is open to the air, so the pressure at point 2 is 0
- There is no head gain

Taking these known variables and assumptions into account and solving for V_2, the energy equation becomes:

$$V_2 = \sqrt{2g(H - H_L)}$$

To find the flow exiting the structure at point 2, multiply both sides of the equation by the orifice area, A.

$$AV_2 = Q = A\sqrt{2g(H - H_L)}$$

where Q = discharge (m³/s, ft³/s)

The point of discharge is the vena contracta, where the flow area is usually contracted from the original orifice area. Also, computations can be simplified by eliminating the head loss term, H_L. Both of these variables are accounted for by applying an orifice coefficient, C, to the right side of the equation. The final form of the orifice equation becomes:

$$Q = CA\sqrt{2gH}$$

where C = orifice coefficient

When dealing with storm sewer design, the orifice coefficient is generally about 0.6. For more in-depth information on orifice coefficients for different situations, see Brater and King's *Handbook of Hydraulics* (1996).

Weirs

Weirs are notches or gaps over which fluid flows. The lowest point of structure surface or edge over which water flows is called the ***crest***, whereas the stream of water that exits over the weir is called the ***nappe***. Depending on the weir design, flow may contract as it exits over the top of the weir, and, as with orifices, the point of maximum contraction is called the vena contracta.

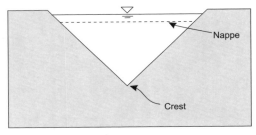

Figure 1-7: Front View of Common Weir

This contraction can be counteracted or suppressed by designing the weir such that its shape conforms to the shape of the channel. This type of weir is called a **suppressed weir**. With a **contracted weir**, the crest and nappe vary from the channel to such a degree that a significant contraction of flow area does occur.

In addition to suppressed and contracted weir types, weirs are also distinguished as either **sharp-crested** or **broad-crested**. A sharp-crested weir has a sharp upstream edge formed so that the nappe flows clear of the crest. Broad-crested weirs have crests that extend horizontally in the direction of flow far enough to support the nappe and fully develop hydrostatic pressures for at least a short distance.

Weirs can also be distinguished by their shapes. The most common shapes are shown in Figure 1-8. The effects of weir shape and other factors previously mentioned are accounted for with modifications to the weir equation (derived in Example 1-4), such as adjustments the weir coefficient. Table 1-1 contains information on coefficients for V-Notch weirs.

	Weir Type	Figure	Equation	Coefficients
Sharp Crested	Rectangular	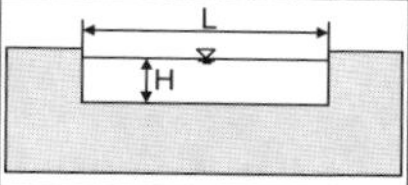	Contracted $Q = C(L- 0.1iH) H^{3/2}$ Suppressed $Q = CLH^{3/2}$ i = Number of iterations	Metric C = 1.84 English C = 3.367
Sharp Crested	V-Notch	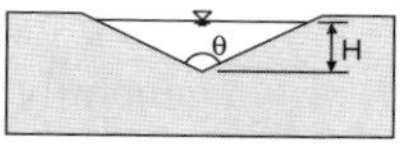	$Q = C\left(\frac{8}{15}\right)\sqrt{2g}\tan\theta\left(\frac{H}{2}\right)^{3/2}$	C varies between 0.611 and 0.570 depending on H and Q*
Sharp Crested	Cipolletti	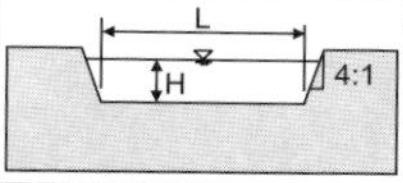	Metric $Q = CLH^{3/2}$ English $Q = CLH^{3/2}$	Metric C = 1.86 English C = 3.367
Non-Sharp-Crested	Broad (Side View)	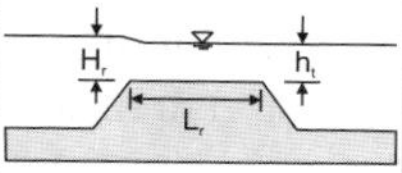	$Q = C_d L H_r^{3/2}$	C_d is a function of H_r, h, and L_r ranging between 1.25 and 3.1*

*Refer to FlowMaster help documentation for more information.

Figure 1-8: Standard Weirs

Table 1-1: V-Notch Weir Coefficients of Discharge — English Units

Head (feet)	Weir Angle, θ (degrees)					
	22.5	30	45	60	90	120
0.5	0.611	0.605	0.569	0.590	0.584	0.581
1.0	0.593	0.590	0.583	0.580	0.576	0.575
1.5	0.586	0.583	0.578	0.575	0.572	0.572
2.0	0.583	0.580	0.576	0.573	0.571	0.571
2.5	0.580	0.578	0.574	0.572	0.570	0.570
3.0	0.579	0.577	0.574	0.571	0.570	0.570

Derived from: Van Havern, Bruce P. Water Resources Measurements, American Water Works Association, 1986

Weirs have the following applications:

- Serving as emergency spillways for regulating high-return event flows overtopping dams and detention ponds
- Regulating the flow in channels
- Measuring flow
- Approximating the flow over roadways acting as broad-crested weirs when flow exceeds a culvert's capacity (see Chapter 4)
- Approximating the interception capacity of unsubmerged drainage inlets in swales (see Chapter 3)
- Approximating the flow allowed through an unsubmerged culvert operating under inlet control (see Chapter 4)

Example 1-4: The Weir Equation

Derive the weir equation for the rectangular weir with a crest of length L and head H, which discharges from a free outfall as shown in Figure 1-9.

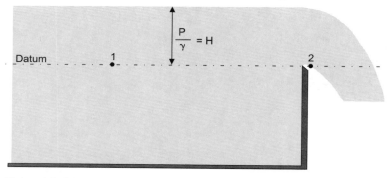

Figure 1-9: Weir Example

Solution

Begin with the energy equation:

$$\frac{p_1}{\gamma} + z_1 + \frac{V_1^2}{2g} + H_G = \frac{p_2}{\gamma} + z_2 + \frac{V_2^2}{2g} + H_L$$

List the known variables and assumptions:

- The datum is at the crest of the weir
- $P_1/\gamma = H$
- Point 2 occurs at the vena contracta
- The elevation heads, z_1 and z_2, are equivalent
- Assume the velocity in the tank is negligible
- The exiting stream pressure at point 2 is 0
- There is no head gain

After applying the known variables and assumptions and solving for V_2, the energy equation becomes:

$$V_2 = \sqrt{2g(H - H_L)}$$

To find the flow, multiply both sides by the flow area, which in this case is the length of the weir, L, multiplied by the height of the head, H.

$$AV_2 = Q = LH\sqrt{2g(H - H_L)}$$

where L = length of weir (m, ft)

To account for head loss, contraction, and other variables, a weir coefficient, C, is applied. Unlike the orifice coefficient, the weir coefficient generally takes into account the constant $2g$. Finally, the weir equation becomes:

$$Q = CLH^{3/2}$$

where C = weir coefficient ($m^{1/2}/s$, $ft^{1/2}/s$)

Unlike the orifice coefficient, the weir coefficient is not unitless. Care has to be taken that the correct coefficient is applied when using a specific unit system. Typical coefficient values for different weir shapes, as well as variations in the equation, can be seen in the previously shown Figure 1-8.

1.4 Friction Losses

There are many equations that approximate the friction losses associated with the flow of a liquid through a given section. Commonly used methods include:

- Manning's equation
- Chézy's (Kutter's) equation
- Hazen-Williams equation
- Darcy-Weisbach (Colebrook-White) equation

These equations can be described by a generalized friction equation:

$$V = kCR^x S^y$$

where V = mean velocity
C = flow resistance factor
R = hydraulic radius
S = friction slope
x, y = exponents
k = factor to account for empirical constants, unit conversion, etc.

The lining material of the flow channel usually determines the flow resistance or roughness factor, C. However, the ultimate value of C may be a function of the channel shape, depth, and fluid velocity.

Manning's Equation

Manning's equation is the most commonly used open channel flow equation. The roughness component, C, is typically assumed to be constant over the full range of flows and is represented by a Manning's roughness value, n. These n-values have been experimentally determined for various materials and should not be used with fluids other than water. Manning's equation is:

$$V = \frac{k}{n} R^{2/3} S^{1/2}$$

where V = mean velocity (m/s, ft/s)
k = 1.49 for U.S. customary units, 1.00 for SI units
n = Manning's roughness value
R = hydraulic radius (m, ft)
S = friction slope (m/m, ft/ft)

Chézy's (Kutter's) Equation

The Chézy equation, in conjunction with Kutter's equation, is widely used in sanitary sewer design and analysis. The roughness component, C, is a function of the hydraulic radius, friction slope, and lining material of the channel. The Chézy equation is:

$$V = C\sqrt{RS}$$

where V = mean velocity (m/s, ft/s)
C = roughness coefficient (see following calculation)
R = hydraulic radius (m, ft)
S = friction slope (m/m, ft/ft)

The roughness coefficient, C, is related to Kutter's n through Kutter's equation. Note that the n-values used in Kutter's equation are actually the same as Manning's n coefficients.

U.S. Standard Units	**S.I. Units**
$$C = \dfrac{41.65 + \dfrac{0.00281}{S} + \dfrac{1.811}{n}}{1 + \dfrac{\left(41.65 + \dfrac{0.00281}{S}\right)n}{\sqrt{R}}}$$	$$C = \dfrac{23 + \dfrac{0.00155}{S} + \dfrac{1}{n}}{1 + \dfrac{\left(23 + \dfrac{0.00155}{S}\right)n}{\sqrt{R}}}$$

where C = roughness coefficient
       n = Manning's roughness value
       R = hydraulic radius (m, ft)
       S = friction slope (m/m, ft/ft)

Hazen-Williams Equation

The Hazen-Williams equation is most frequently used in the design and analysis of pressure pipe systems. The equation was developed experimentally, and therefore should not be used for fluids other than water (and only within temperatures normally experienced in potable water systems). The Hazen-Williams equation is:

$$V = kCR^{0.63}S^{0.54}$$

where V = mean velocity (m/s, ft/s)
       k = 1.32 for U.S. customary units, or 0.85 for SI units
       C = Hazen-Williams roughness coefficient (unitless)
       R = hydraulic radius (m, ft)
       S = friction slope (m/m, ft/ft)

Darcy-Weisbach (Colebrook-White) Equation

The Darcy-Weisbach equation is a theoretically based equation commonly used in the analysis of pressure pipe systems. It applies equally well to any flow rate and any incompressible fluid, and is general enough to be applied to open channel flow systems. In fact, the ASCE Task Force on Friction Factors in Open Channels (1963) supported the use of the Darcy-Weisbach equation for free-surface flows. This recommendation has not yet been widely accepted because the solution to the equation is difficult and not easily computed using non-computerized methods. With the increasing availability of computer solutions, the Darcy-Weisbach equation will likely gain greater acceptance because it successfully models the variability of effective channel roughness with channel material, geometry, and velocity.

The roughness component in the Darcy-Weisbach equation is a function of both the channel material and the Reynolds number, which varies with velocity and hydraulic radius.

$$V = \sqrt{\frac{8g}{f} RS}$$

where V = flow velocity (m/s, ft/s)
          g = gravitational acceleration (m/s^2, ft/s^2)
          f = Darcy-Weisbach friction factor (unitless)
          R = hydraulic radius (m, ft)
          S = friction slope (m/m, ft/ft)

The Darcy-Weisbach friction factor, f, can be found using the Colebrook-White equation for fully developed turbulent flow, as follows:

Free Surface

Full Flow (Closed Conduit)

$$\frac{1}{\sqrt{f}} = -2\log\left(\frac{k}{12R} + \frac{2.51}{Re\sqrt{f}}\right)$$

$$\frac{1}{\sqrt{f}} = -2\log\left(\frac{k}{14.8R} + \frac{2.51}{Re\sqrt{f}}\right)$$

where k = roughness height (m, ft)
          R = hydraulic radius (m, ft)
          Re = Reynolds number (unitless)

This iterative search for the correct value of f can become quite time-consuming for hand computations and computerized solutions of many pipes. Another method, developed by Swamee and Jain, solves directly for f in full-flowing circular pipes. This equation is:

$$f = \frac{1.325}{\left[\log_e\left(\frac{k}{3.7D} + \frac{5.74}{Re^{0.9}}\right)\right]^2}$$

where f = friction factor (unitless)
          k = roughness height (m, ft)
          D = pipe diameter (m, ft)
          Re = Reynolds number (unitless)

Typical Roughness Factors

Typical pipe roughness values for each of these methods are shown in Table 1-2. These values will vary depending on the manufacturer, workmanship, age, and other factors. For this reason, the following table should be used only as a guideline.

Table 1-2: Typical Roughness Coefficients

Material	Manning's Coefficient	Hazen-Williams	Darcy-Weisbach Roughness Height	
	n	C	k (mm)	k (ft)
Asbestos cement	0.011	140	0.0015	0.000005
Brass	0.011	135	0.0015	0.000005
Brick	0.015	100	0.6	0.002
Cast-iron, new	0.012	130	0.26	0.00085
Concrete:				
Steel forms	0.011	140	0.18	0.006
Wooden forms	0.015	120	0.6	0.002
Centrifugally spun	0.013	135	0.36	0.0012
Copper	0.011	135	0.0015	0.000005
Corrugated metal	0.022	–	45	0.15
Galvanized iron	0.016	120	0.15	0.0005
Glass	0.011	140	0.0015	0.000005
Lead	0.011	135	0.0015	0.000005
Plastic	0.009	150	0.0015	0.000005
Steel:				
Coal-tar enamel	0.010	148	0.0048	0.000016
New unlined	0.011	145	0.045	0.00015
Riveted	0.019	110	0.9	0.003
Wood stave	0.012	120	0.18	0.0006

1.5   Pressure Flow

For pipes flowing full, many of the friction loss calculations are greatly simplified because the flow area, wetted perimeter, and hydraulic radius are all functions of pipe radius (or diameter). Table 1-3 presents the three pipe friction loss equations that are commonly used to design pressure pipe systems.

There is much more information presented about pressure piping systems in Chapter 6, including further discussion on pumping systems, minor losses, and network analysis.

Table 1-3: Three Pipe Friction Loss Equations

Equation	Q (m³/s); D (m)	Q (cfs); D (ft)	Q (gpm); D (in.)
Darcy-Weisbach	$S_f = \dfrac{0.083\,fQ^2}{D^5}$	$S_f = \dfrac{0.025\,fQ^2}{D^5}$	$S_f = \dfrac{0.031\,fQ^2}{D^5}$
Hazen-Williams	$S_f = \dfrac{10.7}{D^{4.87}}\left(\dfrac{Q}{C}\right)^{1.852}$	$S_f = \dfrac{4.73}{D^{4.87}}\left(\dfrac{Q}{C}\right)^{1.852}$	$S_f = \dfrac{10.5}{D^{4.87}}\left(\dfrac{Q}{C}\right)^{1.852}$
Manning	$S_f = \dfrac{10.3(nQ)^2}{D^{5.33}}$	$S_f = \dfrac{4.66(nQ)^2}{D^{5.33}}$	$S_f = \dfrac{13.2(nQ)^2}{D^{5.33}}$

Example 1-5: Pressure Pipe Friction Losses

Use the FlowMaster program to compare the head loss computed by the Hazen-Williams equation to the head loss computed by the Darcy-Weisbach equation for a pressure pipe having the following characteristics: 12-in diameter cast iron pipe (new) one mile in length with a flow rate of 1,200 gallons per minute (with water at 65°F).

Solution

Although there are no elevations or pressures given, these values are not needed to determine the head loss in the pipe. Setting up FlowMaster to solve for the "Elevation at 1" allows us to use zero elevation and zero pressure assumptions and fill in the rest of the pipe characteristics.

For the Hazen-Williams equation, a C coefficient of 130 is assumed. This value results in 18.8 ft of head loss (which agrees with the computed 18.8-ft elevation at point 1). Using Darcy-Weisbach, a roughness height of 0.00085 ft is assumed. The solution indicates a head loss of 18.9 ft, which is only a 0.1-ft difference from the value predicted by Hazen-Williams.

Discussion

If the same system is analyzed with 2,000 to 3,000 gallons per minute of flow, however, the difference in head loss between the two equations becomes almost 10 feet.

Why such a big difference? For starters, the two methodologies are completely unrelated, and the estimated roughness coefficients were taken from a list of approximate values. If the Hazen-Williams equation is used with a roughness value of 125, the results are much closer. This difference should emphasize the fact that models are only as good as the data that is input into them, and the engineer needs to fully understand all of the assumptions that are being made before accepting the results.

1.6   Open-Channel Flow

Open-channel flow analysis is more complex than pressure flow analysis because the flow area, wetted perimeter, and hydraulic radius are not necessarily constant as they are in a uniform pipe section under full-flow conditions. Because of this considerable difference, additional characteristics become important when dealing with open-channel flow.

Uniform Flow

Uniform flow refers to the hydraulic condition in which the discharge and cross-sectional area (and therefore velocity) are constant throughout the length of the channel. For a pipe flowing full, the only required assumptions are that the pipe be straight and have no contractions or expansions. For an open channel, additional assumptions include:

- The depth of flow must be constant (that is, the hydraulic grade line must be parallel to the channel bed). This depth of flow is called ***normal*** depth.
- Because the velocity is constant, the velocity head does not change through the length of the section; therefore, the energy grade line is parallel to both the hydraulic grade line and the channel bed.

In channels that are prismatic, the flow conditions will typically approach uniform flow if the channel is sufficiently long. When this occurs, the net force on the fluid approaches zero because the gravitational force is equal to the opposing friction forces from the channel bottom and walls.

Example 1-6: Uniform Flow

A concrete trapezoidal channel has a bottom width of 4 m and 45-degree side slopes. If the channel is on a 1-percent slope and is flowing at a depth of 1 m throughout its length, how much flow is being carried (use Manning's equation)? How much flow would the same channel carry if it were a rectangular channel 4 m wide?

Solution

Because the channel is flowing at the same depth throughout, we can assume that normal depth has been achieved (that is, the friction slope is equal to the channel slope). We will assume a Manning's n of 0.013 for concrete.

From the trapezoidal geometry, we can easily calculate the area and wetted perimeter, and then the hydraulic radius, as follows:

$$A = (4 \text{ m} \times 1 \text{ m}) + 2 \times (0.5 \times 1 \text{ m} \times 1 \text{ m}) = 5.00 \text{ m}^2$$

$$P_w = 4 \text{ m} + 2 \times (1 \text{ m} \times 2^{0.5}) = 6.83 \text{ m}$$

$$R = A / P_w = 5.00 \text{ m}^2 / 6.83 \text{ m} = 0.73 \text{ m}$$

Manning's equation for velocity can then be solved. The discharge can be computed as

$$V = (1.00/0.013) \times 0.73^{2/3} \times 0.01^{1/2} = 6.25 \text{ m/s}$$

$$Q = V \times A = 6.25 \text{ m/s} \times 5.00 \text{ m}^2 = 31.2 \text{ m}^3/\text{s}$$

To answer the second part of the question, we simply repeat the steps for a rectangular section shape.

$$A = (4 \text{ m} \times 1\text{m}) = 4 \text{ m}^2$$

$$P_w = 4 \text{ m} + 2 \times (1\text{m}) = 6 \text{ m}$$

$$R = 4 \text{ m}^2 / 6 \text{ m} = 0.67 \text{ m}$$

$$V = (1.00/0.013) \times 0.67^{2/3} \times 0.01^{1/2} = 5.87 \text{ m/s}$$

$$Q = 5.87 \text{ m/s} \times 4 \text{ m}^2 = 23.5 \text{ m}^3/\text{s}$$

As we would expect, this discharge is less than the discharge of the trapezoidal section.

Specific Energy and Critical Flow

Of course, channels do not always flow at normal depth. If they did, it would make the engineer's task quite simple. A more in-depth look at non-uniform flow is presented in Chapter 7, but this chapter will continue by focusing on another important concept — specific energy.

For any flow section, the *specific energy* is defined as the sum of the depth of flow and the velocity head.

$$E = y + \frac{V^2}{2g}$$

where E = specific energy (m, ft)
y = depth of flow (m, ft)
V = mean velocity (m/s, ft/s)
g = gravitational acceleration (m/s^2, ft/s^2)

If we assume the special case of an infinitely short section of open channel (with essentially no friction losses and no change in elevation), we see that the general energy equation can be reduced to an equality of specific energies. In other words,

$$E_1 = y_1 + \frac{V_1^2}{2g} = y_2 + \frac{V_2^2}{2g} = E_2$$

Recall that the velocity of the section is directly related to the area of flow, and that the area of flow is a function of channel depth. This means that, for a given discharge, the specific energy at each point is solely a function of channel depth and more than one depth may exist with the same specific energy. If the channel depth is plotted against specific energy for a given flow rate, the result is similar to the graph shown in Figure 1-10.

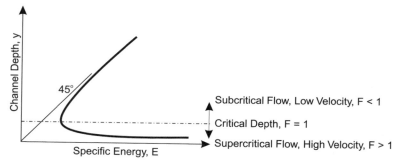

Figure 1-10: Specific Energy

As this figure shows, a depth exists for which the specific energy is at a minimum. This depth is called the *critical* depth. If the velocity is higher than critical velocity (that is, the depth is less than critical depth), the flow is considered *supercritical*. If the velocity is lower than critical velocity (the depth is greater than critical depth), the flow is *subcritical*.

The velocity at critical depth is equal to the *wave celerity*—the speed at which waves will ripple outward from a pebble tossed into the water. A unitless value called the *Froude number*, *F*, represents the ratio of actual fluid velocity to wave celerity. The Froude number is computed as follows:

$$F = \frac{V}{\sqrt{gD}}$$

where F =   Froude number (unitless)
        D =   hydraulic depth of the channel, defined as A/T
        A =   flow area (m², ft²)
        T =   top width of flow (m, ft)
        V =   fluid velocity (m/s, ft/s)
        g =   gravitational acceleration (m/s², ft/s²)

By definition, when the flow is at critical depth (that is, the velocity is equal to the wave celerity), the Froude number must be equal to 1. The equation can therefore be rewritten and re-factored to form the following equality:

$$\frac{A^3}{T} = \frac{Q^2}{g}$$

where A =   flow area (m², ft²)
        T =   top width of flow (m, ft)
        Q =   channel flow rate (m³/s, ft³/s)
        g =   gravitational acceleration (m/s², ft/s²)

This equation can now be used to determine the depth for which this equality holds true, which is critical depth. For simple geometric shapes, the solution is relatively easy to determine. However, quite a few iterations may be required to find the solution for an irregularly shaped channel such as a natural streambed. In fact, several valid critical depths may exist for irregular channels.

Example 1-7: Critical Depth

What is the critical depth for a grassy triangular channel with 2H:1V side slopes and a 0.5% slope when the flow is 3.00 m³/s? If the channel is actually flowing at a depth of 1.2 m, is the flow critical, subcritical, or supercritical?

Solution

For such a simple geometry, we can quickly create a relationship between the flow area, top width, and depth of flow:

$$T = 4y, \; A = 0.5 \times T \times y = 0.5 \times 4y \times y = 2y^2 \; m^2$$

Inserting these values into the previous equation for critical depth, we can algebraically solve for the channel depth:

$$(2y^2)^3 / 4y = Q^2 / g$$

$$8y^6 / 4y = Q^2 / g$$

$$2y^5 = Q^2 / g$$

$$y^5 = Q^2 / 2g$$

$$y = (Q^2 / 2g)^{1/5} = [\, (3.00 \; m^3/s)^2 / (2 \times 9.8 \; m/s^2) \,]^{0.2} = (0.46 \; m^5)^{0.2} = 0.86 \; m$$

The critical depth for this section is 0.86 m. The actual flow depth of 1.2 m is greater than critical depth, so the flow is subcritical.

1.7 Computer Applications

It is very important for students (and practicing engineers) to fully understand the methodologies behind hydraulic computations. Once these concepts are understood, the solution process can become repetitive and tedious—the type of procedure that is well-suited to computer analysis.

There are several advantages to using computerized solutions for common hydraulic problems:

- The amount of time to perform an analysis can be greatly reduced.
- Computer solutions can be more detailed than hand calculations. Performing a solution manually often requires many simplifying assumptions.
- The solution process may be less error-prone. Unit conversion and the rewriting of equations to solve for any variable are just two examples of mistakes frequently introduced with hand calculations. A well-tested computer program helps to avoid these algebraic and numeric errors.
- The solution is easily documented and reproducible.
- Because of the speed and accuracy of a computer model, more comparisons and design trials can be performed. The result is the exploration of more design options, which eventually leads to better, more efficient designs.

In order to prevent an "overload" of data, this chapter deals primarily with steady-state computations. After all, an introduction to hydraulic calculations is tricky enough without throwing in the added complexity of a constantly changing system.

The assumption that a system is under steady-state conditions is oftent perfectly acceptable. Minor changes that occur over time or irregularities in a channel cross-section are frequently negligible, and a more detailed analysis may not be the most efficient or effective use of time and resources.

There are circumstances when an engineer may be called upon to provide a more detailed analysis, including unsteady flow computations. For a storm sewer, the flows may rise and fall over time as a storm builds and subsides. For water distribution piping, a pressure wave may travel through the system when a valve is closed abruptly (the same "water-hammer" effect can probably be heard in your house if you close a faucet quickly).

As an engineer, it is important to understand the purpose of an analysis; otherwise, appropriate methods and tools to meet that purpose cannot be selected.

1.8   FlowMaster

FlowMaster is an easy-to-use program that helps civil engineers with the hydraulic design and analysis of pipes, gutters, inlets, ditches, open channels, weirs, and orifices. FlowMaster computes flows and pressures in conduits and channels using common head loss equations such as Darcy-Weisbach, Manning's, Kutter's, and Hazen-Williams. The program's flexibility allows the user to choose an unknown variable and automatically compute the solution after entering known parameters. FlowMaster also calculates rating tables and plots curves and cross-sections. You can view the output on the screen, copy it to the Windows clipboard, save it to a file, or print it on any standard printer. FlowMaster data can also be viewed and edited using tabular reports called FlexTables.

FlowMaster enables you to create an unlimited number of worksheets to analyze uniform pressure-pipe or open-channel sections, including irregular sections (such as natural streams or odd-shaped man-made sections). FlowMaster does not work with networked systems such as a storm sewer network or a pressure pipe network. For these types of analyses, StormCAD, WaterCAD, or SewerCAD should be used instead.

The theory and background used by FlowMaster have been reviewed in this chapter and can be accessed via the FlowMaster on-line help system. General information about installing and running Haestad Methods software can be found in Appendix A.

FlowMaster replaces solutions such as nomographs, spreadsheets, and BASIC programs. Because FlowMaster gives you immediate results, you can quickly generate output for a large number of situations. For example, you can use FlowMaster to:

- Analyze various hydraulic designs
- Evaluate different kinds of flow elements
- Generate professional-looking reports for clients and review agencies

1.9 Tutorial Example

The following solution gives step-by-step instructions on how to solve an example problem using the FlowMaster computer program (included on the CD-ROM that accompanies this textbook) developed by Haestad Methods.

Problem Statement

Using Manning's equation, design a triangular concrete channel with equal side slopes, a longitudinal slope of 5%, a peak flow capacity of 0.6 m³/s, and a maximum depth of 0.3. Also, design a concrete trapezoidal channel with equal side slopes and a base width of 0.2 that meets the same criteria. Create a cross-section of each channel and a curve of discharge versus depth for each channel. Assume the water is at 20°C.

Solution

- Upon opening FlowMaster, click **Create New Project** in the **Welcome to FlowMaster** dialog. Enter a filename and click **Save**.

- Select **Triangular Channel** from the **Create a New Worksheet** dialog and click **OK**.

- In the **Triangular Channel** dialog, select **Manning's Formula** from the **Friction Method** pull-down menu. Enter a label for the worksheet and click **OK**.

- Select **Global Options** from the **Options** menu and change the unit system to **System International**, if it has not already been done, by selecting it from the pull-down menu in the **Unit System** field. Click **OK** to exit the dialog. If you changed the unit system, you will be prompted to confirm the unit change. Click **Yes**.

- The worksheet dialog should appear. Because discharge, channel slope, and depth are given, the variable you need to solve for is the side slopes of the channel. Select **Equal Side Slopes** from the **Solve for:** menu at the top of the dialog.

- Enter the channel slope (you can change the units to percent by double left-clicking the units), depth, and discharge into the appropriate fields and select the Manning's *n* for concrete. Click **Solve**. The equal side slopes should be 1.54 H:V.

- To design the trapezoidal section, first click **Close** on the triangular section worksheet to save it. Then click **Create...** at the bottom of the **Worksheet List**.

- Select the **Trapezoidal Channel** and **OK**. Repeat the same steps as before to design the triangular channel. The equal side slopes should be 0.80 H:V. Click **Close** to exit the worksheet.

Creating Channel Cross-Sections

- Open the triangular section worksheet by highlighting it and selecting the **Open** button

- Click the **Report** button on the bottom of the triangular channel worksheet. Select **Cross Section...**

- Type a report title and click **OK.** Figure 1-11 provides a graphical representation of both the triangular and trapezoidal channel designs. Click **Print** if you want to print a copy of the cross-section. Click **Close** to exit the report. Finally, click **Close** to exit the triangular section worksheet. The drawing for the trapezoidal section cross-section is created in the same way from its worksheet.

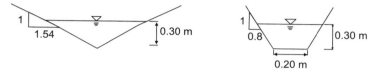

Figure 1-11: Triangular and Trapezoidal Channel Designs

Creating Discharge versus Depth Curves

- Open the trapezoidal section worksheet by highlighting it and selecting the **Open** button.
- Because discharge needs to be on the *y*-axis (the ordinate) of the graph, you need to change **Equal Side Slopes** in the **Solve For:** field to **Discharge**.
- Click **Report...** at the bottom of the worksheet. Select **Rating Curve** from the drop-down list.
- In the **Graph Setup** dialog, select **Discharge** from the pull-down menu in the field labeled **Plot.** Select **Depth** from the pull-down menu in the field labeled **vs.**
- To scale the plot properly, make the minimum depth 0 m and the maximum depth 0.3 m. Choose an increment based on how smooth you want to make the curve. An increment of 0.1 will give the plot 3 points, an increment of 0.01 will give the plot 30 points, etc. Click **OK**. Click **Print Preview** at the top of the window, and then click **Print** to print out a report featuring the rating curve you have just created. Click **Close** to exit the **Print Preview** window. Click **Close** again to exit the **Plot Window**.
- Perform the same procedure for the triangular section. Your curves should match those in Figures 1-12 and 1-13.

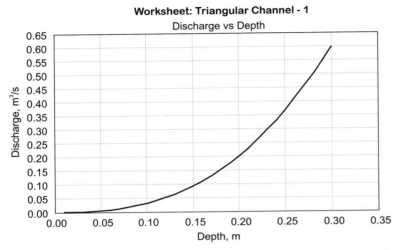

Figure 1-12: Comparison of Discharge versus Depth for the Trapezoidal Channel Design

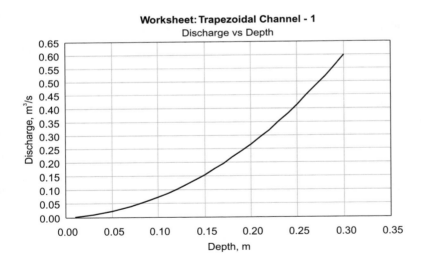

Figure 1-13: Comparison of Discharge versus Depth for the Triangular Channel Design

1.10 Problems

Solve the following problems using the FlowMaster computer program. Unless stated otherwise, assume water is at 20°C.

1. The cross-section of a rough, rectangular, concrete ($k = 0.2 \times 10^{-2}$ ft) channel measures 6 × 6 ft. The channel slope is 0.02 ft/ft. Using the Darcy-Weisbach friction method, determine the maximum allowable flow rate through the channel to maintain one foot of freeboard (freeboard is the vertical distance from the water surface to the overtopping level of the channel). For these conditions, find the following characteristics (note that FlowMaster may not directly report all of these):

   a) Flow area
   b) Wetted perimeter
   c) Hydraulic radius
   d) Velocity
   e) Froude number

2. A 450-mm circular concrete ($n = 0.013$) pipe constructed on a 0.6-percent slope carries 0.1 m³/s.

   a) Using Manning's equation and normal depth assumptions, what are the depth and velocity of flow?

   b) What would the velocity and depth be if the pipe were constructed of corrugated metal ($n = 0.024$) instead of concrete?

3. A trapezoidal channel carries 2.55 m³/s at a depth of 0.52 m. The channel has a bottom width of 5 m, a slope of 1.00 percent, and 2H:1V side slopes.

   a) What is the appropriate Manning's roughness coefficient?

   b) How deep would the water be if the channel carried 5 m³/s?

4. Use Manning's equation to analyze an existing brick-in-mortar ($n = 0.015$) triangular channel with 3H:1V side slopes and a 0.05 longitudinal slope. The channel is intended to carry 7 cfs during a storm event.

   a) If the maximum depth in the channel is 6 in, is the existing design acceptable?

   b) What would happen if the channel were replaced by a concrete ($n = 0.013$) channel with the same geometry?

5. A pipe manufacturer reports that it can achieve Manning's roughness values of 0.011 for its concrete pipes, which is lower than the 0.013 reported by its competitors. Using Kutter's equation, determine the difference in flow for a 310-mm circular pipe with a slope of 2.5% flowing at one-half of the full depth.

6. A grass drainage swale is trapezoidal, with a bottom width of 6 ft and 2H:1V side slopes. Using the friction method you feel is appropriate, answer the following questions:

   a) What is the discharge in the swale if the depth of flow is 1 ft and the channel slope is 0.005 ft/ft?

   b) What would the discharge be with a slope of 0.010 ft/ft?

7. A paved highway drainage channel has the geometry shown in the following figure. The maximum allowable flow depth is 0.75 ft (to prevent the flow from encroaching on traffic), and the Manning's n-value is 0.018 for the type of pavement used.

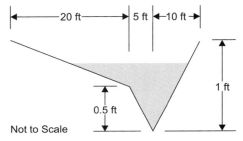

Figure for Problem 7

   a) What is the capacity of the channel given a 2% longitudinal slope?

   b) Create a rating curve to demonstrate how the capacity varies as the channel slope varies from 0.5% to 5%. Choose an increment that will generate a reasonably smooth curve.

8. Using the Hazen-Williams equation, determine the minimum diameter of a new cast iron pipe ($C = 130$) for the following conditions: the upstream end is 51.8 m higher than the downstream end, which is 2.25 km away. The upstream pressure is 500 kPa, and the desired downstream pressure and flow rate are 420 kPa and 11,000 l/min, respectively. What is the minimum diameter needed? Assume pipes are available in 50-mm increments.

9. 2,000 gallons of water per minute flow through a level, 320-yard-long, 8-in-diameter cast iron pipe ($C = 130$, $k = 2.5908e^{-4}$ m) to a large industrial site. If the pressure at the upstream end of the pipe is 64 psi, what will the pressure be at the industry? Is there a significant difference between the solutions produced by the Hazen-Williams method and the Darcy-Weisbach method?

10. Develop a performance curve for the pipe in Problem 9 that shows the available flow to the industry with residual pressures ranging from 20 psi to 80 psi (assume the source can maintain 64 psi regardless of flow rate). Create similar curves for 10-in and 12-in diameter pipes and compare the differences in flow.

11. Using the Darcy-Weisbach equation, find the minimum-sized of circular corrugated metal storm drain ($k = 1.0 \times 10^{-3}$ ft) that will carry 1.5 cfs with a maximum depth of 6 inches. The drain carries water down a hill 3 ft high to a pond with a free outfall 75 ft away. What pipe size should be used? Assume pipes are available in 3-in increments. What would the maximum capacity of this pipe be? What would the capacity of the pipe be when it is flowing full?

12. A channel with the cross-section shown in the following figure has a Manning's coefficient of 0.040 from station 0 to station 3 and 0.054 from station 3 to station 8. The flow through the channel is 13 m³/s, and the water surface is 1.7 m high. Find the following:

   a)   Weighted Manning's coefficient

   b)   Slope of the channel

   c)   Top width

   d)   Wetted perimeter

   e)   Flow regime (supercritical or subcritical)

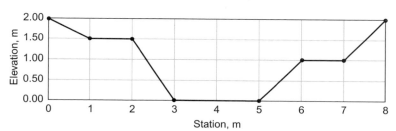

Figure for Problems 12 & 13

13. A stream with the cross-section shown in the previous figure has a flow rate of 5 m³/s. The stream has a longitudinal slope of 0.002 m/m and a natural stony bottom (n = 0.050, stations 0 to 8).

   a)   Using Manning's equation, what is the water surface elevation of the stream?

   b)   What is the maximum capacity of the channel?

   c)   How would the capacity of the channel be affected if you were to pave the center of the channel (n = 0.013) between stations 3 and 5?

14. A rectangular concrete channel with a width of 1 m and a height of 0.5 m is on a slope of 0.008 m/m. Design a concrete circular channel for which the depth is half of the diameter and the flow area is the same as that of the rectangular channel. Which channel is more efficient and by how much?

15. A weir is placed in a rectangular channel to measure the flow. The discharge from the rectangular channel enters a trapezoidal channel with a stony bottom. The trapezoidal channel is 0.50 m wide at the base with 2:1 (H:V) equal side slopes. The weir is a sharp-crested, v-notch weir with a crest 0.43 m above the channel bottom, a weir coefficient of 0.58, and a notch angle of 1.57 radians. The height of the water above the weir is 0.70 m, and the depth of water in the trapezoidal channel is measured to be 0.40 m.

    What is the flow rate? What is the slope of the trapezoidal channel (using Manning's formula)? If the discharge is increased until the elevation of the water surface in the trapezoidal channel reaches 0.61 m, what will the headwater elevation be at the weir?

16. The outlet structure on a pond is used to regulate the flow out of the pond for different storm events. An outlet structure must be designed to discharge 2.20 m^3/min when the water surface elevation in the pond reaches 1.52 m, and 6.29 m^3/min when the water surface elevation reaches 2.60 m. The outlet structure will be a circular orifice and a sharp-crested rectangular weir combination, with the centroid of the orifice at an elevation of 0.90 m and the weir crest at an elevation of 2.50 m. Both will discharge to free outfall conditions.

    Assume an orifice coefficient of 0.6. Find the orifice diameter needed to supply the correct discharge when the water surface reaches the first specified elevation. What will the discharge from the orifice be when the water surface reaches the second specified elevation? Find the width of the weir needed to supply the extra discharge necessary to meet the requirement. Use Manning's formula where necessary.

17. An approximately trapezoidal, clean, natural stream carries the discharge from a pond down a 0.001 slope. The maximum depth in the channel is 0.5 m. The channel has equal side slopes of 3.0 (H:V) and a bottom width of 1.0 m. The pond discharges water through a circular orifice into the channel. The centroid of the orifice is located 1.0 m above the bottom of the channel.

    Assume an orifice coefficient of 0.6. Design the orifice to discharge the maximum flow rate possible without exceeding the maximum allowed depth in the channel when the water surface in the pond reaches 4.6 m above the channel bottom. Use Manning's formula when necessary.

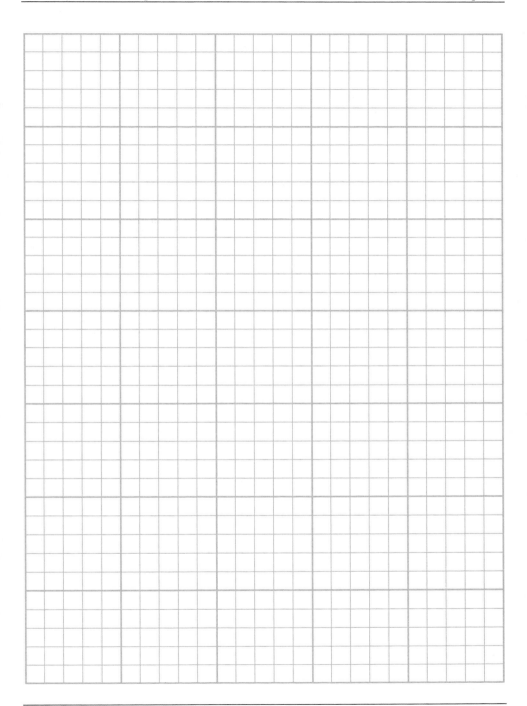

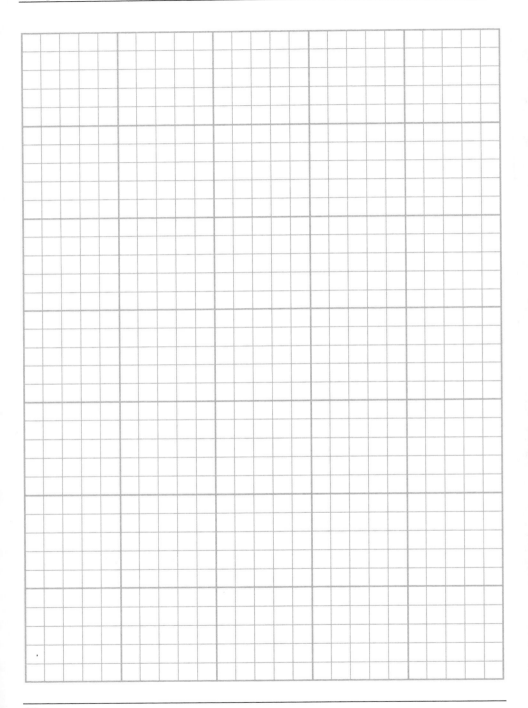

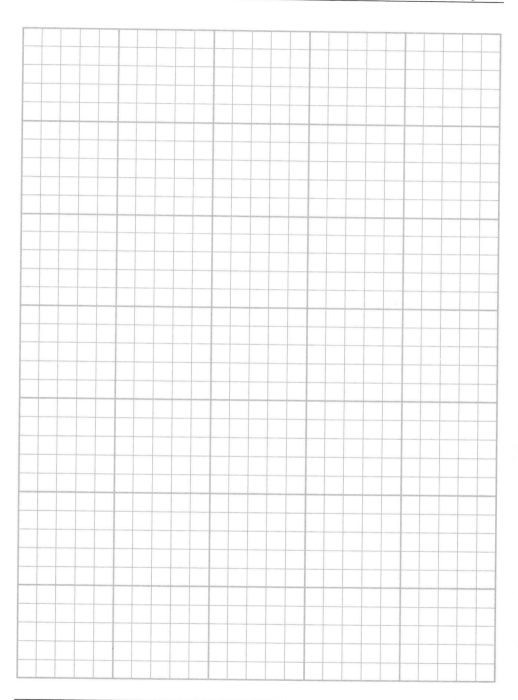

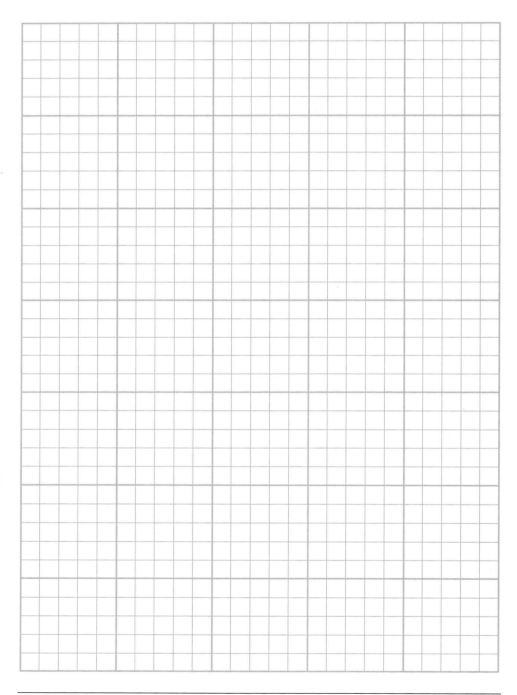

Basic Hydrology

Hydrology is the study of water on and below the earth's surface and in the atmosphere. The discussion in this chapter is limited to rainfall and the resulting surface runoff. Data on surface runoff flow rates and volumes provide the loads used to design and evaluate storm sewers, culverts, ditches, and detention ponds. Several of these structures are covered in more detail in other chapters.

2.1 Rainfall

Rainfall data is fundamental for determining the amount of stormwater generated by a particular storm event. This section describes the properties of rainfall used in modeling.

Basic Rainfall Characteristics

For the design engineer, the most important characteristics of rainfall are:

- The *depth,* or *volume,* of rainfall during a specified time interval (or its average *intensity* over that time interval)
- The *duration* of the rainfall
- The *area* over which the rainfall occurs
- The average *recurrence interval* of a rainfall amount
- The *temporal* and *spatial distributions* of rainfall within the storm

Return Period and Frequency

The probability that a storm event of a certain magnitude will occur in any given year is expressed in terms of event frequency and return period.

The ***return period***, or the recurrence interval, represents, on average, the length of time expected to elapse between rainfall events of equal or greater magnitude. Although a recurrence interval is expressed in years, it is actually based on probability of occurrence.

For example, a five-year return period represents a storm event that is expected to occur once every five years on average. This does not mean that two storm events of that size will not occur in the same year, nor does it mean that the next storm event of that size will not occur for another 20 years. It just means that the average will be once every five years (that is, there is a 20 percent chance of occurrence in any given year).

The ***frequency***, or exceedance probability, is a measure of how often a specific rainfall event will be equaled or exceeded, and is simply the inverse of the return period.

Example 2-1: Computing a Recurrence Interval

What is the recurrence interval for a storm event that has a 20 percent probability of being equaled or exceeded within any given year? For one that has a two percent probability of exceedence?

Solution

For a storm event with a 20 percent probability of being equalled or exceeded in a given year, the recurrence interval is computed as

$$1 / 0.20 = 5 \text{ years}$$

For an event with a two-percent probability, the recurrence interval is

$$1 / 0.02 = 50 \text{ years}$$

Types of Rainfall Data

Historic rainfall data is compiled and analyzed to predict storm characteristics. Rainfall data is available from a variety of sources, including governmental organizations and agencies. The data can be presented in various formats, including intensity-duration-frequency (IDF) curves, cumulative rainfall depths, and rainfall hyetographs. In infrastructure design, a synthetic rainfall distribution is often applied to the total rainfall depth for a storm of given duration and recurrence frequency. In the United States, the most frequently applied synthetic rainfall distributions are four 24-hour distributions developed by the Natural Resources Conservation Service, U.S. Department of Agriculture.

Intensity-Duration-Frequency Data

For a selected storm duration, a rainfall intensity exists that corresponds to a given exceedance probability or recurrence interval. A rainfall ***intensity-duration-frequency (IDF) curve*** illustrates the average rainfall intensities corresponding to a particular storm recurrence interval for various storm durations (see Figure 2-1). These curves are the result of the statistical analysis of rainfall data for a particular area.

Given the information on the graph shown in Figure 2-1, you can determine that the average one-hour rainfall intensity expected to be equaled or exceeded, on average, once every 100 years is 56.0 mm/hr.

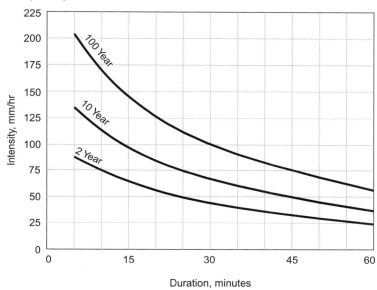

Figure 2-1: Example Set of IDF Curves

Although graphical rainfall curves are acceptable for hand calculations, they are not well-suited to computer analyses. Data are therefore input into hydrologic software either as equations or in a tabular format. Creating a rainfall table from a set of IDF curves is a simple matter of manually picking values from the curves. For example, Table 2-1 can be created from the data presented in the IDF curves of Figure 2-1.

Table 2-1: Example IDF Table

Rainfall Intensities (mm/hr)			
Storm Durations	Return Period		
	2 Years	10 Years	100 Years
5 min	88	135	204
10 min	75	114	168
15 min	65	97	142
30 min	44	66	100
60 min	24	37	56

Computer programs commonly access IDF data in the form of an equation. Several forms have been developed to analytically describe the graphical I-D-F relationships. The most common forms of these equations are:

$$i = \frac{a}{(b+D)^n} \qquad i = \frac{a(R_P)^m}{(b+D)^n} \qquad i = a + b(\ln D) + c(\ln D)^2 + d(\ln D)^3$$

where i = intensity of rainfall (mm/hr, in/hr)
          D = rainfall duration (minutes or hours)
          R_P = return period (years)
          a, b, c, d, m, and n are coefficients

When applying IDF data to system design, you must use data developed for the specific geographic location where the system is to be constructed. A single set of IDF curves can normally be used for areas as large as a city or small county. Many drainage jurisdictions and agencies such as weather bureaus can provide the engineer with IDF data recommended for their particular geographical location. Engineers should understand when and by whom the IDF curves were created, as more recently updated resources may be available.

In the United States, such information can be found in several National Weather Service publications. For example, the NWS publication TP 40 (Hershfield, 1961) presents maps showing precipitation depths over the United States for storm durations from 30 minutes to 24 hours and for recurrence intervals from 1 to 100 years. TP 40 was partially superceded by a later publication known as HYDRO-35 for the central and eastern United States (Frederick et al., 1977), and by the NOAA Atlas 2 for the 11 coterminous western states (Miller et al., 1973). Updated atlases for the Midwestern United States (Huff and Angle, 1992) and the northeastern United States and southeastern Canada (McKay and Wilkes, 1995) have also been published.

Temporal Distributions and Hyetographs for Design Storms

Some types of hydrologic analyses require the distribution of precipitation over the duration of the storm. A **_temporal rainfall distribution,_** such as the one shown in Figure 2-2, shows the cumulative progression of rainfall depth throughout a storm. The y-axis is represented by a simple rain gauge that fills over the period represented on the x-axis. **_Total depth_** is simply the final depth in the gauge. The average intensity (i) during any time segment is represented by the slope of the rainfall curve during that interval. The steeper the slope, the greater the average intensity is for a given segment.

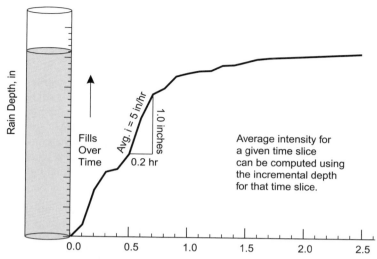

Figure 2-2: Temporal Distribution of Rainfall

The temporal distribution shown in Figure 2-2 can also be represented using a bar graph that shows how much of the total rainfall occurs within each time interval during the course of an event. A graph of this nature is called a ***rainfall hyetograph.*** Hyetographs can be displayed in terms of incremental rainfall depth measured within each time interval as shown in Figure 2-3, or as the average intensity calculated for each interval by dividing incremental depth by the time interval.

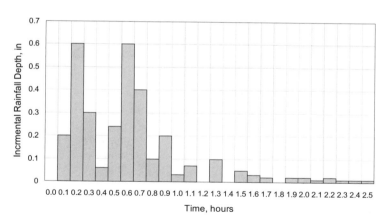

Figure 2-3: A Hyetograph of Incremental Rainfall Depth versus Time

The design of stormwater management facilities typically requires a complete rainfall hyetograph. For such situations, engineers commonly use *synthetic* temporal distributions of rainfall, which are essentially systematic and reproducible methods for varying the rainfall intensity throughout a design event.

The selected length Δt of the time increment between the data points used to construct a temporal rainfall distribution depends on the size (area) and other characteristics of the drainage basin. As a rule of thumb, the time increment should be no larger than about one-fourth to one-fifth of the basin lag time (t_l), or about one-sixth of the *time of concentration* (t_c) of the basin. In any case, the smallest time increment for which rainfall data are generally available is about five minutes. In small urban drainage basins where it is often necessary to use time increments as small as one or two minutes, the data must be extrapolated.

In addition to selecting an appropriate Δt, the engineer must select the total duration to be used when developing a design storm hyetograph. In many cases, the storm duration will be specified by the review agency having jurisdiction over the area in which a stormwater conveyance facility will be built; this approach promotes consistency from one design to another.

Many methods have been proposed for distributing a total rainfall depth throughout a storm to develop a design storm hyetograph. The NRCS developed one of the more commonly used methods in the United States (SCS, 1986). With this method, Table 2-2 is used to find fractions of the total accumulated rainfall depth for storms with 24-hour durations. (Figure 2-4 depicts Table 2-2 graphically.) The storms are classified into various types, with each type being recommended for use in a certain U.S. geographical region, as shown in Figure 2-5. If necessary, interpolation may be used to obtain values not shown in Table 2-2. Nonlinear interpolation methods are recommended for this purpose.

Table 2-2: SCS Dimensionless Storm Distributions (SCS, 1986)

t (hr)	Type I	Type IA	Type II	Type III
0	0.000	0.000	0.000	0.000
1	0.017	0.020	0.011	0.010
2	0.035	0.050	0.022	0.020
3	0.055	0.082	0.035	0.031
4	0.076	0.116	0.048	0.043
5	0.099	0.156	0.063	0.057
6	0.126	0.206	0.080	0.072
7	0.156	0.268	0.098	0.091
8	0.194	0.425	0.120	0.114
9	0.254	0.520	0.147	0.146
10	0.515	0.577	0.181	0.189
11	0.624	0.624	0.235	0.250
12	0.682	0.664	0.663	0.500
13	0.728	0.701	0.772	0.750
14	0.766	0.736	0.820	0.811
15	0.799	0.769	0.854	0.854
16	0.830	0.800	0.880	0.886
17	0.857	0.830	0.902	0.910
18	0.882	0.858	0.921	0.928
19	0.905	0.884	0.937	0.943
20	0.926	0.908	0.952	0.957
21	0.946	0.932	0.965	0.969
22	0.965	0.956	0.978	0.981
23	0.983	0.978	0.989	0.991
24	1.000	1.000	1.000	1.000

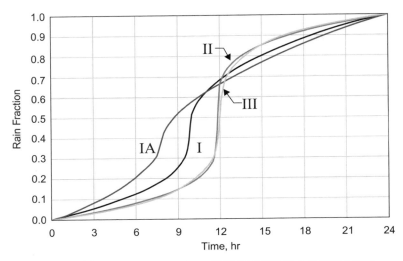

Figure 2-4: *Graphical Representation of NRCS (SCS) Rainfall Distributions*

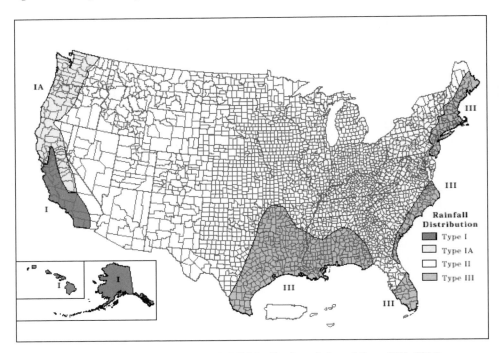

Figure 2-5: *Coverage of NRCS (SCS) Rainfall Distributions (adapted from SCS, 1986)*

Example 2-2: Developing a Design Storm Hyetograph from SCS Distributions

Develop a design storm hyetograph for a 50-year, 24-hour storm in Boston, Massachusetts. Assume that $\Delta t = .1$ hr is a reasonable choice for the drainage basin to which the design storm will be applied.

Solution

Figure 2-5 illustrates that a Type III storm distribution is a reasonable choice for Boston. From TP 40, the total depth of a 50-year, 24-hour storm in Boston is estimated to be 6.0 inches. Table 2-3 illustrates the calculation of the storm hyetograph.

The first column of the table is the time, in hours, since the beginning of the storm, and is tabulated in 1-hr increments for the total storm duration of 24 hours. (In actuality, the Δt used in the calculations would be 0.1 hr; the 1-hr increment is used here for brevity.) The second column is the fraction of the total storm depth that has accumulated at each time during the storm. These values are obtained by interpolation from Table 2-2 for the Type III storm distribution. The third column contains the cumulative rainfall depths for each time during the storm and is obtained by multiplying each fraction in the second column by the total storm depth of 6.0 in. The fourth column contains the incremental depths of rainfall within each time interval during the storm; these values are computed as the difference between the current and preceding values in the third column.

Table 2-3: 50-Year, 24-Hour Storm Hyetograph for Boston, Massachusetts

t (hr)	Fraction	Cum. P (in)	Incr. P (in)
0	0.000	0.000	
1	0.010	0.060	0.060
2	0.020	0.120	0.060
3	0.031	0.186	0.066
4	0.043	0.258	0.072
5	0.057	0.342	0.084
6	0.072	0.432	0.090
7	0.091	0.546	0.114
8	0.114	0.684	0.138
9	0.146	0.876	0.192
10	0.189	1.134	0.258
11	0.250	1.500	0.366
12	0.500	3.000	1.500
13	0.750	4.500	1.500
14	0.811	4.866	0.366
15	0.854	5.124	0.258
16	0.886	5.316	0.192
17	0.910	5.460	0.144
18	0.928	5.568	0.108
19	0.943	5.658	0.090
20	0.957	5.742	0.084
21	0.969	5.814	0.072
22	0.981	5.886	0.072
23	0.991	5.946	0.060
24	1.000	6.000	0.054

The resulting graph of cumulative precipitation is shown in Figure 2-6, and the hyetograph is shown in Figure 2-7. The height of each bar on the hyetograph is the average rainfall intensity during that time interval, and the area of each bar is the incremental rainfall depth during that time interval. Because the time increment is 1 hr (1-hr increment is shown for simplicity; actual Δt is 0.1 hr), the value for the height of the bar (in units of in/hr) is equal to the incremental depth for that time increment (in inches).

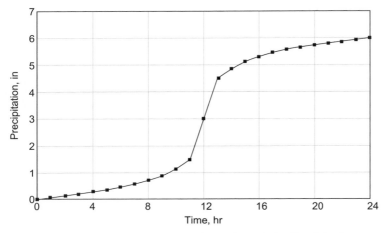

Figure 2-6: Graph of Derived Design Storm Cumulative Precipitation

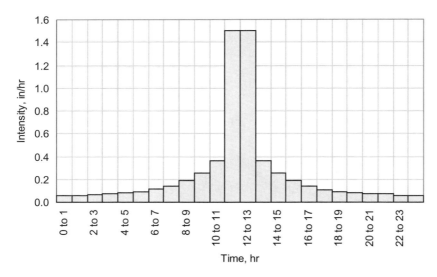

Figure 2-7: Derived Design Storm Hyetograph

2.2 Rainfall Abstractions and Runoff Volume

Only a portion of the total rainfall occurring over a drainage basin contributes to surface runoff and stream flow. In fact, a simple comparison of rainfall and runoff records for most locations in the United States shows that the equivalent depth of runoff is typically about 30 to 50 percent of the precipitation depth.

To obtain the loading information necessary to design and model structures such as storm sewers, culverts, and detention facilities, it is necessary to calculate the runoff volumes and/or flow rates resulting from the storm events of interest. This section presents three techniques for computing total runoff volume: (1) the *Horton equation*, (2) the *runoff coefficient,* and (3) the *NRCS curve number equation.*

Watershed Area

A *watershed* is an area that drains to a single point of discharge. The first step in computing runoff at a point of interest (such as a culvert, inlet, or property outfall) is to delineate its watershed on a contour map. Because water flows downhill, delineating a watershed is simply a matter of identifying an outfall and locating the watershed boundary such that any rain that falls within the boundary will be directed toward that point of discharge. The delineated area is then measured using a planimeter, or graphical or computer-aided methods. Because river and stream systems collect water, a watershed may have any number of sub-watersheds within it. The focus of the analysis and the determination of how large a watershed must be to be analyzed separately depend on the scope and purpose of the project at hand. Figure 2-8 shows the collection channels for two typical natural watersheds.

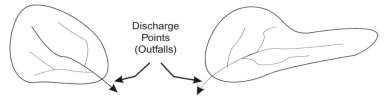

Figure 2-8: Typical Natural Watersheds with Collection Channels

After the watershed is delineated and measured, the modeler can proceed to the next step of computing rainfall abstractions and runoff depth. To determine the total runoff volume, runoff depth is multiplied by the watershed area.

Rainfall Abstractions

Rainfall that does not contribute to direct surface runoff may be intercepted by vegetation, infiltrated into the ground surface, retained as depression storage in puddles and small irregularities in the land surface, or returned to the atmosphere through transpiration and evaporation. Collectively, these *losses* of rainfall are called *abstractions.* The rainfall that remains after abstractions have occurred comprises the surface runoff and is called *effective precipitation.*

The four basic types of abstractions are interception, depression storage, infiltration, and evaporation. Evaporation, however, is not typically considered in modeling stormwater conveyances.

Interception

Interception refers to the capture of rainfall on the leaves and stems of vegetation before it reaches the ground surface. Water intercepted by vegetation is returned to the atmosphere by evaporation during dry-weather periods.

Depression Storage

Excess water begins to pond on the land surface when the rainfall intensity exceeds the infiltration capacity of a soil during a storm event. The ponded water fills small depressions and irregularities in the ground surface, and additional water is held on the surface through the phenomenon of surface tension. The water held in depressions is called *depression storage,* and it either evaporates during dry weather periods or infiltrates into the soil. Non-infiltrated rainfall that remains after surface depressions and irregularities have been filled contributes to surface runoff.

Infiltration

When rainfall occurs on a *pervious* surface, some of the rainwater infiltrates into the ground. The infiltrated water may contribute to groundwater recharge, or it may be taken up by the roots of vegetation and subsequently transpired through the leaves of plants. Infiltrated water also may be evaporated from the soil during dry-weather periods between storm events, or it may move laterally through the near-surface soils and reappear as surface water in a stream.

Determining Runoff Volume

In its most general form, the relationship of runoff (effective precipitation) to infiltration and abstractions is (see Figure 2-9):

$$D_r = D_p - D_{li} - D_i - D_s - D_e \quad \text{for} \quad D_p > D_{li} \text{ and } D_r > D_s$$

$$D_r = 0 \quad \text{for} \quad D_p \leq D_{li} \text{ or } D_r \leq D_s$$

where D_r = total depth of runoff (effective precipitation)
    D_p = total depth of precipitation (rainfall)
    D_{li} = total initial loss (interception)
    D_i = total depth infiltrated after initial losses
    D_s = total depression storage depth
    D_e = transpiration and evaporation losses (often ignored for short-duration stormwater events)

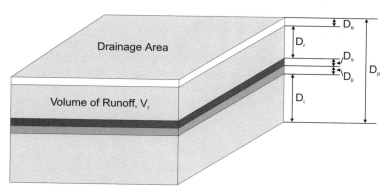

Figure 2-9: Precipitation, Abstraction, and Runoff Volume

Volume of runoff is then expressed by

$$V_r = D_r \times A$$

where
V_r = runoff volume
A = contributing drainage area
D_r = total depth of runoff

Note: Some hydrology literature refers to runoff volume in terms of depth (in in. or mm), in which case the depth would be multiplied by the contributing area to get the true volume.

Example 2-3: Computing Runoff Volume

A 2.5-hour storm deposits 2.0 inches of rainfall over a catchment (watershed) area of 3 acres. If the interception capacity is 0.3 inches, the depression storage is 0.2 inches, the calculated total infiltration is 0.7 inches, and evaporation is negligible, find the total depth of effective precipitation and the total runoff volume for the drainage area.

Solution

Total runoff depth is computed as:

$$D_r = 2.0 - 0.3 - 0.7 - 0.2 - 0 = 0.8 \text{ in}$$

And total runoff volume is:

$$V_r = (0.8 \text{ in} \div 12 \text{ in/ft}) \times 3 \text{ ac} = 0.2 \text{ ac-ft} = 8,712 \text{ ft}^3$$

Although the concept of computing runoff volume just described is a simple one, the problem of determining the amount of rainfall lost to abstractions remains. The following subsections describe a few of the methods used in accounting for abstractions—the Horton equation, the runoff coefficient, and the NRCS (SCS) curve number equation.

Horton Infiltration Equation

A widely used method of representing the infiltration capacity of a soil is the *Horton equation* (Horton, 1939). The Horton equation models a decreasing rate of infiltration over time, which implies that the rate of infiltration decreases as the soil becomes more saturated. For conditions in which the rainfall intensity is always greater than the infiltration capacity (that is, the rainwater supply for infiltration is not limiting), this method expresses the infiltration rate as

$$f(t) = f_c + (f_0 - f_c)e^{-k(t-t_0)}$$

where
    $f(t)$ = the infiltration rate (in/hr or mm/hr) at time t (min)
    f_c = a steady-state infiltration rate that occurs for sufficiently large t
    f_0 = the initial infiltration rate at the time that infiltration begins (that is, at time $t = t_0$)
    k (min^{-1}) = a decay coefficient

It can be shown theoretically that the steady-state infiltration rate f_c is equal to the saturated vertical hydraulic conductivity of the soil.

Estimation of the parameters f_c, f_0, and k in the preceding equation can be difficult because of the natural variabilities in antecedent moisture conditions and soil properties. Table 2-4 provides some values recommended by Rawls et al. (1976), although such tabulations should be used with caution. Singh (1992) recommends that f_0 be taken as roughly five times the value of f_c.

Table 2-4: Typical Values of Horton Infiltration Parameters (Rawls et al., 1976)

Soil Type	f_0 (in/hr)	f_c (in/hr)	k (min^{-1})
Alphalpha loamy sand	19.0	1.4	0.64
Carnegie sandy loam	14.8	1.8	0.33
Dothan loamy sand	3.5	2.6	0.02
Fuquay pebbly loamy sand	6.2	2.4	0.08
Leefield loamy sand	11.3	1.7	0.13
Tooup sand	23.0	1.8	0.55

Often, the rainfall intensity during the early part of a storm is less than the potential infiltration capacity of the soil; thus, the supply of rainwater is a limiting factor on the infiltration rate. During the time period when the water supply is limiting, the actual infiltration rate is equal to the rate at which rainwater is supplied to the ground surface. This effect is illustrated in Figure 2-10. Later in the storm when the rainfall rate is greater than the infiltration rate, the actual infiltration rate will be greater than that predicted by the preceding equation because infiltration was limited early in the storm.

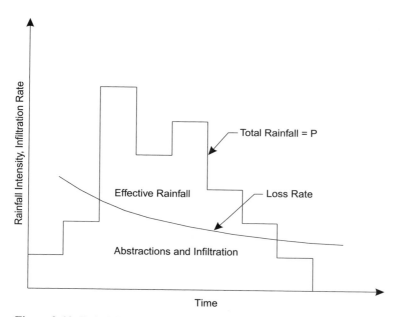

Figure 2-10: Rainfall Intensity Can Limit Infiltration Rate during the Early Part of the Storm

Land Use and Cover Considerations

When applying a physically based equation such as Horton's, care should be taken to consider the impacts of land use and cover conditions. If the parameters used to solve for infiltration consider soil conditions only, the computed runoff may not be applicable.

Example 2-4: Using Horton's Equation to Determine Infiltration Rate

Using Horton's equation, find the infiltration rate at time 2.0 hours for Dothan loamy sand. The rainfall duration is 4 hours, and for this event, it takes 0.5 hours to reach the interception capacity, at which time infiltration begins.

Solution

From Table 2-4, $f_0 = 3.5$ in/hr; $f_c = 2.6$ in/hr; and $k = 0.02$ min⁻¹. Thus, $f(2\text{ hr}) = 2.6$ in/hr + (3.5 in/hr − 2.6 in/hr)$e^{-0.02(2 - 0.5)} = 3.47$ in/hr.

Runoff Coefficient

The concept of the ***runoff coefficient*** assumes that the effective rainfall intensity i_e is a fraction of the gross rainfall intensity i, or

$$i_e = Ci$$

where C = runoff coefficient $(0 \le C \le 1)$

A good way to visualize the C coefficient is to treat it in terms of percent of rainfall. For example, a C of 0.85 would yield a runoff amount (effective precipitation) that is 85 percent of the gross rainfall. The C coefficient is used with the rational method for peak runoff rate estimation, which is described in Section 2.3.

Example 2-5: Using the Runoff Coefficient to Compute Effective Rainfall Intensity

For a rainfall event with an average intensity of 2.0 in/hr falling onto a drainage area having a C coefficent = 0.70, determine the effective rainfall intensity.

Solution

$$i_e = C_i = 0.70 \times 2.0 \text{ in/hr} = 1.4 \text{ in/hr}$$

Table 2-5 is a listing of recommended runoff coefficients corresponding to various types of land uses. It should be noted, however, that some locales have developed runoff coefficient tables that also consider soil type. Coefficients should be selected carefully for proper application to the particular locale and soil conditions.

Table 2-5: Runoff Coefficients for Use in the Rational Method (Schaake et al., 1967)

Type of Area or Development	C
Types of Development	
Urban business	0.70 – 0.95
Commercial office	0.50 – 0.70
Residential development	
Single-family homes	0.30 – 0.50
Condominiums	0.40 – 0.60
Apartments	0.60 – 0.80
Suburban residential	0.25 – 0.40
Industrial development	
Light industry	0.50 – 0.80
Heavy industry	0.60 – 0.90
Parks, greenbelts, cemeteries	0.10 – 0.30
Railroad yards, playgrounds	0.20 – 0.40
Unimproved grassland or pasture	0.10 – 0.30
Types of Surface Areas	
Asphalt or concrete pavement	0.70 – 0.95
Brick paving	0.70 – 0.80
Roofs of buildings	0.80 – 0.95
Grass-covered sandy soils	
Slopes 2% or less	0.05 – 0.10
Slopes 2% to 8%	0.10 – 0.16
Slopes over 8%	0.16 – 0.20
Grass-covered clay soils	
Slopes 2% or less	0.10 – 0.16
Slopes 2% to 8%	0.17 – 0.25
Slopes over 8%	0.26 – 0.36

When a drainage basin consists of a mixture of land uses, a composite runoff coefficient may be computed for the basin by weighting individual runoff coefficients for each land use by their respective areas, as demonstrated in Example 2-6.

Example 2-6: Determining the Weighted Runoff Coefficient

Estimate the runoff coefficient for a drainage basin that is made up of 15 acres of park and 30 acres of medium-density, single-family housing.

Solution

From Table 2-5, the runoff coefficients for the park and residential areas are estimated to be 0.20 and 0.40, respectively. The composite runoff coefficient for the entire drainage basin of 45 acres is therefore

$$C = [15(0.20) + 30(0.40)]/45 = 0.33$$

NRCS (SCS) Curve Number Method

In the 1950s, the U.S. Department of Agriculture Soil Conservation Service (SCS; now the Natural Resource Conservation Service or NRCS) developed a procedure to partition the total depth of rainfall represented by a design storm hyetograph into initial abstractions, retention, and effective rainfall (SCS, 1969).

Initial rainfall abstractions consist of all rainfall losses occurring before the beginning of surface runoff, including interception, infiltration, and depression storage. *Retention* refers to the continuing rainfall losses following the initiation of surface runoff, which are predominantly due to continuing infiltration. Conservation of mass requires that

$$F = P - I_a - P_e$$

where F = equivalent depth of retention (in, mm)
P = total rainfall depth in storm (in, mm)
I_a = equivalent depth of initial abstractions (in, mm)
P_e = depth of effective precipitation (in, mm)

An assumption made in the development of the curve number method is:

$$\frac{F}{S} = \frac{P_e}{P - I_a}$$

where S = maximum possible retention (in, mm)

The value of the maximum possible retention, S, depends on the soil type and land use condition in the drainage basin. The value of S does not include I_a. In essence, the assumption represented by this equation is that the ratio of actual retention to maximum possible retention of water during a storm is equal to the ratio of effective rainfall to maximum possible effective rainfall (total rainfall less initial abstractions). Substitution of $F = P - I_a - P_e$ into the previous equation yields

$$P_e = \frac{(P - I_a)^2}{(P - I_a) + S}$$

for values of $P > I_a$. Data analyzed by the NRCS indicated that I_a is related to S, and on average supported the use of the relationship $I_a = 0.2S$. Thus, the equation becomes

$$P_e = \frac{(P - 0.2S)^2}{P + 0.8S}$$

when $P > 0.2S$ ($P_e = 0$ when $P \le 0.2S$). Because the initial abstraction I_a consists of interception, depression storage, and infiltration prior to the onset of direct runoff, it may be appropriate in some applications to assume that $I_a = 0.1S$ or $I_a = 0.3S$ instead of $I_a = 0.2S$. For example, the relationship $I_a = 0.1S$ might be appropriate in a heavily urbanized area where there is little opportunity for initial abstractions to occur. The preceding equation must be modified when the relationship between I_a and S is assumed to be different from $I_a = 0.2S$.

The use of this equation for estimating the depth of effective rainfall during a storm requires an estimate of the maximum possible retention S. NRCS conducted research to approximate S for various soil and cover conditions. In order to provide engineers with tables having a manageable range of coefficients that varying between 0 and 100, the original values for S were rearranged using the following simple relationship:

$$CN = \frac{1000}{S + 10}$$

where CN = runoff curve number
S = maximum possible retention (in)

Rearranging, S is related to the **curve number**, CN, as

$$S = \frac{1000}{CN} - 10$$

Practical values of CN range from about 30 to 98, with larger values being associated with more impervious land surfaces. The NRCS has tabulated curve numbers as a function of soil type, land use, hydrologic condition of the drainage basin, and antecedent moisture condition.

Soil Group

Soils in the United States have been classified by the NRCS into four hydrologic groups: Groups A, B, C, and D. **Group A** soils have high infiltration rates (low runoff potential), even when they are thoroughly wetted. Typical Group A soils are well-drained sands and gravels. **Group D** soils are at the opposite end of the spectrum, having low infiltration rates (high runoff potential). Typical Group D soils are clays, shallow soils over nearly impervious material, and soils with a high water table. **Group B** and **Group C** soils are in the mid-range of the spectrum.

In the United States, hydrologic soil group information can be determined from the NRCS soil survey of the county in which the project is located. Note that when a drainage basin undergoes urbanization, the hydrologic soil group may change due to compaction of the soil by heavy construction equipment or mixing of soils as a consequence of grading operations.

Cover Type

The surface conditions of a drainage area have a significant impact on runoff. For example, in the exaggerated case of a sandy (Group A) soil completely paved with asphalt, the soil itself will have no impact on the amount of runoff. Even for pervious conditions, cover type plays a significant role in the amount of runoff from a site. For example, a heavily forested area will yield runoff volumes that differ from those of a lawn or plowed field.

Hydrologic Condition

The *hydrologic condition* of rangeland, meadow, or pasture is defined to be "good" if it is lightly grazed and has vegetative cover on more than 75 percent of the area. Conversely, a "poor" hydrologic condition corresponds to a heavily grazed area with vegetation covering less than 50 percent of the surface.

Antecedent Moisture Condition

When rainfall events occur in quick succession, the time period between storms may be too short for the soils to dry to their average or normal moisture conditions. When rainfall occurs on soils that are already wet, the net result is that runoff volumes and peaks will be higher than normal. The NRCS (SCS) method accounts for this possibility by allowing the curve number to depend on an *antecedent moisture (AMC) condition.* Three AMC classifications exist. Normal conditions correspond to AMC-II. AMC-I corresponds to a drier condition, and AMC-III to a wetter condition.

Curve numbers corresponding to AMC-I and AMC-III conditions can be computed from AMC-II condition curve numbers using the following equations (Chow et al., 1988). The computed CN should be rounded to the nearest whole number.

$$CN_I = \frac{4.2CN_{II}}{10 - 0.058CN_{II}}$$

$$CN_{III} = \frac{23CN_{II}}{10 + 0.13CN_{II}}$$

where CN_I, CN_{II}, and CN_{III} = curve numbers for AMC-I, -II, and -III, respectively.

Curve Number Tables

Table 2-6 provides a listing of curve numbers that account for both cover conditions and soil type for normal antecedent moisture conditions (AMC-II). The curve numbers shown for the urban and suburban land use conditions are based on the percentages of directly connected impervious areas in the drainage basin as shown in the table, and should be used with caution when the actual percentage of imperviousness in a drainage basin differs from this assumed value. When necessary, a composite curve number can be developed as an area-weighted average of individual curve numbers. The composite CN should be rounded to the nearest whole number.

Additional information on hydrologic condition and curve numbers for land uses other than those contained in Table 2-6 can be found in the National Engineering Handbook, Section 4: Hydrology (NEH-4) (SCS, 1969) and TR-55 (SCS, 1986).

Table 2-6: Runoff Curve Numbers for Urban Areas (SCS, 1986)[1]

Cover Type and Hydrologic Condition	Avgerage Percent Impervious Area[2]	Curve Numbers for Hydrologic Soil Group			
		A	B	C	D
Fully developed urban areas (vegetation established)					
Open space (lawns, parks, golf courses, cemeteries, etc.)[3]:					
Poor condition (grass cover < 50%)		68	79	86	89
Fair condition (grass cover 50% to 75%)		49	69	79	84
Good condition (grass cover > 75%)		39	61	74	80
Impervious areas:					
Paved parking lots, roofs, driveways, etc. (excluding right-of-way)		98	98	98	98
Streets and roads:					
Paved; curbs and storm sewers (excluding right-of-way)		98	98	98	98
Paved; open ditches (including right-of-way)		83	89	92	93
Gravel (including right-of-way)		76	85	89	91
Dirt (including right-of-way)		72	82	87	89
Western desert urban areas:					
Natural desert landscaping (pervious area only)[4]		63	77	85	88
Artificial desert landscaping (impervious weed barrier, desert shrub with 1 to 2 inch sand or gravel mulch and basin borders)		96	96	96	96
Urban districts:					
Commercial and business	85	89	92	94	95
Industrial	72	81	88	91	93
Residential districts by average lot size:					
1/8 acre or less (town houses)	65	77	85	90	92
1/4 acre	38	61	75	83	87
1/3 acre	30	57	72	81	86
1/2 acre	25	54	70	80	85
1 acre	20	51	68	79	84
2 acres	12	46	65	77	82
Developing urban areas					
Newly graded area (pervious areas only no vegetation)[5]		77	86	91	94
Idle lands (CNs are determined using cover types similar to those in 2-2(c) (SCS, 1986)					

[1]Average runoff condition, and Ia = 0.2s.
[2]The average percent impervious area shown was used to develop the composite CNs. Other assumptions are as follows: impervious areas are directly connected to the drainage system, impervious areas have a CN of 98, and pervious areas are considered equivalent to open space in good hydrologic condition.
[3]CNs shown are equivalent to those of pasture. Composite CNs may be computed for other combinations of open space cover type.
[4]Composite CNs for natural desert landscaping should be computed using Figures 2-3 or 2-4 (in SCS, 1986) based on the impervious area percentage (CN = 98) and the pervious area CN. The pervious area CNs are assumed equivalent to desert shrub in poor hydrologic condition.
[5]Composite CNs to use for the design of temporary measures during grading and construction should be computed using Figures 2-3 or 2-4 (in SCS, 1986) based on the degree of development (impervious area percentage) and the CNs for the newly graded pervious areas.

Example 2-7: Estimating Runoff Depth and Volume Using the NRCS (SCS) Curve Number Method (Modified from SCS, 1986)

Estimate the curve number, depth of runoff (effective precipitation), and runoff volume for a 1,000-acre drainage basin if the total depth of precipitation is 5.0 inches. All soils in the basin are in hydrologic soil group C. The proposed land use is 50 percent detached houses with 0.25-acre lots; 10 percent townhouses with 0.125-acre lots; 25 percent schools, parking lots, plazas, and streets with curbs and gutters; and 15 percent open space, parks, and schoolyards with good grass cover. Use an antecedent soil moisture condition of AMC-III. The detached housing and townhouse areas have directly connected impervious area percentages similar to those assumed in Table 2-6.

Solution

The composite curve number corresponding to AMC-II conditions is computed as a weighted average, as shown in Table 2-7.

Table 2-7: Calculations for Example 2-7

Land Use	Area (ac)	CN	Product
Detached houses (0.25-acre lots)	500	83	41,500
Townhouses (0.125-acre lots)	100	90	9,000
Streets, plazas, etc.	250	98	24,500
Open space, parks, etc.	150	74	11,100
Sums	**1,000**		**86,100**

Thus, the composite CN is computed as

$$CN = 86,100 \div 1,000 = 86$$

The curve number corresponding to AMC-III moisture conditions is found to be

$$CN_{III} = \frac{23(86)}{10 + 0.13(86)} = 93$$

The maximum possible retention for this basin at AMC-III is

$$S = (1000 \div 93) - 10 = 0.75 \text{ in}$$

Initial abstractions are estimated to be

$$I_a = 0.2S = 0.15 \text{ in}$$

Because $P > I_a$, the depth of runoff (effective precipitation) is estimated as

$$P_e = [5.0 - 0.2(0.75)]^2/(5.0 + 0.8(0.75)] = 4.20 \text{ in}$$

The total volume of runoff is therefore

$$V_r = (4.2 \text{ in} / 12 \text{ in/ft}) (1000 \text{ ac}) = 350 \text{ ac-ft}$$

2.3   Computing Peak Runoff Flow Rate

To design stormwater conveyance or detention systems, the engineer must obtain information on runoff flow rates. Two basic levels of analysis exist. The first level is a peak flow calculation to determine the maximum runoff flow rate at a given point resulting from a storm event. This level of analysis is often sufficient for designing storm sewers and culverts whose only function is to convey runoff away from areas where it is unwanted. The second level, which is more complex, consists of the generation of a runoff *hydrograph,* which provides information on flow rate versus time and runoff volume. This type of information is necessary in the analysis of detention and retention facilities where time and volume considerations are critical. In some situations, hydrograph analysis is also required for storm sewer analyses.

After you determine the required analysis approach, you must choose techniques for computing how much of the rainfall will contribute to surface runoff and, in the case of a hydrograph analysis, how this flow will be distributed through time. These techniques are sometimes dictated by local regulations.

Time of Concentration

The maximum amount of flow coming from any watershed is related to the amount of time it takes for the entire watershed to be contributing to the flow. In other words, it may start raining right now, but it could be several minutes (or even hours) before the water that falls on some parts of the watershed actually makes its way to the discharge point.

Some places in a watershed are hydraulically closer to the discharge point than others, but for peak flow generation only the most hydraulically remote location is considered crucial. The amount of time that it takes for the first drop of water falling on this location to work its way to the discharge point is called the *time of concentration.*

Many methods for calculating time of concentration are given in various private, federal, and local publications. Although each of these methods is different (in some cases only slightly), they are all based on the type of ground cover, the slope of the land, and the distance along the flow path. In most locales, there is also a minimum time of concentration (typically 5 to 10 minutes) recommended for small watersheds, such as a section of a parking lot draining to a storm sewer. Some methods predict the response time directly, whereas others predict the velocity of flow. The predicted velocity coupled with estimates of the flow path length can then be used to estimate the response time.

With few exceptions, methods for prediction of basin response time are empirical in nature. Consequently, large errors in response time estimates can be expected to occur if these methods are not carefully selected and applied, and these errors can significantly affect peak runoff estimates. The method selected for estimation of t_c should be one that was developed for basin conditions similar to those in the drainage basin for which an estimate is desired.

Table 2-8 lists several commonly used methods for estimation of the time of concentration of a drainage basin. Figure 2-11 illustrates average overland flow velocities as a function of land use characteristics and surface slope. When flows are channelized in gutters, open channels, or storm sewers, Manning's equation may be used to estimate the velocity of flow (see Chapter 1).

Table 2-8: Commonly Used Methods for Estimation of the Time of Concentration, in minutes

Equation	Source	Remarks
$t_c = 60LA^{0.4} / DS^{0.2}$	Williams (1922)	L = basin length (mi), A = basin area (mi^2), D = diameter (mi) of a circular basin of area A, and S = basin slope (percent). The basin area should be smaller than 50 mi^2.
$t_c = KL^{0.77} / S^n$	Kirpich (1940)	Developed for small drainage basins in Tennessee and Pennsylvania, with basin areas from 1 to 112 ac. L = basin length(ft), S = basin slope (ft/ft), $K = 0.0078$ and $n = 0.385$ for Tennessee; $K = 0.0013$ and $n = 0.5$ for Pennsylvania. The estimated t_c should be multiplied by 0.4 if the overland flow path is concrete or asphalt, or by 0.2 if the channel is concrete-lined.
$t_c = (2LN / 3S^{0.5})^{0.47}$	Hathaway (1945), Kerby (1959)	Drainage basins with areas of less than 10 acres and slopes of less than 0.01. This is an overland flow method. L = overland flow length from basin divide to a defined channel (ft), S = overland flow path slope (ft/ft), and N is a flow retardance factor ($N = 0.02$ for smooth impervious surfaces; 0.10 for smooth, bare packed soil; 0.20 for poor grass, row crops, or moderately rough bare surfaces; 0.40 for pasture or average grass; 0.60 for deciduous timberland; and 0.80 for conifer timberland, deciduous timberland with deep ground litter, or dense grass).
$t_c = 300(L / S)^{0.5}$	Johnstone and Cross (1949)	Developed for basins in the Scotie and Sandusky River watersheds with areas between 25 and 1,624 mi^2. L = basin length (mi), and S = basin slope (ft/mi).
$t_c = \{(0.007I + c) / S^{0.33}\} \times (IL / 43,200)^{-0.67} L / 60$	Izzard (1946)	Hydraulically derived formula. I = effective rainfall intensity (in/hr), S = slope of overland flow path (ft/ft), L = length of overland flow path (ft), and c is a roughness coefficient ($c = 0.007$ for smooth asphalt, 0.012 for concrete pavement, 0.017 for tar and gravel pavement, and 0.060 for dense bluegrass turf).
$t_c = 0.94I^{-0.4}(Ln / S^{0.5})^{0.6}$	Henderson and Wooding (1964)	Based on kinematic wave theory for flow on an overland flow plane. I = rainfall intensity (in/hr), L = length of overland flow (ft), n = Manning's roughness coefficient, S = overland flow plane slope (ft/ft).
$t_c = 1.8(1.1 - C)L^{0.5} / S^{0.333}$	Federal Aviation Agency (1970)	Developed based on airfield drainage data. C = Rational Method runoff coefficient, L = overland flow length (ft), and S = slope (percent).
$t_c = \dfrac{1}{60}\sum (L/V)_i$	Soil Conservation Service (1986)	Time of concentration is developed as a sum of individual travel times. L = length of an individual flow path (ft) and V = velocity of flow over an individual flow path (ft/s). V may be estimated using Figure 2-11 or using Manning's equation.

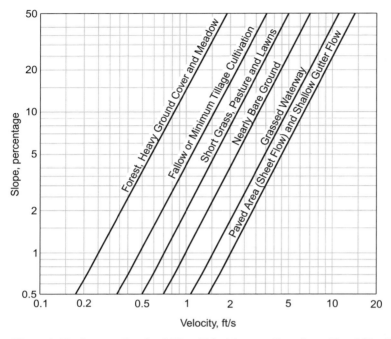

Figure 2-11: Average Overland Flow Velocities as a Function of Land Use Characteristics and Surface Slope

Example 2-8: Time of Concentration

An urbanized drainage basin is shown in Figure 2-12. Three types of flow conditions exist from the furthest point of the drainage basin to its outlet. Estimate the time of concentration based on the following data:

Reach	Flow Description	Slope (%)	Length (ft)
A to B	Overland (forest)	7	500
B to C	Overland (shallow gutter)	2	900
C to D	Storm sewer with manholes, inlets, etc. ($n = 0.015$, dia. $= 3$ ft)	1.5	2,000
D to E	Open channel, gunite-lined, trapezoidal ($B = 5$ ft, $y = 3$ ft, $z = 1:1$, $n = 0.019$)	0.5	3,000

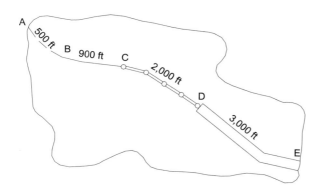

Figure 2-12: Flow Paths in a Drainage Basin for Calculation of t_c

Solution

For the reach from A to B, the average flow velocity is $V = 0.7$ ft/s. The travel time for that reach is therefore

$$t_{AB} = L/V = 500/0.7 = 714 \text{ s}$$

Similarly, for the reach from B to C, the average flow velocity is $V = 2.8$ ft/s. The travel time for that reach is therefore

$$t_{BC} = L/V = 900/2.8 = 321 \text{ s}$$

To compute the travel time in the storm sewer from C to D, Manning's equation is employed to compute the pipe-full velocity:

$$V = \frac{1.49}{n}\left(\frac{D}{4}\right)^{2/3} S^{1/2} = \frac{1.49}{0.015}\left(\frac{3}{4}\right)^{2/3} (0.015)^{1/2} = 10 \text{ ft/s}$$

The travel time for that reach is therefore

$$t_{CD} = L/V = 2000/10 = 200 \text{ s}$$

Travel time in the open channel from D to E is computed using the bank-full velocity, again found via Manning's equation:

$$V = \frac{1.49}{n} R^{2/3} S^{1/2} = \frac{1.49}{0.019}(1.78)^{2/3}(0.005)^{1/2} = 8.2 \text{ ft/s}$$

The travel time for that reach is therefore

$$t_{DE} = L/V = 3000/8.2 = 366 \text{ s}$$

The time of concentration is the sum of the four individual travel times and is

$$t_c = 1{,}601 \text{ sec} = 0.44 \text{ hr}$$

The Rational Method

The Rational Method is an equilibrium-based approach to peak flow estimation that uses rainfall intensity data and watershed characteristics to predict peak flows for a rainfall event. The Rational Method is a popular choice for storm sewer design because this type of design usually considers only peak flows, and because of the simplicity of the calculations involved.

At the most fundamental level, the Rational Method assumes that a steady state is attained such that the rainfall inflow rate of water onto a drainage basin is equal to the outflow rate of water from the basin. If one expresses the volumetric inflow rate as the product of the basin area A and the effective rainfall intensity i_e, the outflow rate Q is obtained as $Q = i_e A$. Further, if one accounts for abstractions, the effective intensity is a product of the actual rainfall intensity and a runoff coefficient, resulting in

$$Q = CiA$$

where Q = runoff rate (ac-in/hr, ha-mm/hr)
          C = runoff (abstractions) coefficent
          i = rainfall intensity (in/hr, mm/hr)
          A = drainage area (ac, ha)

Because 1 ac-in/hr = 1.008 cfs $\approx$ 1 cfs, engineers performing calculations by hand typically ignore the conversion factor and simply assume that the discharge Q is in units of cfs. In SI units, a conversion factor of 0.278 will yield Q in units of m^3/s.

The time of concentration is the smallest time for which the entire basin is contributing runoff to the basin outlet; therefore, the storm duration must be at least as long as the time of concentration if a steady-state condition is to be achieved. Also, steady-state conditions dictate that the storm intensity be spatially and temporally uniform. It is not reasonable to expect that rainfall will be spatially uniform over a large drainage basin, or that it will be temporally uniform over a duration at least as long as the time of concentration when t_c (and hence A) is large. Therefore, these conditions limit the applicability of the Rational Method to small drainage basins. An upper limit of 200 acres has been suggested by some, but the limit should really depend on the storm characteristics of the particular locale. These local characteristics may limit the applicability of the Rational Method to basins smaller than 10 acres in some cases.

When several drainage basins (or subbasins) discharge to a common facility such as a storm sewer or culvert, the time of concentration should be taken as the longest of all the individual times of concentration, and should include pipe travel times when appropriate. Further, the total drainage area served (the sum of the individual basin areas) should be no larger than the 200-acre limit (or smaller where applicable) of the Rational Method.

The basic steps for applying the Rational Method are as follows:

Step 1: Apply I-D-F Data

Develop or obtain a set of intensity-duration-frequency (IDF) curves for the locale in which the drainage basin resides. Assume that the storm duration is equal to the time of concentration and determine the corresponding intensity for the recurrence interval of interest. Note that the assumption that the storm duration and time of concentration are equal is conservative in that it represents the highest intensity for which the entire drainage area can contribute.

Step 2: Compute Watershed Area

The basin area A can be estimated using topographic maps, computer tools such as CAD or GIS software, or by field reconnaissance. The time of concentration may be estimated using the procedures discussed in the preceding subsection.

Step 3: Choose C Coefficients

The runoff coefficient C may be estimated using Table 2-5 if the land use is homogeneous in the basin, or a composite C value may be estimated if the land use is heterogeneous (see Example 2-6).

Step 4: Solve Peak Flow

Finally, the peak runoff rate from the basin can be computed using the equation $Q = CiA$.

The following example illustrates the use of the Rational Method for several subbasins draining into a common storm sewer system.

Example 2-9: Computing Flows for Multiple Subbasins with the Rational Method

Figure 2-13 is a plan view of a storm sewer system draining three subbasins. Use the Rational Method to determine the peak discharge in each pipe and size each pipe assuming the pipes flow full. Assume also that the pipes will be concrete with $n = 0.013$. Perform the calculations for a storm recurrence interval of 25 years. Subbasin and pipe characteristics and IDF data for the 25-year event are tabulated as follows:

Subbasin	A (ac)	C	t_c (min)
A	6.0	0.6	20
B	4.0	0.8	10
C	4.5	0.8	15

Pipe	Length (ft)	Slope (%)
1	500	1.0
2	400	1.2
3	500	0.9

Duration (min)	Intensity (in/hr)
5	8.40
10	7.02
15	5.96
20	5.26
30	4.42
60	2.97

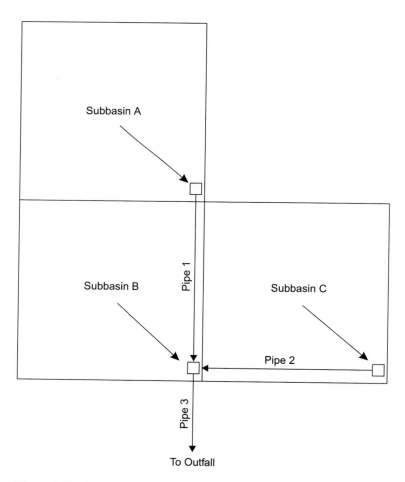

Figure 2-13: System for Example 2-9

Solution

Flow into Pipe 1 occurs from Subbasin A only. Using the time of concentration as the storm duration, the 25-year rainfall intensity is 5.26 in/hr. The peak discharge used in sizing Pipe 1 is therefore

$$Q = 0.6(5.26)(6.0) = 19 \text{ cfs}$$

Assuming that Pipe 1 is flowing full, its required diameter D may be found using Manning's equation as follows:

$$D = \left(\frac{Qn}{0.464 S^{1/2}} \right)^{3/8} = \left(\frac{19(0.013)}{0.464(0.01)^{1/2}} \right)^{3/8} = 1.87 \text{ ft}$$

Rounding up to the next commercially available size, Pipe 1 should have a diameter of 24 inches.

The cross-sectional area of Pipe 1 is therefore 3.14 ft^2, and the average velocity in Pipe 1 is

$$V = Q/A = 19/3.14 = 6.1 \text{ ft/s}$$

The travel time in Pipe 1 is

$$t = L/V = 500/6.1 = 82 \text{ s} = 1.4 \text{ minutes}$$

Pipe 2 is treated the same way as Pipe 1, recognizing that runoff from Subbasin C only enters Pipe 2. The peak discharge from Subbasin C is $Q = 22$ cfs, and the required diameter of Pipe 2 is $D = 24$ in. The travel time in Pipe 2 is $t = 57$ s $= 1.0$ min.

Pipe 3 must be sized to handle the runoff from all three of the subbasins, which have a total area of $A = 14.5$ acres. The runoff coefficient for the combined areas is computed as a composite value and is

$$C = \frac{6(0.6) + 4(0.8) + 4.5(0.8)}{14.5} = 0.72$$

The time of concentration is computed as the longest of the travel times to the upstream end of Pipe 3. These travel times are (1) the time of concentration of Subbasin B (10 minutes), (2) the time of concentration of Subbasin A plus the travel time in pipe 1 (20 + 1.4 = 21.4 min), and (3) the time of concentration of Subbasin C plus the travel time in Pipe 2 (15 + 1.0 = 16.0 min). Thus, the time of concentration for Pipe 3 is 21.4 minutes, and the corresponding rainfall intensity (by interpolation) is 5.14 in/hr.

The peak discharge for Pipe 3 is

$$Q = 0.72(5.14)(14.5) = 54 \text{ cfs}$$

The required diameter of Pipe 3 (rounded to the nearest standard size) is 36 inches.

NRCS (SCS) Peak Flow Estimation

The NRCS (SCS) has developed a simple procedure for estimation of peak runoff rates for small drainage basins. Graphical and tabular solutions to this procedure are presented in Technical Release 55 (TR-55) (SCS, 1986), and tabular and regression-based solutions are presented in the U.S. Department of Transportation Federal Highway Administration's Hydrologic Engineering Circular No. 22 (HEC-22) (Brown et al., 1996). The HEC-22 regression procedure is described in this subsection.

For use with this method, the drainage basin should have a fairly homogeneous distribution of CN, and the composite CN should be at least 40. The basin should also have one main channel, although branches are acceptable if they have approximately equal times of concentration. Further, this method was developed for use with 24-hour storm rainfall depths. Its use with other storm durations is not advised.

This method is implemented by first applying the following equation to estimate the depth of effective precipitation during a storm. The peak discharge is estimated as

$$Q_p = q_u A P_e$$

where Q_p= the peak flow rate (cfs)
   q_u = the unit peak flow rate (cfs/mi^2/in)
   A = the drainage basin area (mi^2)
   P_e = the depth of effective precipitation (in)

The unit peak flow rate is estimated as

$$q_u = 10^K$$

where

$$K = C_0 + C_1 \log_{10} t_c + C_2 (\log_{10} t_c)^2$$

C_0, C_1, and C_2 are coefficients listed in Table 2-9 as a function of the SCS 24-hour design storm distribution type and the ratio I_a/P, and t_c is the time of concentration (hr). P is the 24-hour rainfall depth, and I_a is the depth of initial abstractions. For convenience, the ratio I_a/P is tabulated in Table 2-10 as a function of the curve number. The ratio I_a/P should not be less than 0.1, nor larger than 0.5. The time of concentration should be in the range of 0.1 to 10 hours.

Table 2-9: Coefficients for SCS (NRCS) Peak Discharge Method (FHWA, 1996)

Storm Type	Ia/P	C_0	C_1	C_2
I	0.10	2.30550	-0.51429	-0.11750
	0.15	2.27044	-0.50908	-0.10339
	0.20	2.23537	-0.50387	-0.08929
	0.25	2.18219	-0.48488	-0.06589
	0.30	2.10624	-0.45696	-0.02835
	0.35	2.00303	-0.40769	-0.01983
	0.40	1.87733	-0.32274	0.05754
	0.45	1.76312	-0.15644	0.00453
	0.50	1.67889	-0.06930	0
IA	0.10	2.03250	-0.31583	-0.13748
	0.15	1.97614	-0.29899	-0.10384
	0.20	1.91978	-0.28215	-0.07020
	0.25	1.83842	-0.25543	-0.02597
	0.30	1.72657	-0.19826	0.02633
	0.35	1.70347	-0.17145	0.01975
	0.40	1.68037	-0.14463	0.01317
	0.45	1.65727	-0.11782	0.00658
	0.50	1.63417	-0.09100	0
II	0.10	2.55323	-0.61512	-0.16403
	0.15	2.53125	-0.61698	-0.15217
	0.20	2.50928	-0.61885	-0.14030
	0.25	2.48730	-0.62071	-0.12844
	0.30	2.46532	-0.62257	-0.11657
	0.35	2.41896	-0.61594	-0.08820
	0.40	2.36409	-0.59857	-0.05621
	0.45	2.29238	-0.57005	-0.02281
	0.50	2.20282	-0.51599	-0.01259
III	0.10	2.47317	-0.51848	-0.17083
	0.15	2.45395	-0.51687	-0.16124
	0.20	2.43473	-0.51525	-0.15164
	0.25	2.41550	-0.51364	-0.14205
	0.30	2.39628	-0.51202	-0.13245
	0.35	2.35477	-0.49735	-0.11985
	0.40	2.30726	-0.46541	-0.11094
	0.45	2.24876	-0.41314	-0.11508
	0.50	2.17772	-0.36803	-0.09525

Table 2-10: I_a/P for Selected Rainfall Depths and Curve Numbers (Adapted from FHWA, 1996)

P (in)	Curve Number, CN											
	40	45	50	55	60	65	70	75	80	85	90	95
0.50	0.50	0.50	0.50	0.50	0.50	0.50	0.50	0.50	0.50	0.50	0.44	0.21
1.00	0.50	0.50	0.50	0.50	0.50	0.50	0.50	0.50	0.50	0.35	0.22	0.11
1.50	0.50	0.50	0.50	0.50	0.50	0.50	0.50	0.44	0.33	0.24	0.15	0.10
2.00	0.50	0.50	0.50	0.50	0.50	0.50	0.43	0.33	0.25	0.18	0.11	0.10
2.50	0.50	0.50	0.50	0.50	0.50	0.43	0.34	0.27	0.20	0.14	0.10	0.10
3.00	0.50	0.50	0.50	0.50	0.44	0.36	0.29	0.22	0.17	0.12	0.10	0.10
3.50	0.50	0.50	0.50	0.47	0.38	0.31	0.24	0.19	0.14	0.10	0.10	0.10
4.00	0.50	0.50	0.50	0.41	0.33	0.27	0.21	0.17	0.13	0.10	0.10	0.10
4.50	0.50	0.50	0.44	0.36	0.30	0.24	0.19	0.15	0.11	0.10	0.10	0.10
5.00	0.50	0.49	0.40	0.33	0.27	0.22	0.17	0.13	0.10	0.10	0.10	0.10
5.50	0.50	0.44	0.36	0.30	0.24	0.20	0.16	0.12	0.10	0.10	0.10	0.10
6.00	0.50	0.41	0.33	0.27	0.22	0.18	0.14	0.11	0.10	0.10	0.10	0.10
6.50	0.46	0.38	0.31	0.25	0.21	0.17	0.13	0.10	0.10	0.10	0.10	0.10
7.00	0.43	0.35	0.29	0.23	0.19	0.15	0.12	0.10	0.10	0.10	0.10	0.10
7.50	0.40	0.33	0.27	0.22	0.18	0.14	0.11	0.10	0.10	0.10	0.10	0.10
8.00	0.38	0.31	0.25	0.20	0.17	0.13	0.11	0.10	0.10	0.10	0.10	0.10
8.50	0.35	0.29	0.24	0.19	0.16	0.13	0.10	0.10	0.10	0.10	0.10	0.10
9.00	0.33	0.27	0.22	0.18	0.15	0.12	0.10	0.10	0.10	0.10	0.10	0.10
9.50	0.32	0.26	0.21	0.17	0.14	0.11	0.10	0.10	0.10	0.10	0.10	0.10
10.00	0.30	0.24	0.20	0.16	0.13	0.11	0.10	0.10	0.10	0.10	0.10	0.10
10.50	0.29	0.23	0.19	0.16	0.13	0.10	0.10	0.10	0.10	0.10	0.10	0.10
11.00	0.27	0.22	0.18	0.15	0.12	0.10	0.10	0.10	0.10	0.10	0.10	0.10
11.50	0.26	0.21	0.17	0.14	0.12	0.10	0.10	0.10	0.10	0.10	0.10	0.10
12.00	0.25	0.20	0.17	0.14	0.11	0.10	0.10	0.10	0.10	0.10	0.10	0.10
12.50	0.24	0.20	0.16	0.13	0.11	0.10	0.10	0.10	0.10	0.10	0.10	0.10
13.00	0.23	0.19	0.15	0.13	0.10	0.10	0.10	0.10	0.10	0.10	0.10	0.10
13.50	0.22	0.18	0.15	0.12	0.10	0.10	0.10	0.10	0.10	0.10	0.10	0.10
14.00	0.21	0.17	0.14	0.12	0.10	0.10	0.10	0.10	0.10	0.10	0.10	0.10
14.50	0.21	0.17	0.14	0.11	0.10	0.10	0.10	0.10	0.10	0.10	0.10	0.10
15.00	0.20	0.16	0.13	0.11	0.10	0.10	0.10	0.10	0.10	0.10	0.10	0.10

When ponding or swampy areas exist in a drainage basin, the peak discharge should be reduced to account for the temporary storage of runoff. In this case, an adjusted peak flow Q_{pa} should be computed as

$$Q_{pa} = F_p Q_p$$

where F_p is an adjustment factor obtained from Table 2-11. Ponds and swampy areas lying along the flow path used for computation of the time of concentration should not be included in the area percentage in Table 2-11. Neither channel nor reservoir routing can be accommodated with this method.

Table 2-11: Adjustment Factor, F_p, for Ponds and Swampy Areas (FHWA, 1996)

Pond and Swamp Area (percent)	F_p
0	1.00
0.2	0.97
1.0	0.87
3.0	0.75
5.0	0.72

Example 2-10: Computing Peak Discharge Using the NRCS Method

Compute the peak discharge from the 1,000-acre (1.56 mi^2) drainage basin described in Example 2-7, but using AMC-II soil moisture conditions. The rainfall distribution is an SCS Type II distribution, and the time of concentration of the drainage basin is 0.9 hours. There are no ponds or swampy areas in the basin.

Solution

From Example 2-7, $P = 5.0$ inches and $CN = 86$ for AMC-II. For this condition, the maximum possible retention $S = 1.63$ inch, and the effective precipitation is $P_e = 3.46$ inches.

From Table 2-10, the ratio I_a/P is 0.10; and from Table 2-9 the coefficients C_0, C_1, and C_2 are $C_0 = 2.55323$, $C_1 = -0.61512$, and $C_2 = -0.16403$, respectively. Therefore,

$$K = 2.55323 - 0.61512 \, \log_{10}(0.9) - 0.16403[\log_{10}(0.9)]^2 = 2.58104$$

The unit peak flow rate is

$$q_u = 10^{2.58104} = 381 \text{ cfs/mi}^2/\text{in}$$

The peak discharge from the drainage basin is computed as

$$Q_p = 381(1.56)(3.46) = 2,060 \text{ cfs}$$

2.4 Computing Hydrographs

A *hydrograph* represents the flow rate as it varies over time at a particular location within a watershed. The integrated area under the hydrograph represents the total hydrograph volume of water. Base flow represents subsurface flow from groundwater that discharges into the conveyance channel. Many storm conveyance channels are dry at the beginning of a rainfall event, which equates to a base flow of zero as long as the water table does not rise into the channel during the storm. Figure 2-14 displays the various components of a surface runoff hydrograph, with a base flow of zero.

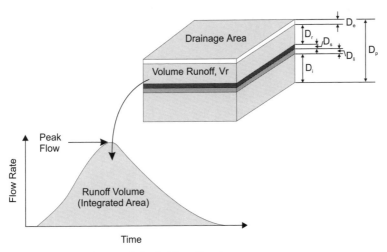

Figure 2-14: Hydrograph Definition Sketch

Estimation of a complete runoff hydrograph, as opposed to merely the peak rate of runoff, is necessary to account for the effects of storage in a drainage basin. Because a hydrograph accounts for volume and flow variations over an entire rainfall event, it is useful for analyzing complex watersheds and designing detention ponds. Hydrographs enable you to assess of the effects of storage associated with natural ponds and lakes, and with artificial stormwater detention and/or retention facilities. Hydrograph estimation is also necessary in order to assess the impacts of storm duration and/or hyetograph shape on runoff production, and in cases when two or more adjacent drainage basins (or subbasins) are discharging to a common stream.

Procedures for estimating unit hydrographs and performing discrete convolution are presented in this and the following section. *Unit hydrograph estimation methods* involve several basic steps:

1. Establish a design storm rainfall hyetograph.

2. Convert the design storm rainfall hyetograph into a runoff (effective rainfall) hyetograph by subtraction of rainfall abstractions.

3. Estimate a unit hydrograph for the drainage basin of interest.

4. Merge the runoff (effective rainfall hyetograph) and the unit hydrograph using discrete convolution to produce what is called a *direct runoff hydrograph,* which represents the surface runoff hydrograph for the complex storm pattern represented by the rainfall hyetograph.

5. If appropriate, add *base flow* to the direct runoff hydrograph to obtain the *total hydrograph* representing both surface runoff and base flow.

Creating Runoff (Effective Rainfall) Hyetographs

The first step in calculating a runoff hydrograph from a given rainfall hyetograph is to calculate a runoff (effective rainfall) hyetograph. Provided that the data is available, the most accurate way to do this is to develop a runoff hyetograph by modeling abstractions and infiltration within each time-step of a rainfall event. To do this, subtract the interception from the beginning of a gross rainfall hyetograph, subtract infiltration from what remains after interception has been accounted for, and subtract depression storage from what remains after both interception and infiltration have been accounted for. This approach is physically based and is not limited to use with any particular storm duration or rainfall hyetograph shape.

Example 2-11: Computing an Effective Rainfall Hyetograph

Develop a runoff (effective rainfall) hyetograph for a watershed with an initial loss (interception capacity) of 0.3 in., a depression storage capacity of 0.2 in., and Horton infiltration parameters of $f_0 = 1.5$ in/hr, $f_c = 0.3$ in/hr, and $k = 0.04$ min^{-1}. The rainfall hyetograph is tabulated as follows:

t (min)	P (in.)
0 – 10	0.24
10 – 20	0.46
20 – 30	1.17
30 – 40	0.58
40 – 50	0.35
50 – 60	0.17

Solution

The interception capacity of 0.3 in. is subtracted first. Because 0.24 in. of rainfall occurs during the first 10 minutes of the storm, all of that rainfall plus an additional 0.06 in. of rainfall occurring in the second 10 minutes of the storm is lost to interception. Thus, after accounting for interception, the rainfall hyetograph is:

t (min)	P (in.)
0 – 10	0
10 – 20	0.4
20 – 30	1.17
30 – 40	0.58
40 – 50	0.35
50 – 60	0.17

The infiltration rate, $f(t)$, can be calculated and tabulated as a function of t using the Horton equation (see Section 2.2), where t_0 is the time at which rainwater first begins to infiltrate ($t_0 = 10$ min in this example, because rainfall prior to that time is lost to interception and hence is not available for infiltration). The first column in the following table is the time since the beginning of rainfall, and the second is the time since the beginning of infiltration. The third column is the computed infiltration rate.

The fourth column contains incremental infiltration depths for each 10-minute period during the storm. For example, the first value of $F = 0.22$ in. is computed as the average of the current and preceding infiltration rates, multiplied by the time interval of $\Delta t = 10$ min $= 1/6$ hr (for example, $0.22 = [(1.50 + 1.10)/2]/6)$.

t (min)	$t - t_0$ (min)	$f(t)$ (in/hr)	Incr. F (in)
0			
10	0	1.5	
20	10	1.1	0.22
30	20	0.84	0.16
40	30	0.66	0.13
50	40	0.54	0.1
60	50	0.46	0.08

Subtraction of the infiltration depth in each time interval from the corresponding rainfall depth remaining after interception leads to the following hyetograph (any negative values produced should be set equal to zero):

t (min)	P (in)
0-10	0
10 – 20	0.18
20 – 30	1.01
30 – 40	0.45
40 – 50	0.25
50 – 60	0.09

Finally, subtraction of the depression storage capacity of 0.2 in. leads to the following effective rainfall hyetograph:

t (min)	P_e (in)
10 – 20	0
10 – 20	0
20 – 30	0.99
30 – 40	0.45
40 – 50	0.25
50 – 60	0.09

The rainfall hyetograph and the effective rainfall hyetograph are illustrated in Figures 2-15 and 2-16. Note that the effective rainfall intensities are less than the actual rainfall intensities. Note also that effective rainfall, and hence surface runoff, does not begin (in this example) until 20 minutes after the beginning of the storm.

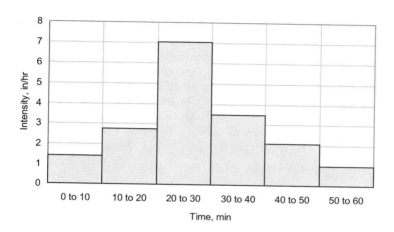

Figure 2-15: Rainfall Hyetograph for Example 2-11

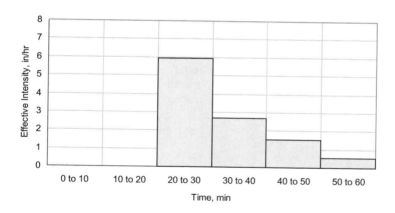

Figure 2-16: Effective Rainfall (Runoff) Hyetograph for Example 2-11

Unit Hydrographs

A *unit hydrograph* is an important intermediate step in computing a full runoff hydrograph for design or analysis purposes. After a unit hydrograph is established for a particular basin, the data can be used to compute the complete runoff hydrographs resulting from various rainfall events. The basic theory rests on the assumption that the runoff response of a drainage basin to an effective rainfall input is linear. Practically speaking, this assumption means that the concepts of proportionality and superposition can be applied. For example, it means that the direct runoff caused by two inches of effective rainfall in a given time interval is four times as great as that caused by 0.5 in. of effective rainfall in the same amount of time. It also means that the total amount of time for the basin to respond to each of these rainfall depths is the same. Consequently, the base length, in hours, of each of the direct runoff hydrographs is the same.

Visualizing and Developing Unit Hydrographs

By definition, the Δt-hour (or Δt-minute) unit hydrograph of a drainage basin is the direct runoff hydrograph produced by one inch of effective rainfall falling uniformly in time and space over the drainage basin during a duration Δt time units. By conservation of mass, the volume of runoff produced (represented by the area under a graph of the unit hydrograph) must be equal to one inch of runoff (effective rainfall) times the drainage basin area (see Figure 2-17). It may be observed from this definition that the unit hydrographs for two drainage basins must be different from one another, because the basin areas (as well as other factors) are different.

Figure 2-18 provides a metaphor to help demonstrate the abstract principals of a unit hydrograph. A sprinkler system is uniformly distributed over an entire drainage area. Constant rainfall is modeled by using the sprinklers to apply a constant rate of water until exactly one inch of runoff is generated, at which time the sprinklers are turned off. Δt represents the duration of time that the sprinklers are on. A stream gauge is set on the downstream end of the contributing drainage area to record the runoff hydrograph resulting from the one inch of runoff. The resulting hydrograph represents the *unit hydrograph* generated for the drainage area.

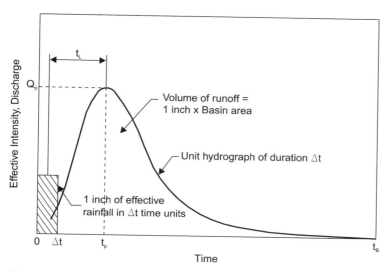

Figure 2-17: Unit Hydrograph Resulting from 1 in. of Effective Rainfall (Runoff) over Time (Δt)

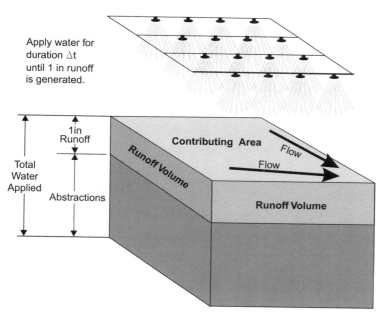

Figure 2-18: Visualizing the Unit Hydrograph Concept

The time t_L in Figure 2-17, which is the length of time from the center of Δt to the peak discharge on the unit hydrograph, is the **basin lag time.** This response time can be thought of as an approximate average of all possible travel times for runoff in a drainage basin. In practice (and as shown in the figure), it is usually assumed to be the amount of time between the center of mass of a pulse of effective rainfall and the peak of the resultant hydrograph. The basin lag time is often used instead of time of concentration when estimating the complete runoff hydrograph.

Two basic categories of unit hydrographs exist: (1) unit hydrographs for gauged watersheds and (2) *synthetic unit hydrographs.* Most commonly, rainfall and runoff records for a drainage basin do not exist, and one must resort to synthesis of a unit hydrograph based on information that can be gathered about the basin. Extensive literature exists on various ways to calculate synthetic unit hydrographs, including procedures proposed by Clark, Snyder, and Singh. This text introduces the development of synthetic unit hydrographs by applying the NRCS (SCS) method. The Haestad Press book *Hydrology and Runoff Modeling* provides details on other synthetic unit hydrographs methods.

NRCS Synthetic Unit Hydrographs

The NRCS analyzed a large number of unit hydrographs derived from rainfall and runoff records for a wide range of basins and basin locations and developed an average *dimensionless unit hydrograph* (SCS, 1969). Times on the horizontal axis of the dimensionless unit hydrograph are expressed in terms of the ratio of time to time of peak discharge (t/t_p), and discharges on the vertical axis are expressed in terms of the ratio of discharge to peak discharge (Q/Q_p). Figure 2-19 shows the NRCS dimensionless unit hydrograph, and Table 2-21 lists its ordinates.

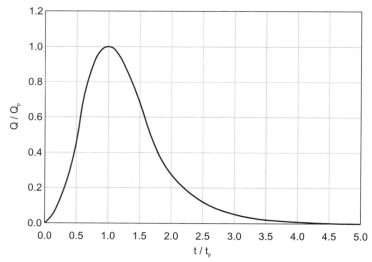

Figure 2-19: The NRCS (SCS) Dimensionless Unit Hydrograph

Table 2-12: Ordinates of the SCS (NRCS) Dimensionless Unit Hydrograph (SCS, 1969)

t/t_p	Q/Q_p	t/t_p	Q/Q_p
0	0.000	1.7	0.460
0.1	0.030	1.8	0.390
0.2	0.100	1.9	0.330
0.3	0.190	2.0	0.280
0.4	0.310	2.2	0.207
0.5	0.470	2.4	0.147
0.6	0.660	2.6	0.107
0.7	0.820	2.8	0.077
0.8	0.930	3.0	0.055
0.9	0.990	3.2	0.040
1.0	1.000	3.4	0.029
1.1	0.990	3.6	0.021
1.2	0.930	3.8	0.015
1.3	0.860	4.0	0.011
1.4	0.780	4.5	0.005
1.5	0.680	5.0	0.000
1.6	0.560		

Application of the dimensionless unit hydrograph method involves estimation of the lag time t_L of the drainage basin. Lag is typically approximated as $0.6t_c$ in NRCS (SCS) unit hydrograph computations. The time to peak of the synthetic unit hydrograph of duration Δt is then computed as:

$$t_p = \frac{\Delta t}{2} + t_L$$

The NRCS recommends that Δt should be equal to $0.133t_c$, or equal to $0.222t_L$ (SCS, 1969). A small variation from this is acceptable. The Δt chosen for development of the synthetic unit hydrograph must be consistent with the Δt chosen for development of the design storm and effective rainfall hyetographs.

The peak discharge Q_p (in cfs) of the synthetic unit hydrograph is calculated as

$$Q_p = \frac{645.33 KAQ}{t_p}$$

where $645.33 =$ conversion factor $= (1 \text{hr}/3600 \text{ s}) (1 \text{ft}/12 \text{ in}) [(5280 \text{ft})^2/1 \text{ mi}^2]$
        $K = 0.75$ is constant based on geometric shape of dimensionless unit hydrograph
        (NEH-4)
        $Q = 1$ in. is the runoff depth for unit hydrograph calculation
        $A =$ the drainage basin area (mi^2)
        $t_p =$ the time to peak (hr)

Simplifying yields

$$Q_p = \frac{484A}{t_p}$$

The coefficient 484 appearing in the numerator of this equation includes a unit conversion factor and is an average value for many drainage basins. It may be reduced to about 300 for flat or swampy basins, or increased to about 600 for steep or mountainous basins. Care needs to be taken when the factor 484 is changed, as the base length and/or shape of the synthetic unit hydrograph must also be changed to ensure that it represents a volume of water equivalent to one inch of effective rainfall over the drainage basin area.

Once t_p and Q_p have been estimated using the preceding equations, the desired synthetic unit hydrograph can be graphed and/or tabulated using the dimensionless unit hydrograph shown in Figure 2-19 and Table 2-12.

Example 2-12: Developing an NRCS (SCS) Synthetic Unit Hydrograph

Develop a synthetic unit hydrograph for a 1.5-mi^2 drainage basin in Memphis, Tennessee having a time of concentration of 90 minutes. Assume that the basin slopes are moderate so that the factor 484 can be applied in computing Q_p.

Solution

Employing the guidelines for estimation of Δt, its value should be no larger than

$0.133t_c = 0.133(90) = 12$ min

A duration of $\Delta t = 10$ minutes is selected, and the synthetic unit hydrograph will be a 10-minute unit hydrograph. The basin lag is estimated as

$t_L = 0.6t_c = 54$ min

The time to peak for the synthetic unit hydrograph is

$t_p = (10/2) + 54 = 59$ min $= 0.98$ hr

The peak discharge is estimated as

$Q_p = 484(1.5)/0.98 = 740$ cfs.

Ordinates of the synthetic unit hydrograph are given in Table 2-13. The first column of the table is the time t, in minutes, and is tabulated in $\Delta t = 10$ min intervals. The second column is the dimensionless time ratio t/t_p, where $t_p = 59$ min. The third column is the dimensionless discharge ratio, and is determined using the dimensionless time ratio and interpolation from Table 2-12. The fourth and last column contains the ordinates of the 10-min unit hydrograph, which are computed as the products of the dimensionless discharge ratios and $Q_p = 740$ cfs.

Table 2-13: SCS (NRCS) Synthetic Unit Hydrograph Computations for Example 2-12

(1) t (min)	(2) t/t_p	(3) Q/Q_p	(4) Q (cfs)	(5) t (min)	(6) t/t_p	(7) Q/Q_p	(8) Q (cfs)
0	0.00	0.00	0	140	2.37	0.16	118
10	0.17	0.08	59	150	2.54	0.12	89
20	0.34	0.24	178	160	2.71	0.09	67
30	0.51	0.49	363	170	2.88	0.07	52
40	0.68	0.79	585	180	3.05	0.05	37
50	0.85	0.96	710	190	3.22	0.04	30
60	1.02	1.00	740	200	3.39	0.03	22
70	1.19	0.93	688	210	3.56	0.02	15
80	1.36	0.81	599	220	3.73	0.02	15
90	1.53	0.64	474	230	3.90	0.01	7
100	1.69	0.47	348	240	4.07	0.01	7
110	1.86	0.35	259	250	4.24	0.01	7
120	2.03	0.26	192	260	4.41	0.01	7
130	2.20	0.21	155	270	4.58	0.00	0

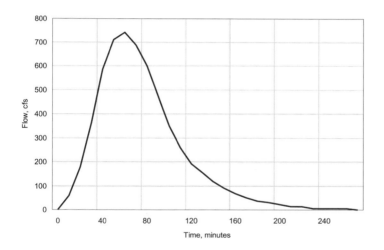

Figure 2-20: Synthetic Unit Hydrograph for Example 2-12

Discrete Convolution

A unit hydrograph represents the runoff hydrograph from a drainage basin subjected to one inch of runoff (effective precipitation) applied over a duration of Δt. However, a runoff (effective rainfall) hyetograph typically contains many Δt time periods, each of which has its own associated runoff depth. In *discrete convolution,* the direct runoff hydrograph resulting from a complete rainfall hyetograph is computed by applying a unit hydrograph to each discrete time step within the hyetograph.

To conceptualize discrete convolution, refer to Figures 2-21 and 2-22. The first figure illustrates a runoff (effective rainfall) hyetograph consisting of $n_p = 3$ rainfall pulses, each of duration $\Delta t = 10$ minutes, with the depth of each pulse denoted by P_i ($i = 1, 2 \ldots n_p$). The second figure shows a unit hydrograph with $n_u = 11$ non-zero ordinates shown at Δt time intervals, with the nonzero ordinates denoted by U_j ($j = 1, 2 \ldots n_u$). (Note that the ordinates of the unit hydrograph are in units of cfs per inch of runoff, and thus the notation of this subsection is different from the previous subsection in which unit hydrograph ordinates were denoted by discharge Q.) The time increment Δt used for development of the runoff (effective rainfall) hyetograph must be the same as the Δt duration of excess rainfall used to create the unit hydrograph.

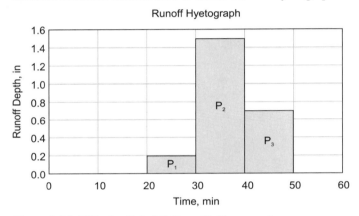

Figure 2-21: Effective Rainfall (Runoff) Hyetograph

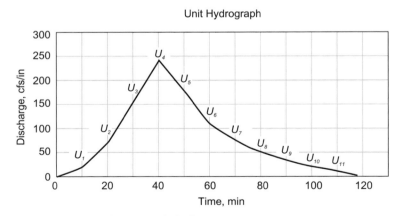

Figure 2-22: Unit Hydrograph Ordinates

Because unit hydrograph theory assumes that drainage basins behave linearly, the ordinates Q_j of the runoff hydrograph produced by P_1 inches of effective rainfall must be equal to $Q_j = P_1 U_j$. These ordinates are shown in the third column of Table 2-14 (the first and second columns of the table reproduce the information in Figure 2-22). These ordinates were calculated by multiplying each unit hydrograph ordinate by the runoff depth for pulse $P_1 = 0.2$ in. The values in column three are shifted down such that the time at which the runoff hydrograph in column three begins is the same as the time at which the first pulse of effective rainfall begins.

The fourth and fifth columns in Table 2-14 are computed by multiplying the unit hydrograph ordinates in the second column by the effective rainfall depths $P_2 = 1.5$ in. and $P_3 = 0.7$ in., respectively. Again, the time at which each runoff pulse's hydrograph begins corresponds to the time at which each runoff (effective rainfall) pulse begins. The sum of the runoff hydrograph ordinates in each row of the table (shown in the sixth column) is an ordinate of the direct runoff hydrograph caused by the complete rainfall event.

Table 2-14: Discrete Convolution

(1) t (min)	(2) U (cfs/in)	(3) P_1U (cfs)	(4) P_2U (cfs)	(5) P_3U (cfs)	(6) Q (cfs)
0	0				0
10	20				0
20	70	0			0
30	160	4	0		4
40	240	14	30	0	44
50	180	32	105	14	151
60	110	48	240	49	337
70	75	36	360	112	508
80	50	22	270	168	460
90	33	15	165	126	306
100	21	10	113	77	200
110	10	7	75	53	134
120	0	4	50	35	89
130		2	32	23	57
140		0	15	15	30
150			0	7	7
160				0	0

Figure 2-23 shows the runoff hydrograph resulting from each rainfall pulse and the total runoff hydrograph for the entire rainfall event.

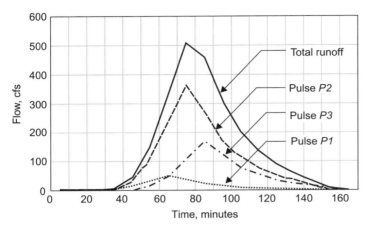

Figure 2-23: Summing of Hydrographs from Individual Rainfall Pulses

Example 2-13: Computing a Runoff Hydrograph

Compute the direct runoff hydrograph for the Memphis, Tennessee drainage basin described in Example 2-12. Use the unit hydrograph developed for the basin in that example, and use the runoff (effective rainfall) hyetograph developed in Example 2-11.

Solution

There are a total of $n_p = 4$ runoff (effective rainfall) pulses, and a total of $n_u = 26$ non-zero unit hydrograph ordinates. Thus, there will be a total of $n_q = 29$ non-zero direct runoff hydrograph ordinates.

Table 2-15 illustrates the tabular calculation (discrete convolution). The first column is the time since the beginning of rainfall in $\Delta t = 10$ minute increments (the duration of the unit hydrograph and the duration of the effective rainfall pulses). The second column contains the ordinates of the unit hydrograph from Example 2-12. The third through the sixth columns are the unit hydrograph ordinates multiplied by the effective rainfall depths. Note that the first entry (the first zero) in each column corresponds to the time at which the corresponding effective rainfall pulse begins ($t = 20$ min for the first pulse, $t = 30$ min for the second pulse, and $t = 40$ min for the third pulse; see Figure 2-16). The seventh column is the sum of the previous four, and is the direct runoff hydrograph.

Table 2-15: Discrete Convolution to Obtain Direct Runoff Hydrograph

(1) *t* (min)	(2) *U* (cfs/in)	(3) 0.99*U*	(4) 0.45*U*	(5) 0.25*U*	(6) 0.09*U*	(7) *Q* (cfs)
0	0					0
10	59					0
20	178	0				0
30	363	58	0			58
40	585	176	27	0		203
50	710	359	80	15	0	454
60	740	579	163	45	5	792
70	688	703	263	91	16	1073
80	599	733	320	146	33	1231
90	474	681	333	178	53	1244
100	348	593	310	185	64	1152
110	259	469	270	172	67	977
120	192	345	213	150	62	769
130	155	256	157	119	54	585
140	118	190	117	87	43	436
150	89	153	86	65	31	336
160	67	117	70	48	23	258
170	52	88	53	39	17	197
180	37	66	40	30	14	150
190	30	51	30	22	11	115
200	22	37	23	17	8	85
210	15	30	17	13	6	65
220	15	22	14	9	5	49
230	7	15	10	8	3	36
240	7	15	7	6	3	30
250	7	7	7	4	2	19
260	7	7	3	4	1	15
270	0	7	3	2	1	13
280		7	3	2	1	12
290		0	3	2	1	6
300			0	2	1	2
310				0	1	1
320					0	0

2.5 Problems

1. The following data is from Huff and Angle (1992). The numbers indicate the total rainfall (inches) expected in Chicago, Illinois for storm recurrence intervals of 2, 5, 10, 25, 50 and 100 years and durations from 5 minutes to 24 hours. Plot a series of IDF curves showing the rainfall intensities for each recurrence interval for storm durations between 5 minutes and 2 hours.

Duration	Recurrence Interval (years)					
	2	5	10	25	50	100
24 hrs	3.11	3.95	4.63	5.60	5.63	7.36
2 hr	1.83	2.33	2.74	3.31	3.86	4.47
1 hr	1.46	1.86	2.18	2.63	3.07	3.51
30 min	1.15	1.46	1.71	2.07	2.42	2.77
15 min	0.84	1.07	1.25	1.51	1.76	1.99
10 min	0.68	0.87	1.02	1.23	1.44	1.62
5 min	0.37	0.47	0.56	0.67	0.78	0.89

2. Use the data in Problem 1 and the SCS Type II distribution to develop a 25-year, 24-hour storm for Chicago.

3. During a 40-mm rainfall event, the interception capacity of the watershed is estimated to be 11 mm, the depression storage is 9 mm, and the infiltration is 7 mm. What is the total volume of runoff from the 2.56 ha watershed?

4. A proposed development consists of the following land use areas:

Land Use	Area (ac)
Condominiums	2.75
Greenbelt	0.89
Commercial	1.37

The time of concentration is estimated to be 25 min. Using the Rational Method IDF data from Problem 1, calculate the peak runoff resulting from a 10-yr storm. Use the midpoint in the range of C coefficients in Table 2-5.

5. A suburban watershed has a time of concentration of 2.5 hours and the following land use characteristics:

Land Cover	Area (mi²)	CN_{II}
Commercial & business	4	92
¼ acre housing	14	75
Parking lots, roofs & driveways	0.78	98

a) Use the NRCS (SCS) CN method to determine volume of runoff resulting from a 6-in storm. Assume that AMC-I applies.

b) Use the SCS Method to determine the peak discharge from the watershed.

6. Develop a unit hydrograph for a drainage basin with an area of 3.5 mi². Use a time of concentration of 120 min. Assume that a shape factor of 484 applies and that the time of concentration is 2 hours.

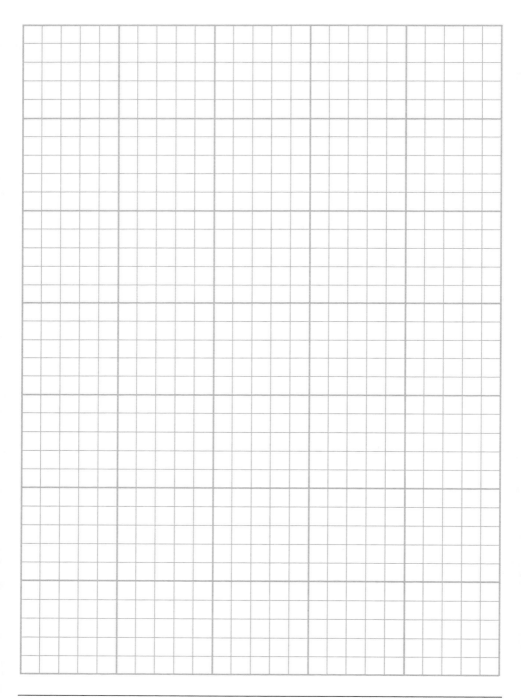

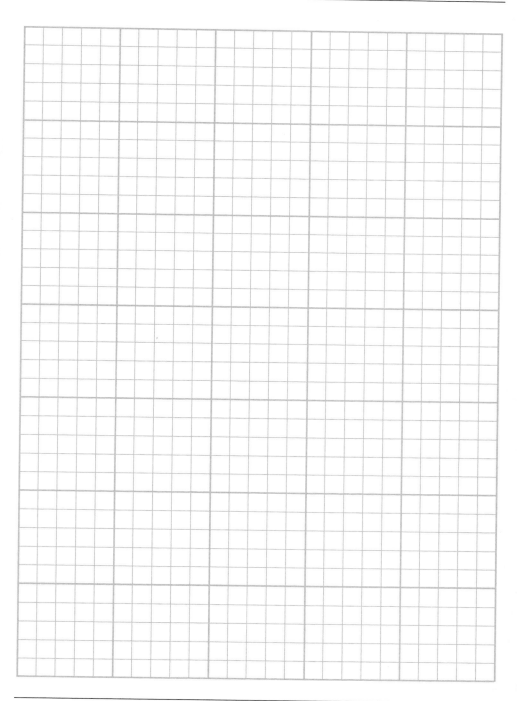

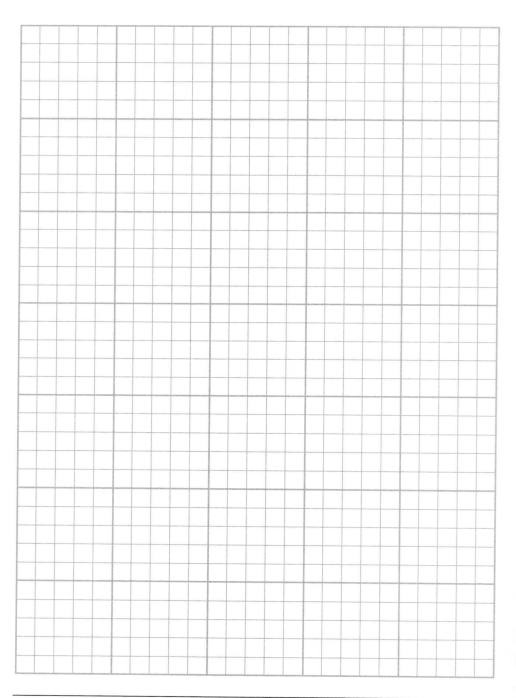

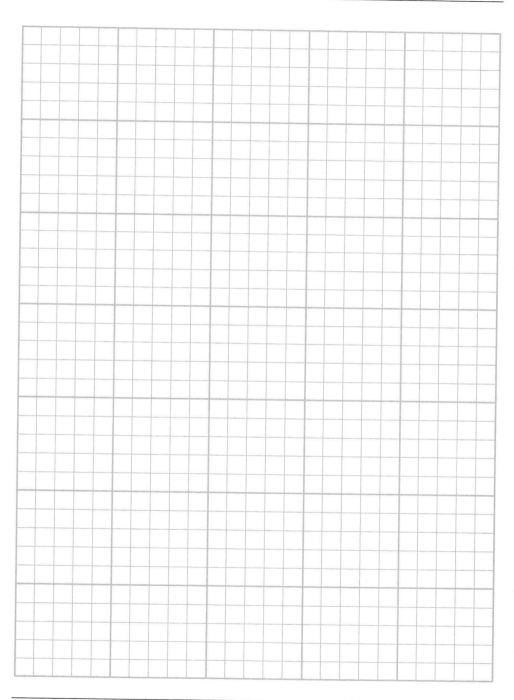

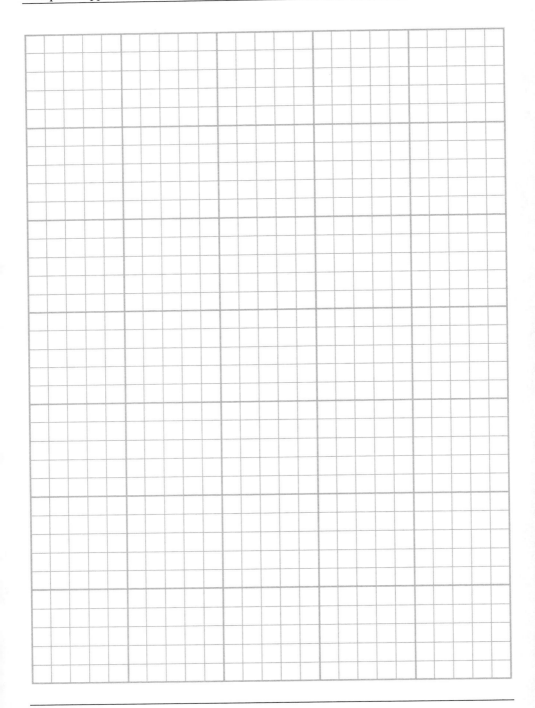

Inlets, Gravity Piping Systems, and Storm Sewer Design

3.1   Inlet Design Overview

Road and highway designs must include sufficient drainage provisions in order to minimize the danger resulting from stormwater runoff and to optimize traffic efficiency under most weather conditions. The key objective when designing inlets is to minimize the spread of water across a roadway and in the gutter. In stormwater drainage, the **gutter** is the channel on the side of the road through which stormwater runoff is conveyed to storm sewer inlets. **Spread** is the top width of the flowing water on the road, measured from the curb.

The allowable spread length, which is generally determined by local or state regulations, is based on the classification of the road. For example, a road with a higher speed limit should have a smaller allowable spread than a road designed for slower speeds because of the increased risk of hydroplaning. In addition to spread width, roadway classification also dictates the return period of the design storm to use in calculating the spread at a point. Table 3-1, from the Federal Highway Administration's (FHWA) HEC-22 *Urban Drainage Design Manual* (Brown, Stein and Warner, 1996), provides an overview of different road conditions and the design criteria these conditions necessitate. We recommend you refer to the FlowMaster or StormCAD on-line help for further explanations, as well as the HEC-22 manual.

The incoming surface flow (and spread) observed can be controlled by the efficiency and spacing of the inlets located upstream along the road. One additional factor to consider is whether the inlet is located on grade or in a sag, as the design criteria and the equations involved differ. **Inlets on grade** are located on a slope and intercept a portion of the water as it flows past. ***Inlets in sag*** are located at a point where runoff from a given area will ultimately collect, and these inlets are normally designed to capture 100 percent of the surface flow; otherwise, flooding will occur in the surrounding area.

Table 3-1: Suggested Minimum Design Frequencies and Spreads for Gutter Sections on Grade

Road Classification		Design Return Period	Design Spreads
High Volume or Bi-directional	<70 km/hr (45 mph)	10-year	Shoulder + 1 m (3 ft)
	>70 km/hr (45 mph)	10-year	Shoulder
	Sag Point	50-year	Shoulder + 1 m (3 ft)
Collector	Low Volume	10-year	½ Driving Lane
	High Volume	10-year	Shoulder
	Sag Point	10-year	½ Driving Lane
Local Streets	Low Volume	5-year	½ Driving Lane
	High Volumes	10-year	½ Driving Lane
	Sag Point	10-year	½ Driving Lane

3.2 Gutter Sections on Grade

The main curb and gutter section types are the uniform section and the composite section, as illustrated in Figure 3-1 with their defining variables. ***Uniform gutter sections*** have a constant slope across the section. ***Composite gutter sections*** are defined by a continuous gutter depression, *a,* measured from the bottom of the curb to the projected road cross-slope at the curb. The frontal flow, Q_w, is normally defined as the flow in the depressed section of the gutter or the flow over the grate width in the case of a grate inlet (grate inlets are discussed later in this chapter).

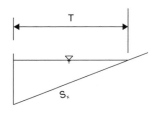

Uniform Road Section

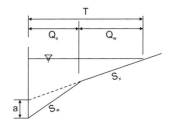

Composite Road Section

Q_w = Flow in depressed section (m³/s, ft³/s)
Q_s = Side flow (m³/s, ft³/s)
S_w = Gutter cross-slope (m/m, ft/ft)
S_x = Road cross-slope (m/m, ft/ft)
T = Total width of flow or spread (m, ft)
a = Continuous gutter depression (mm, in)

Figure 3-1: Uniform and Composite Gutter Sections

Runoff in gutters on grade is treated as open channel flow, and Manning's equation is applicable. Because the friction along the curb height is negligible compared to the friction against the pavement width (spread) of flow, Manning's formula was modified, becoming the following equation for calculating flow in uniform gutter sections:

$$Q = \frac{K_c}{n} S_x^{1.67} S_L^{0.5} T^{2.67}$$

where K_c =   0.376 (0.56 in U.S. units)
           n =   Manning's coefficient
           S_L =   road longitudinal slope (m/m, ft/ft)

Using this equation, the spread, T, in a uniform gutter section can be explicitly calculated for a given flow rate, Q. However, in the case of composite gutters, T can no longer be expressed as an explicit function of Q. Rather, an iterative process is required to calculate the spread.

On a road with a grade, the spread will be at a maximum just upstream of the inlet. Note that the spread at this location is independent of the inlet's ability to capture flow and its efficiency. The spread for a specific roadway is a function of the discharge in the gutter. To decrease the flow to an inlet, reduce inlet spacing so that they serve as collection points for smaller watersheds.

For composite sections, the variable E_0 is introduced to account for the added conveyance of a depressed gutter. E_0 is the ratio of flow in the depressed section, Q_w, to the total gutter flow, and is expressed as:

$$E_0 = \left\{ 1 + \frac{S_W}{S_X} \left[\left(1 + \frac{S_W/S_X}{(T/W)-1} \right)^{2.67} - 1 \right] \right\}^{-1}$$

In the case of a grate inlet in a uniform section, the variable E_0 is also useful, with the frontal flow, Q_w, now defined as the gutter flow contained in the width of the grate. In this case, E_0 becomes:

$$E_0 = 1 - \left(1 - W_g/T \right)^{2.67}$$

where W_g =   width of grate inlet (m, ft)

Drainage inlets typically capture frontal flow more efficiently than side flow. In drainage inlet design, it is good practice to maximize E_0 by increasing the gutter cross-slope, or by increasing the width of the gutter depression or the grate extending into the road.

3.3 Inlets on Grade

Designs of inlets on grade are based on how much flow will be intercepted for a given total flow (gutter discharge) to the inlet. Inlet design equations solve for this efficiency.

$$E = \frac{Q_i}{Q}$$

where E =   inlet efficiency
         Q_i =   intercepted flow (m³/s, cfs)
         Q =   total gutter flow (m³/s, cfs)

Flow that is not intercepted by a drainage inlet on grade is bypassed and carried over to another inlet downstream, or is "lost" to a stream or pond, for example.

Grate Inlets on Grade

Grate inlets, as shown in Figure 3-2, tend to be more efficient than curb inlets when on a grade. Curb inlets are discussed in the next section of this chapter.

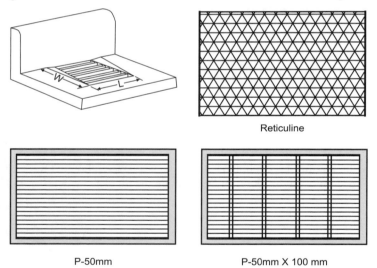

Reticuline

P-50mm   P-50mm X 100 mm

Figure 3-2: Grate Inlet in a Gutter and Some Typical Grate Types

Two concerns must be addressed in the grate inlet design process. First, the engineer needs to choose a grate type appropriate for the roadway being designed. Bicycle traffic, for example, would limit the engineer to grate types with both longitudinal and transverse bars in order to prevent bicycle accidents. Second, grate inlets have a higher propensity to clog than other types of inlets. If debris is prevalent in runoff at the point of design, adequate provisions must be made to account for inlet clogging, such as utilizing a combination (grate and curb) inlet at these points.

As shown in Figure 3-1, the total gutter flow is composed of frontal flow, Q_w (the flow in the depressed gutter or over the grate width), and side flow, Q_s. The total efficiency of the grate inlet is determined by calculating the grate's ability to capture frontal flow and side flow.

R_f is the ratio of intercepted frontal flow to the total frontal flow, and is expressed as:

$$R_f = 1 - K_{cf}(V - V_0)$$

where K_{cf} =   0.295 (0.090 in U.S. units)
         V =   average velocity in the gutter at the location of the inlet (m/s, ft/s)
         V_0 =   splash-over velocity of the inlet (m/s, ft/s)

The **splash-over velocity** is the minimum velocity of the gutter flow capable of inducing enough momentum for some of the flow to skip over the grate opening and be carried over downstream. The splash-over velocity is a function of the grate type and the grate length, and can be found in Appendix A of the HEC-22 manual or obtained from the grate manufacturer. If the gutter velocity is less than the splash-over velocity, all frontal flow is intercepted and R_f equals 1.0.

The ratio, R_s, of side flow intercepted to total side flow is expressed as:

$$R_s = \left(1 + \frac{K_{cs}V^{1.8}}{S_x L^{2.3}}\right)^{-1}$$

where K_{cs} =   0.0828 (0.15 in U.S. units)
        L =   grate length (m, ft)

The total intercepted flow is expressed as:

$$Q_i = Q_w R_f + Q_s R_s$$

The total efficiency of the grate inlet on grade is expressed as:

$$E = R_f E_0 + R_s(1 - E_0)$$

Curb Inlets on Grade

Curb inlets are openings within the curb itself (see Figure 3-3), and they are used in areas where grate inlets are prone to clogging.

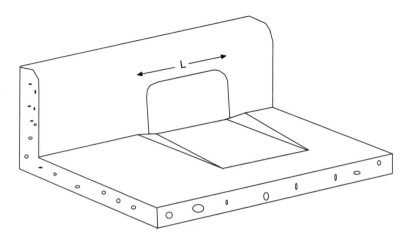

Figure 3-3: Curb Inlet

The efficiency of a curb inlet is based on the ratio of the actual inlet length to the inlet length necessary to capture 100% of the total runoff. Curb inlets are often inset into the pavement to create a *local depression*. A local depression, as shown in Figure 3-4, is a depression of the gutter at the location of the inlet only, as opposed to a gutter depression, which is continuous along the curb.

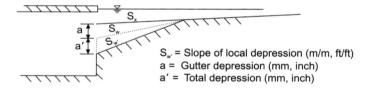

S_w = Slope of local depression (m/m, ft/ft)
a = Gutter depression (mm, inch)
a′ = Total depression (mm, inch)

Figure 3-4: Local Depression at a Curb Inlet

The curb opening length, L_T, that would be required to intercept 100% of a flow, Q, on a roadway section with a uniform cross-slope is defined as:

$$L_T = K_c Q^{0.42} S_L^{0.3} \left(\frac{1}{nS_x} \right)^{0.6}$$

where $K_c = 0.817$ (0.60 in U.S. units)

To account for local depressions or gutter depressions, an additional composite or equivalent slope, S_e, is necessary:

$$S_e = S_x + S_w'E_0$$

where S_w' = gutter cross-slope at the inlet location measured from the pavement cross-slope, S_x (m/m, ft/ft)

       E_0 = ratio of flow in the depressed section to the total gutter flow upstream of the inlet (does not account for local depression).

To calculate L_T with a composite gutter, replace the road cross-slope, S_x, with the equivalent slope, S_e, in the equation solving for L_T.

The efficiency of a curb opening on grade shorter than the required length for total interception is:

$$E = 1 - \left(1 - \frac{L}{L_T}\right)^{1.8}$$

Combination Inlets on Grade

Combination inlets, shown in Figure 3-5, consist of both grate and curb openings. The curb inlet functions as a sweep, removing debris from the runoff before it can clog the grate inlet.

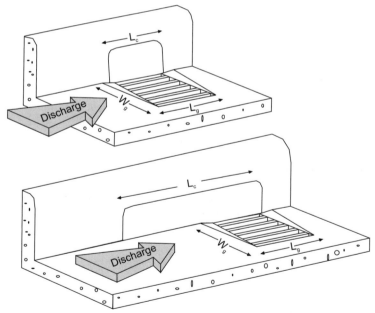

Figure 3-5: Typical Combination Inlets

If the curb inlet length is equal to the grate inlet length, the flow intercepted by the combination inlet is assumed to be equivalent to that intercepted by the grate inlet alone.

The curb inlet is often extended upstream of the grate for more efficient removal of debris than when the curb opening length equals the grate length. The total flow intercepted by this configuration is calculated as the sum of:

- The flow intercepted by the portion of the curb opening located upstream of the grate
- The flow that bypassed the upstream curb opening and is intercepted by the grate alone (the flow intercepted by the portion of the curb opening adjacent to the grate is neglected)

3.4 Inlets in Sag

Inlets located in sag are assumed to capture 100 percent of flow because, once collected, the runoff in the sag has no other place to go. As opposed to inlets located on a grade, the size and type of inlet directly affects the spread. As shown in Table 3-1, the HEC-22 manual typically recommends employing a larger rainfall return period for designing an inlet located in sag than for designing an inlet located on grade.

The computations for calculating the amount of flow intercepted by inlets in sag are based on the principles of weir flow and orifice flow discussed in Chapter 1.

For an unsubmerged inlet operating as a weir, the flow capacity is calculated as:

$$Q_{iw} = C_w P d^{1.5}$$

where Q_{iw} = flow intercepted by the inlet operating as a weir (m³/s, ft³/s)
C_w = weir coefficient, which varies depending on the flow condition and inlet structure.
P = perimeter of the inlet (m, ft)
d = flow depth at the curb (m, ft)

Note that for a grate inlet, the perimeter does not include the length along the curb. Also, if the gutter is depressed (locally or continuously), the perimeter, P, of the grate is calculated as:

$$P = L + 1.8W$$

where L = grate length (m, ft)
W = grate width (m, ft)

The depth, d, for both types of inlets is measured from the projected pavement cross-slope. For a curb inlet, the perimeter is equivalent to the length of the inlet.

If the inlet is submerged and is operating as an orifice, its capacity becomes:

$$Q_{io} = C_o A (2gd_0)^{0.5}$$

where Q_{io} = flow intercepted by the inlet operating as an orifice (m³/s, ft³/s)
      C_0 = orifice coefficient (varies based on the class of inlet and its configuration)
      A = area of the opening (m², ft²)
      g = 9.81 m/s² (32.16 ft/s² in U.S. customary units)
      d_0 = effective head at the orifice (m, ft)

Note that for a grate inlet, the effective head, d_0, is simply the water depth along the curb. For a curb inlet, the effective head is expressed as:

$$d_0 = d_i - \frac{h}{2}(\sin\theta)$$

where d_i = depth at lip of curb opening (m, ft)
      h = curb throat opening height (m, ft) (see Figure 3-6)
      θ = inclination of the curb throat measured from the vertical direction as shown in Figure 3-6

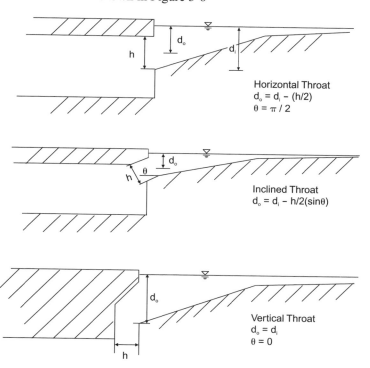

Figure 3-6: Different Curb Inlet Throat Types

Grates alone are not typically recommended for installation in sags because of their propensity to clog and exacerbate ponding during severe weather. A combination inlet may be a better alternative. At low flow depths, the capacity of a combination inlet for which the grate inlet length equals the curb inlet length is equivalent to the capacity of the grate inlet alone. At higher flow depths for the same type of inlet, both the curb inlet and grate inlet act as orifices. The total intercepted flow is then calculated as the sum of the flows intercepted by the grate and curb openings.

3.5   Inlet Design Overview

This section provides a quick overview of features necessary to solve inlet problems using software from Haestad Methods. FlowMaster can be used to analyze the hydraulic performance of individual inlets. StormCAD is used to model inlets in storm sewer networks.

Inlet and Gutter Problems Using FlowMaster

FlowMaster can compute the capacities of gutters and drainage inlets using the methodology put forth in the FHWA's HEC-22 *Urban Drainage Design Manual* (Brown, Stein, and Warner, 1996). Given a type of inlet and design constraints, it can also compute the inlet size required. With FlowMaster you can solve for different variables associated with the following structures by selecting them from the list of available worksheets:

- Gutter sections on grade
- Grate inlets
- Curb inlets
- Combination inlets
- Slot inlets
- Ditch inlets

For a more in-depth tutorial on the use of FlowMaster, see Chapter 1.

When creating a new inlet worksheet, you will be required to name the worksheet by providing a label. Additionally, you will need to specify whether the inlet is on grade or in sag by selecting the appropriate radio button. When editing an inlet's worksheet, remember that there are multiple tabs on which you have to enter data. For example, the combination inlet worksheet has a **Gutter** tab, an **Inlet** tab, a **Grate** tab, and a **Curb** tab.

In the worksheet for a gutter section, you can provide a discharge and solve for the resulting spread, or you can enter a spread and have FlowMaster solve for the allowable discharge. In the worksheet for an inlet, you can either solve for an inlet's efficiency based upon the entered parameters, or you can size the inlet to meet specified design criteria.

Set the variable you want to solve for by selecting it from the pull-down menu in the **Solve For:** field. Then, click **Solve**. The calculated values will appear in the fields highlighted in yellow.

Inlet and Gutter Network Problems Using StormCAD

StormCAD, like FlowMaster, calculates and designs drainage inlets by applying the HEC-22 methodology. Unlike FlowMaster, StormCAD will design an entire gutter network as opposed to just one inlet at a time. The gutter network dictates what happens to flow on the surface when it bypasses an inlet and is routed downstream to another inlet.

To edit an inlet's properties, first double-click on that inlet in the drawing pane and select the **Inlet** tab at the top of the dialog. In the **Inlet** field, select an inlet from the pull-down menu, which lists all the inlets currently defined in the **Inlet Library**. To examine the characteristics of the inlet selected, click the ellipsis **(...)** button next to this field. The **Inlet Library** dialog will appear. The Inlet Library is a separately saved file and editable library allowing customization for local regulations. Select the inlet of interest and click **Edit...** to examine or change its properties, or click the **Insert** button to create a new inlet. To exit an inlet's properties dialog in the library, click **OK** or **Cancel**. To exit the **Inlet Library**, click **Close**.

In the **Inlet** tab of an **Inlet Editor** dialog, the **Inlet Opening** section displays variables for the type of inlet chosen. Gutter characteristics can be entered under **Inlet Section**.

Finally, you have to specify an inlet location by clicking either the **On Grade** or **In Sag** radio button. If the inlet is on grade, fill in the **Longitudinal Slope** of the road and the **Manning's *n*** value for the pavement. You must also select a **Bypass Target** to establish the connectivity of the gutter network. The *bypass target* is another inlet or outlet in the same project (the target element does not have to be an element in the same pipe network) where the flows bypassing the current inlet will be carried. If no bypass target is chosen, all bypass flow will automatically carry over to the outlet of the sewer network that the inlet is part of (in this case, the bypassed flow is not accounted for in the sewer network). Click **OK** to exit the dialog. To view a graphical representation of the gutter network in plan view, select **Gutter Network** from the **Tools** pull-down menu.

3.6 Gradually Varied Flow

When performing an open channel hydraulic analysis, the change in water depth along the length of a section may be so gradual that the entire section can be assumed to have a constant water depth (such as normal depth) without any loss of accuracy. In other systems, however, such as storm sewers, there may be some sort of restriction that prevents the water depth from equaling normal depth throughout the length. For example, a high tailwater elevation may force the depth to be above normal depth at the downstream end of a pipe, as shown in Figure 3-7.

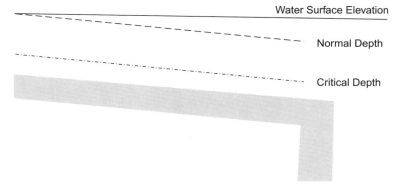

Figure 3-7: Non-Uniform Flow in an Open Channel

When the difference in water depth from one end of a conduit to the other is significant, a gradually varied flow profile analysis is required. Gradually varied flow profile analysis is the process of splitting a channel length into segments and analyzing each segment separately. It is based on several assumptions, including:

- The head loss within any given calculation segment is the same as for uniform flow conditions.
- The velocity is the same across the entire cross-section.
- The slope of the conduit is less than 10 percent.
- The roughness coefficient is constant throughout the reach under consideration and is independent of the depth of flow.
- The depth of flow changes gradually along the length of the conduit, starting from some controlling boundary condition (usually the tailwater elevation); there are no sudden increases or decreases in depth.
- If the pipe is sufficiently long, the depth of flow will approach normal depth.

Flow Classification

The first step in performing a gradually varied flow analysis is to identify the flow classification that is expected to occur in the conduit based on the slope of the channel, the normal depth, the critical depth, and the controlling boundary condition.

Slope Classification

Once the normal depth and critical depth have been computed for the section, the conduit slope can be determined. If the normal depth is above critical depth, the slope is said to be *mild*. If the normal depth is equal to the critical depth, the slope is said to be *critical*. If normal depth is below critical depth, the slope is said to be *steep*.

There are two other slope types to consider: a *horizontal* channel and a channel on an *adverse* slope (an "uphill"-sloping channel). For these slope types, normal depth is undefined.

For a gradually varied flow profile, the first letter of the slope type is used in the identification of the profile. For example, a channel with a hydraulically steep slope is a type S, a channel with a hydraulically mild slope is a type M, and so forth.

Flow Zone Classification

In a gradually varied flow analysis, the flow is assumed to stay within the same zone throughout the length of the conduit. For example, the flow will not jump from subcritical to supercritical within the same profile type. There are three zones where flow profiles can occur:

- Zone 1: Flow depth is above both normal and critical depths
- Zone 2: Flow depth is between normal depth and critical depth
- Zone 3: Flow depth is below both normal and critical depths

A given profile will exist in only one of these zones. Because normal depth is undefined for horizontal slopes and adverse slopes, Zone 1 flow does not exist for these profile types.

Profile Classifications

Once the slope classification and flow zone have been determined, the profile type can be defined, and the engineer can determine how to proceed with the hydraulic grade computations. Figure 3-8 shows the basic profile types.

To perform the computations, the engineer must determine from the profile type whether the flow is subcritical or supercritical (based on the location of actual depths compared to critical depth). In order to prevent excessive velocities that could cause pipe scour or channel erosion, most storm sewers are designed with mild slopes to carry subcritical flows. For this type of flow, the hydraulic control is at the downstream end of the section, and the profile calculation proceeds toward the upstream end. When the flow depth is above normal depth (as in an M1 profile), this type of analysis is called a *backwater* analysis. When the flow depth is between critical depth and normal depth, it is called a *drawdown* analysis.

When supercritical flows are encountered, the controlling section is at the upstream end of the conduit, and the computations proceed from upstream to downstream. This calculation type is a *frontwater* analysis.

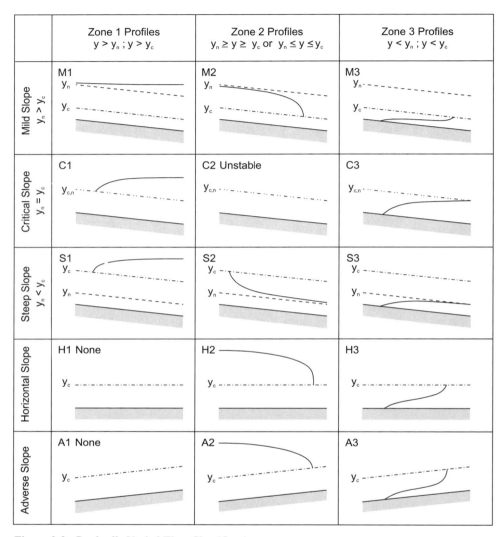

Figure 3-8: Gradually Varied Flow Classifications

Energy Balance

Even for gradually varied flow, the solution is still a matter of balancing the total energy between the two ends of each segment. The energy equation as it relates to each end of a segment can be written as (note that the pressures for both ends are zero, because it is free surface flow):

$$Z_1 + \frac{V_1^2}{2g} = Z_2 + \frac{V_2^2}{2g} + H_L$$

where Z_1 =   hydraulic grade at the upstream end of the segment (m, ft)
        V_1 =   velocity at the upstream end (m/s, ft/s)
        Z_2 =   hydraulic grade at the downstream end of the segment (m, ft)
        V_2 =   velocity at the downstream end (m/s, ft/s)
        H_L =   head loss due to friction (other losses are assumed to be zero) (m, ft)
        g =   gravitational acceleration constant (m/s^2, ft/s^2)

The friction loss is computed based on the average rate of friction loss along the segment and the segment length. This relationship is:

$$H_L = S_{Avg} \cdot \Delta x = \frac{S_1 + S_2}{2} \Delta x$$

where H_L =   loss across the segment (m, ft)
        S_{Avg} =   average friction loss (m/m, ft/ft)
        S_1 =   friction slope at the upstream end of the segment (m/m, ft/ft)
        S_2 =   friction slope at the downstream end of the segment (m/m, ft/ft)
        Δx =   length of the segment being analyzed (m, ft)

The conditions at one end of the segment are known (through assumption or from a previous calculation). Because the friction slope is a function of velocity, which is a function of depth, the depth at the other end of the segment can be found through iteration. There are two primary methods to obtain the solution: the Standard Step method and the Direct Step method.

Standard-Step Method

This method involves dividing the channel into segments of equal known lengths and solving for the unknown depth at one end of the segment (starting with a known or assumed depth at the other end). The standard-step method is the most popular method of determining the flow profile because it can be applied to any channel, not just prismatic channels.

Direct-Step Method

The direct-step method is based on the same basic energy principles as the standard-step method, but takes a slightly different approach to the solution. Instead of assuming a segment length and solving for the depth at the end of the segment, the direct-step method assumes a depth and then solves for the segment length.

3.7 Mixed Flow Profiles

So far, only conditions for which the entire channel has the same profile type, resulting in the smooth curves of a gradually varied flow analysis, have been discussed. This section explores those cases in which profile types are mixed within the same section and the steps that can be taken to analyze these occurrences.

Sealing Conditions

There may be conditions whereby part of a pipe or culvert section is flowing full, while part of the flow remains open. These conditions are called *sealing* conditions and are analyzed in separate parts. The portion of the section flowing full is analyzed as pressure flow, and the remaining portion is analyzed as gradually varied flow.

Rapidly Varied Flow

Rapidly varied flow is turbulent flow resulting from the abrupt and pronounced curvature of flow streamlines into or out of a hydraulic control. Examples of rapidly varied flow include hydraulic jumps, bends, and bridge contractions.

Hydraulic Jumps

When flow passes rapidly from supercritical to subcritical flow, a phenomenon called a *hydraulic jump* occurs. In storm sewer networks, this often occurs when a steep pipe discharges into a particularly high tailwater, as shown in Figure 3-9.

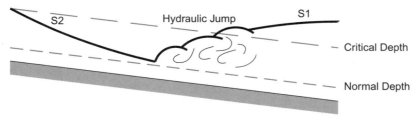

Figure 3-9 Plot of Hydraulic Jump

There are significant losses associated with hydraulic jumps due to the amount of mixing and turbulence that occur. These forces are also highly erosive, so engineers typically try to prevent jumps from occurring in storm sewer systems, or at least predict the location of jumps in order to provide adequate channel, pipe, or structure protection.

3.8 Storm Sewer Applications

Storm sewer analysis occurs in two basic calculation sequences:

- **Hydrology:** Watersheds are analyzed and flows are accumulated from upstream inlets towards the system outlet.

- **Hydraulics:** A tailwater condition is assumed at the outlet, and the flow values (from the hydrology calculations) are used to compute hydraulic grades from the outlet towards the upstream inlets.

Hydrology Model

As the runoff from a storm event travels through a storm sewer, it combines with other flows, and the resulting flows are based on the overall watershed characteristics. As with a single watershed, the peak flow at any location within the storm sewer is assumed to occur when all parts of the watershed are contributing to the flow. Therefore, the rainfall intensity that produces the largest peak flow at a given location is based on the controlling system time at that same location.

The controlling system time is the larger of the *local time of concentration* (to a single inlet) and the *total upstream system time* (including pipe travel times). The controlling time is used for computing the intensity (and therefore the flow) in the combined system.

Example 3-1: Flow Accumulation

A storm sewer inlet has a local time of concentration of eight minutes for a watershed with a weighted CA (that is, the weighted runoff coefficient times the total drainage area) of 1.23 ac. This inlet discharges through a pipe to another storm sewer inlet with a weighted CA of 0.84 ac and a local time of concentration of nine minutes. If the travel time in the pipe is two minutes, what is the overall system CA and corresponding storm duration?

Solution

The total CA can be found by simply summing the CA values from the two inlets. The storm duration, however, must be found by comparing the local time of concentration at the second inlet to the total time for flow from the upstream inlet to reach the downstream inlet.

$$\text{Total } CA = 1.23 \text{ ac} + 0.84 \text{ ac} = 2.07 \text{ ac}$$

$$\text{Upstream Time} = 8 \text{ min} + 2 \text{ min} = 10 \text{ min}$$

The total upstream flow time of 10 min is greater than the local time of concentration at the downstream inlet (9 min). The 10-min value is therefore the controlling time, and should be used as the duration of the storm event.

Other Sources of Water

There may be a number of flow sources for a storm sewer system other than direct watershed inflow. Flow may be piped into an inlet from an external connection, or there could be flow entering an inlet that is the carryover (bypass) flow from another storm sewer inlet.

Design practices for handling carryover flows vary from jurisdiction to jurisdiction. Some local regulations may require that pipes be sized to include all flow that arrives at an inlet, whereas other locales may specify that pipes be sized to accommodate only the flow that is actually intercepted by the upstream inlets. It is the responsibility of the design engineer to ensure that the design is in agreement with the local criteria and policies.

The hydraulics of a storm sewer are often computed as described previously in this chapter. Normal depth may occur in portions of the system, whereas other areas may experience pressure (submerged) conditions. Gradually varied flow and rapidly varied flow may also occur.

Computations start at the system outlet, where a tailwater condition is assumed. There are four basic assumptions for tailwater conditions:

- **Normal Depth:** The depth at the outfall of the farthest downstream pipe is assumed to be equal to normal depth, as in a sufficiently long S2 profile
- **Critical Depth:** The depth at the pipe outfall is assumed to be critical depth, as in subcritical flow to a free discharge
- **Crown Elevation:** The depth is set to the crown (top) of the pipe for free outfall
- **User-Specified Tailwater:** A fixed tailwater depth can also be used, as when there is a known pond or river water surface elevation at the outfall of the storm sewer

Care should be taken to choose an accurate tailwater condition, because this value can affect the hydraulics of much of the system. The designer of a storm sewer system should consider the tailwater depth during storm conditions. An outlet may be above the receiving stream during dry weather, but may be submerged during the design storm event.

3.9 StormCAD

StormCAD is an extremely powerful, easy-to-use program that helps civil engineers design and analyze storm sewer systems. Just draw your network on the screen by using the tool palette, double-click any element to enter data, and click the **GO** button to calculate the network.

Rainfall information is calculated using rainfall tables, equations, or the National Weather Service's HYDRO-35 data. StormCAD also plots Intensity-Duration-Frequency

(IDF) curves. You have a choice of conveyance elements that include circular pipes, pipe arches, boxes and more. Flow calculations handle pressure and varied flow situations including hydraulic jumps, backwater, and drawdown curves. StormCAD's flexible reporting features allow you to customize and print the design and analysis results in report format or as a graphical plot.

How Can You Use StormCAD?

StormCAD is so flexible you can use it for all phases of your project, from the feasibility report to the final design drawings and analysis of existing networks. During the feasibility phase, you can use StormCAD to create several different system layouts with an AutoCAD® or MicroStation™ drawing as the background. For the final design, StormCAD lets you complete detailed drawings with notes that can be used to develop construction plans. In summary, you can use StormCAD to:

- Design multiple storm sewer systems with constraint-based design
- Design/Analyze inlets based on HEC-22 methodology
- Use AASHTO, HEC-22 Energy, standard, absolute, or user-specified ("generic") methods to compute structure losses
- Analyze various design scenarios for storm sewer systems
- Import and export AutoCAD® and MicroStation™ DXF files
- Predict rainfall runoff rates
- Generate professional-looking reports for clients and review agencies
- Generate plan and profile plots of the network

The theory and background used in StormCAD are presented in more detail in the StormCAD on-line help system.

Analysis and Design

StormCAD's automatic design feature allows you to design whole or part of a storm sewer system based on a set of user-defined design constraints. These constraints include minimum/maximum velocity, slope, and cover; choice of pipe invert or crown matching at structures; inlet efficiency; and gutter spread and depth. StormCAD will automatically design the invert elevations and diameters of pipes, as well as the size of a drainage inlet necessary to maintain a given spread (for inlets in sag) or capture efficiency (for inlets on grade).

Profiles

StormCAD also includes an option to automatically generate storm sewer *profiles* — longitudinal plots of the storm sewer. Profiles allow the design engineer, the reviewing agency, the contractor and others to visualize the storm system. They are useful for viewing the hydraulic grade line and determining if the proposed storm sewer is in conflict with other existing or proposed underground utilities.

3.10 Tutorial Examples

The following tutorial provides step-by-step instructions on how to solve the example problem found below using StormCAD (included on the CD that accompanies this textbook).

Tutorial 1 — Design of a Network with Auto Design

A small residential road has three houses. Each house has one storm drain to collect its runoff. The outfall for the system is across the street and drains into a pond. Pipe P-3 leading to the outfall is a 10-m long, concrete box culvert. Pipes P-1 and P-2 are 20-m long, circular concrete pipes. Each structure has a head loss coefficient of 0.5 (using the standard head loss method).

Use Manning's equation to calculate the friction losses through the pipe. The rainfall data and hydrologic data given below. All inlets are **Generic Default 100%**, which are assumed to capture 100 percent of the surface flow.

a)   Use the "Auto Design" feature to find pipe sizes and invert elevations for a 25-year storm if the elevation of the drainage pond's water surface is 262.8 m. The inlet and rainfall information, along with design constraints are given in Figure 3-10.

b)   What would the effect on the system be if the pond's water surface elevation were 0.1 m below the ground elevation at the outfall?

c)   What will happen to the system if the pond's water surface elevation is 262.8 m and an additional flow of 0.5 m³/s is added to I-2?

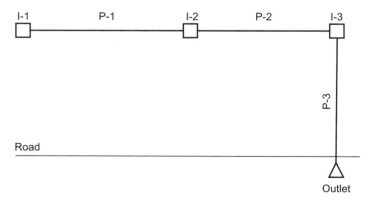

Figure 3-10: Schematic for Tutorial Problem

Inlet Information for Tutorial Problem

Inlet	Ground Elevation (m)	Impervious Area C=0.9 (ha)	Pervious Area C=0.3 (ha)	Time of Concentration (min)
I-1	264.8	0.16	0.18	5
I-2	264.5	0.13	0.15	5
I-3	265.0	0.17	0.13	6
Outlet	264.6	--	--	--

Rainfall Data for Tutorial Problem

Duration (min)	Rainfall Intensity (mm/hr)		
	5 year	10 year	25 year
5	165	181	205
10	142	156	178
15	123	135	154
30	91	103	120
60	61	70	80

Design Constraints for Tutorial Problem

Constraint	Minimum	Maximum
Velocity	1 m/s	3 m/s
Cover	1 m*	--
Pipe Slope	0.5 %	10 %
Match Inverts		

Cover constraints may be relaxed at the outfall, where invert location requirements will typically govern.

PART (a):   *Use the "Auto Design" feature in StormCAD to find pipe sizes and invert elevations for a 25-year storm if the elevation of the drainage pond's water surface is 262.8 m. The design constraints are given above.*

Solution

Project Setup Wizard

- When you start StormCAD, you should be prompted with the **Welcome to StormCAD** dialog. From this dialog you can access the tutorials, open existing projects, and create new ones. Select **Create New Project**, provide a filename, and click **Save**.

- If the **Welcome to StormCAD** dialog does not appear, StormCAD is set to **Hide Welcome Dialog on startup**. To start a new project, select **New** from the **File** menu, enter a filename, and click **Save**. (You can change from **Hide Welcome Dialog** mode to **Show Welcome Dialog** mode in the **Global Options** dialog, which is accessible by selecting **Options** from the **Tools** menu.)

- The **Project Setup Wizard** will appear. Add a project title and any appropriate comments, and click **Next**.

- In the second screen of the **Project Setup Wizard**, select **Manning's Formula** from the pull-down menu in the **Friction Method** field and click **Next**.

- In the third screen of the **Project Setup Wizard**, click the **Schematic** radio button in the **Drawing Scale** section of the dialog. This action will allow you to define the lengths for the pipes without having to worry about scale and spatial placement on the x-y plane. Click **Next**, and then click **Finished**.

Laying Out the System

- Because the units are given mostly in SI, you can simplify data entry by specifying a global unit system for the model. From the **Tools** menu, select **Options.** Then under the **Global** tab, select **System International** from the pull-down list in the **Unit System** field if it has not already been selected. Click **OK**. When changing the unit system, you may be prompted to confirm the switch. If you are prompted, click Yes to confirm the change.

- You do not have to lay out the system exactly as shown in the problem statement. For now, just roughly sketch the schematic following the instructions below.

- Click the **Pipe Layout** button on the vertical toolbar on the left side of the screen.

- To place inlet I-1, click the left mouse button in the workspace.

- To place inlet I-2, move the cursor to the right and click the left mouse button in the location you would like to drop the inlet. Pipe P-1 will be placed automatically.

- Place inlet I-3 in the same manner.

- Click the right mouse button and select the **Outlet** by highlighting it and left clicking. Click the left mouse button to place the outlet.

- Except for the scale, your schematic should look roughly like the one given in the problem statement.

Data Entry

- From the **Analysis** pull-down menu, select **Rainfall Data**, and then select **Table**.

- You need to edit the duration rows and the return period columns in the table to match those given in the problem statement. To do this, click the **Edit Return Periods** button and select either **Delete** or **Add Return Period** to delete the 2-year return period and add the 25-year return period. Edit the duration rows in the table the same way using the **Edit Durations** button. Enter the data for rainfall intensity as you would enter data into a spreadsheet and click **OK**.

- Double-click inlet I-1 to edit the dialog.

- Enter 264.8 m in the **Ground Elevation** field on the **General** tab.

- Click the **Catchment** tab to enter the rational method data for the watershed draining to inlet I-1.

- Enter the impervious area, 0.16 ha, and its Rational coefficient *C*, 0.9, into the table in the **Subwatershed Information** section. Enter the pervious area and its Rational coefficient *C* in the second row. The model will compute the composite *C* coefficient.

- Enter the 5-min T_c in the **Time of Concentration** field.

- Click the **Headlosses** tab. Select **Standard** from the list of **Headloss Methods**. Enter 0.5 in the **Headloss Coefficient** field.

- Edit the data for inlets I-2 and I-3 in the same way using the data found in the tables above, making sure to enter the standard headloss coefficients under the **Headlosses** tab.

- Double-click the outlet to edit its dialog. Enter the ground elevation in the appropriate field.

- A tailwater depth of 262.8 m is given in the problem statement. Therefore, select **User Specified** from the **Tailwater Conditions** field of the dialog. Enter 262.8 m (the elevation of the drainage pond surface) for the tailwater elevation and click **OK**.

- Double-click pipe P-3 to edit its dialog.

- Input 10 m in the **Length** field.

- Select **Box** from the **Section Shape** pull-down menu.

- Select the appropriate material from the **Material** pull-down menu.

- You do not need to enter the upstream and downstream invert elevations under the **General** tab because StormCAD will design these in this example.

- Edit pipes P-1 and P-2 in the same manner. Make sure that both are 20-m-long, circular, concrete pipes. You do not need to enter any new diameters or invert elevations because StormCAD will design these, ignoring any current values.

Running the Model

- Select **Default Design Constraints** from the **Analysis** pull-down menu.

- In the **Default Design Constraints** dialog, select the **Gravity Pipe** tab and enter the minimum and maximum velocities, ground covers, and pipe slopes as shown in Figure 3-11.

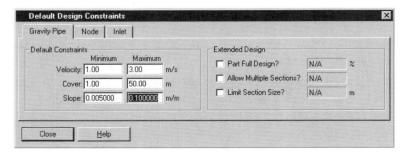

Figure 3-11: Default Pipe Design Constraints in StormCAD

- Select the **Node** tab and select **Inverts** from the **Pipe Matching** field. Click **Close** to exit the dialog.
- Click the **GO** button on the toolbar at the top of the screen. Select **25 year** from the **Return Period** pull-down menu.
- Click the **Design** radio button to design pipe sizes and inverts.
- Click **GO** to design the network. The program will ask you if you want to save the designed data as a new physical alternative, which would give you access to the initial data and the final design within the same model. In this case, click **No**. Click **Close** to exit the dialog.

Answer

- Click the **Tabular Reports** button to examine the newly designed pipe characteristics. Select **Pipe Report** by highlighting it in the **Available Tables** list and click **OK**.
- The length, size, slope, and invert elevations for each pipe can be easily compared using this table. You can also examine the data for any individual pipe under the different tabs of that pipe's dialog.

PART (b): *What would the effect on the system be if the pond's water surface elevation were 0.1 m below the ground elevation at the outfall?*

Solution

- Double-click on the outlet and change the tailwater elevation as dictated by the problem. Close out of this dialog.
- To calculate the model, click the **GO** button in the top toolbar. Switch the calculation type from **Design** to **Analysis**, and click the **GO** button.
- Under the **Results** tab, notice that a warning is displayed, as indicated by a yellow light (if there are no warnings, a green light appears). The warning indicates that flooding occurs at inlet I-2 and that P-3 fails minimum velocity constraint.

- You can also examine conditions by double-clicking the inlet and clicking the **Message** tab in the **Inlet** dialog box. Another way to look at data is to select **Profile** from the **Report** menu. Follow the steps in the **Profile Wizard** to create a profile of the hydraulic grade line within the storm sewer system.

Answer

Flooding will occur at inlet I-2.

PART (c):   *What will happen to the system if the pond's water surface elevation is 262.8 m and an additional flow of 0.5 m³/s is added to I-2?*

Solution

- Double-click the outlet and change the tailwater elevation back to its original level. Click **OK** to accept the change and exit the dialog.
- Double-click inlet I-2. Click the **Flows** tab. Enter 0.5 m³/s in the **Additional Flow** field. Click **OK** to accept the change and exit the dialog.
- Calculate the network in analysis mode as you did in Part (b).

Answer

Flooding will occur at inlet I-2.

Tutorial 2 — Alternatives Analysis with Scenario Manager

The Scenario Manager tool of StormCAD is a versatile utility for analyzing alternative designs and loadings without having to reenter data. Appendix B contains a detailed description of Scenario Manager. In this tutorial, Scenario Manager is used to construct an alternative design to convey additional flows.

Under an alternative scheme, additional flow will enter the network at I-3 and be conveyed under the road via pipe P-3. This scheme adds 1.0 m³/s of flow at inlet I-3. Determine the required size of the box culvert under this alternative.

Solution

Reset the conditions to the original design by resetting the tailwater at O-1 to 262.8 and removing the 0.5 m³/s additional flow at I-2.

- On the **Analysis** drop-down menu, select **Scenarios** and then click **Scenario Wizard**.
- Use the default name of Scenario 2 and click **Next**.
- Scenario 2 will be based on the Base scenario. Click **Next**.
- The calculation type is set to design. Make sure that the Return Period is set to 25 year. Click **Next**.
- The Alternatives that will be changed are the **System Flows**. Check this box and then click **Next**.

- Select the "Create New System Flows Alternative" and then click **Next**. Click **Finish** to return to Scenario Manger.
- Note that with the Scenario section set to Scenario 2, the System Flows alternative is local. All other alternatives are inherited from the Base scenario. Double-click the **System Flow Alternative** to open the dialog window. On the I-3 line, enter 1.0 in the additional flow column, and then click **Close.**
- With Scenarios section set to Scenario 2, click on the **Go – Batch Run** button. In the Batch Run window, select **Scenario 2** and then click on the **Batch** button. Confirm that one batch run will be performed and click on **Yes** to allow StormCAD to create a new Physical Properties alternative.

Answer

Return to the network layout view. Note that the Scenario setting can be used toggle between Base and Scenario 2. With the Scenario set to Scenario 2, double-click P-3 and examine its properties. Note that that box culvert has changed from a 610 × 610 mm size in the Base scenario to a 1220 × 610 box in Scenario 2. All other physical properties are unchanged.

Tutorial 3 — Cost Estimating

StormCAD provides many tools for preparing project cost estimates. See Appendix C for a detailed discussion of Capital Cost Analysis with Haestad Methods' software. The following exercise demonstrates the Unit Cost function and the Cost Table features.

Prepare a cost estimate for materials and installation of the network designed in the previous exercise. The outlet structure has a fixed cost of $1,500, and the box culvert has a unit cost of $125/m.

The following table outlines the cost functions for pipes and inlets.

Data for Cost functions

Structure	Unit Cost Unit	Unit Cost Function Attribute	Cost Function Coefficients			
			a	*b*	*c*	*d*
Circular pipe	$/m	Rise (mm)	0.15	1.1	250	55
Inlet	$/ea.	Depth (m)	200	1.8	0.0	1,000

Solution

- From the **Analysis** pull-down menu, select **Compute Costs** and then select **Unit Cost Functions.**

- Select the **Pipe** tab and then click the **Add** button. Select **Formula Unit Cost Function** as the Unit Cost Function Type and click **OK**. Specify the unit cost, unit, local unit, and enter the data for circular pipe. To view a plot of the function, click on the **Initialize Range** button and then on **Plot**. Close the Plot viewer. Click on **OK** to close the Cost Function dialog.

- To define the cost for the box culvert, click **Add** to add a second cost function. Select **Tabular Unit Cost Function** as the Function Type and click **OK**. Enter "Box Culvert" in the label. In the Unit Cost Data section, enter 610 as the rise (length) and $125 in the unit cost. Then click **OK**.

- To add a cost function for the inlets, select the "**Inlet**" tab. Click **Add** and select **Formula Unit Cost Function** as the Unit Cost Function Type and click **OK**. Click the **Initialize Range** button. Enter "Inlets" as the label. Enter the data for inlets from the cost table. Click **OK** and then close the Cost Function dialog box.

- The next step is to assign the cost data to the structures. Close the Cost Manager and return to the network layout view.

- Double-click **I-1** to open the inlet dialog window. Select the **Cost** tab. Check the **Include in Construction Cost** box and then click the **Insert** button to add the first line of the construction cost table. In the Label column, enter "Material and Installation" and then click the **Advanced** button. In the Cost Item pop up, select **Inlets.** Click **OK** twice to exit the I-1 dialog. Repeat the same procedure for I-2 and I-3.

- Double-click on **P-1** to open the pipe dialog window. Select the **Cost** tab. Check the **Include in Construction Cost** box and then the insert button to add the first line of the construction cost table. In the Label column, enter "Material and Installation," and then click the **Advanced** button. In the Cost Item pop up, select **Circular pipe**. Click **OK** twice to exit the I-1 dialog. Repeat the same procedure for P-2. For P-3 repeat these steps except that unit cost function is to "Box Culvert."

- Double-click on **O-1** to open the Pipe dialog. Select the **Cost** tab. Check the **Include in Construction Cost** box and click the **Insert** button to add the first line of the construction cost table. In the label column, enter "Material and Installation" and then enter $1,500 in the Unit Cost column. Click on **OK**.

- You are now ready to calculate the total project costs. On the **Analysis** drop-down menu, select "**Compute Costs**" to open the Cost Manager. The cost will be calculated for the Base Scenario. Click the **Cost** Reports button and select **Detailed Report** from the Drop down menu. The Detailed Cost Report table will appear. To obtain a hard copy, select **Print Review** and then **Print**.

Answer

The estimated costs for materials and installation are:

Inlets	4,449
Outlet	1,500
Pipe	6,446
TOTAL	$12,395

3.11 Problems

Solve problems 1 through 3 using FlowMaster. Solve problems 4 through 11 using StormCAD.

1. The spread on a proposed road paved with smooth asphalt and having a 1.0-percent longitudinal slope is limited by local regulations to 3.0 m for the sake of automobile safety. The road cross-slope is 2.5%.

    a) What is the maximum allowable discharge on the road if the gutter section is uniform? What is the depth of the flow measured at the curb for this rate of discharge?

    b) An alternative design proposes the addition of a gutter depression with a width of 1.5 meters and a gutter cross-slope of 4.0%. What is the maximum allowable discharge in the gutter under these conditions? What is the depth of the flow at this rate of discharge?

    c) Does the addition of the gutter depression increase or decrease the capacity of the gutter? Why?

2. A proposed gutter section has a road cross-slope of 0.015 m/m and a gutter cross-slope of 0.045 m/m. The gutter is 1.20 m wide and is on a longitudinal slope of 0.02 m/m. The Manning coefficient for the road is 0.013. The predetermined runoff in the gutter is 0.05 m^3/s.

    a) What is the efficiency of a P-50 mm × 100 mm grate inlet that is 0.70 m long and 0.5 m wide? Assume no clogging. What is the intercepted flow? What is the bypassed flow?

    b) What is the efficiency of a 0.70-m-long curb inlet on the same gutter section with no local depression? How does this efficiency compare to the efficiency of the grate inlet in part (a)?

    c) For the curb inlet in part (b), add a local depression that is 20 mm deep and 0.7 m wide. What is the efficiency of the inlet? How does this efficiency compare to the grate inlet in part (a) and the curb inlet in part (b)?

3. An inlet in sag must collect the 50-year peak runoff of 8.0 cfs. The gutter section has a road cross-slope of 2.0% and a gutter cross-slope of 4.0%. The gutter width is 3.0 ft. The local depression is 2.0 in deep and 3.0 ft wide.

    a) What length combination inlet is necessary to maintain a spread of 8.0 ft at the section? The grate is a 3.0-ft wide, P-50 mm type, and the curb inlet has an opening height of 0.7 ft and a vertical throat configuration. Assume the length of the grate will equal the length of the curb opening.

    b) How big would the curb inlet from part (a), acting alone, have to be to maintain the spread width of 8.0 ft under the same conditions? How long would the grate inlet in part (a) have to be to maintain the same spread? Which inlet type is the best solution?

Solve the following problems using StormCAD.

4. Lay out the storm sewer system shown below in StormCAD and enter the data for the network from the tables below. Calculate the results using Manning's equation and the 10-year storm event data tables that follow. Inlet I-1 is on grade with a longitudinal slope of 3%, whereas inlet I-2 is in sag. The tailwater condition at the outlet is free outfall. Assume that there is no clogging of the inlets.

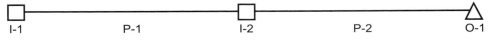

Schematic for Problem 4

Pipe Data for Problem 4

Pipe	Circular Section Size (mm)	Upstream Invert Elevation (m)	Downstream Invert Elevation (m)	Length (m)	Pipe Material (n-value)
P-1	300	115.40	115.10	46	Concrete (0.013)
P-2	300	115.05	114.60	61	Concrete (0.013)

Node Data for Problem 4

Nodes	Ground Elevation (m)	Sump Elevation (m)	Head Loss Method	Head Loss Coefficient
I-1	117.40	115.40	Standard	0.5
I-2	117.15	115.05	Standard	0.5
O-1	118.00	114.60	--	--

Inlet Catchment Data for Problem 4

Inlet	Time of Concentration (min)	Additional Carryover (m³/s)	Area (ha)	Inlet C
I-1	6.3	0	0.45	0.75
I-2	5.2	0	0.22	0.80

Inlet Data for Problem 4

Inlet	Inlet Type	Grate Length (m)	Road Cross-Slope (m/m)	Bypass Target	Manning's n
I-1	Grate DI-1	1.1	0.02	I-2	0.012
I-2	Grate DI-1	1.1	0.02	--	--

Grate DI-1

(Provided in case missing from inlet library)

Structure Width = 0.67 m
Structure Length = 0.67 m

Grate Type =
P-50 mm x 100 mm

Width = 0.76 m Standard
Length = 0.76 m

Rainfall Data for Problem 4

Duration (min)	Rainfall Intensities (mm/hr)		
	5 Year	10 Year	50 Year
5	69.8	78.7	99.6
10	54.6	61.0	77.5
20	40.6	45.2	56.6
30	31.7	36.2	45.7

Fill out an answer table like the one below for each of the following situations:

a) Assume uniform gutters with a slope of 0.02 m/m.

b) Assume continuously depressed gutters with a road cross-slope of 0.02 m/m, a gutter cross-slope of 0.04 m/m, and a gutter width of 0.8 m.

c) Assume continuously depressed gutters as described in (b), as well as inlet lengths increased from 1.1 m to 1.6 m.

d) Explain the reasons for the differences between the three resulting tables.

Answer Table for Problem 4

Inlet	Gutter Spread (m)	Total Flow to Inlet (m³/s)	Intercepted Inlet Flow (m³/s)	Bypassed Inlet Flow (m³/s)	Efficiency (%)
I-1					
I-2					

5. Enter and calculate the storm sewer network shown below using Manning's equation and the rainfall data used in Problem 4. The tailwater condition is free outfall. Assume no clogging of the inlets. Answer the questions that follow.

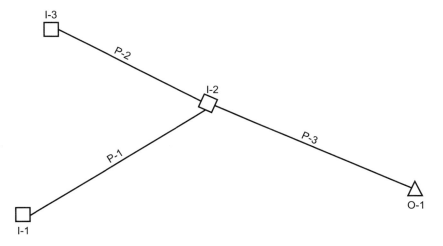

Schematic for Problem 5

Pipe Data for Problem 5

Pipe	Circular Section Size (mm)	Upstream Invert Elevation (m)	Downstream Invert Elevation (m)	Length (m)	Pipe Material (n-value)
P-1	300	425.40	424.70	45	Concrete (0.013)
P-2	450	424.70	424.00	40	Concrete (0.013)
P-3	300	425.00	424.70	54	Concrete (0.013)

Node Data for Problem 5

Node	Ground Elevation (m)	Sump Elevation (m)
I-1	428.00	425.40
I-2	427.50	424.70
I-3	428.60	425.00
O-1	427.10	424.00

Inlet Data for Problem 5

Inlet	Inlet Type	Inlet Length (m)	Road Cross-Slope (m/m)	Inlet Location	Bypass Target	Long. Slope (m/m)	Manning's n
I-1	Curb DI-3A	1	0.02	On Grade	I-2	0.01	0.012
I-2	Curb DI-3A	1	0.02	In Sag	-	-	-
I-3	CurbDI-3A	1	0.02	In Sag	-	-	-

Inlet Catchment Data for Problem 5

Inlet	Time of Concentration (min)	Additional Carryover (m³/s)	Area (ha)	Inlet C
I-1	5.5	0	0.67	0.90
I-2	5.0	0	0.70	0.80
I-3	6.0	0	0.80	0.90

a) Given the design criteria shown in Table 3-1, what minimum gutter cross-slope should the 3-m-wide shoulders have (within 1%) on this high-volume, bi-directional road if the speed limit is 90 km/hr?

b) As an alternative, set all gutter cross-slopes to 4% and replace the curb inlet at I-2 with a grate inlet called "Test." You will need to add this new inlet to the program's inlet library. The inlet has the characteristics given below. What is the minimum grate length for I-2 that would satisfy the 50-year design criteria shown in Table 3-1, assuming no clogging?

Test Inlet Data	
Structure width and length	1.2 m
Grate type	P-50 mm
Grate width	1 m

Grate lengths start at 1 m and are available in increments of 0.5 m

c) Using the same data and inlet designed in part (b), calculate the spread at I-2 assuming 50% clogging.

Solve the following problems using StormCAD. Assume all inlets are **Generic Default 100%**, which means that they are assumed to capture 100% of the surface flow.

6. The data that follows describes the existing storm sewer system shown below. For runoff calculations, assume $C = 0.3$ for pervious land cover and $C = 0.9$ for impervious cover. The ground elevation at the system discharge point is 17.0 m. All pipes are concrete ($n = 0.013$) and circular. Apply a standard head loss coefficient of 0.5 to inlet I-3.

a) Analyze the system for a design return period of 10 years. Assume a free outfall condition. Provide output tables summarizing pipe flow conditions and hydraulic grade lines at the inlets. How is this system performing?

b) Increase the size of pipe P-3 to 450-mm. Rerun the analysis and present the results. How does the system perform with this improvement?

c) Local design regulations require that storm sewer systems handle 25-year return periods without flooding. Rerun the analysis for the improved system in (b). Does the system meet this performance requirement?

d) The above analyses are run using a default Manning's n of 0.013. Many drainage design manuals propose a less conservative design roughness of 0.012. Reanalyze the improved system under 25-year flows using $n = 0.012$. How does this change influence the predicted performance of the system?

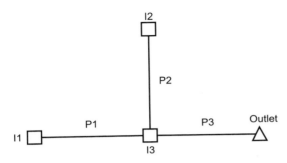

Schematic for Problem 6

Rainfall Data for Problem 6

Duration (min)	Rainfall Intensity (mm/hr)		
	5 year	10 year	25 year
5	165	181	205
10	142	156	178
15	123	135	154
30	91	103	120
60	61	70	80

Inlet Information for Problem 6

Inlet	Ground Elevation (m)	Impervious Area (ha)	Pervious Area (ha)	Time of Concentration (min)
I-1	17.9	0.13	0.32	6.0
I-2	18.0	0.15	0.58	5.0
I-3	17.6	0.08	0.36	5.0

Pipe Information for Problem 6

Pipe	Upstream Invert (m)	Downstream Invert (m)	Diameter (mm)	Length (m)
P-1	16.7	16.15	300	56
P-2	16.8	16.1	375	46
P-3	16.1	15.3	375	54

7. You have been asked by the lead project engineer for a water supply utility to design the stormwater collection system for the proposed ground storage tank and pump station facility shown in the layout. Pipe lengths for P-1, P-2, P-3, and P-4 are 88, 92, 185, and 46 ft, respectively. See the CAD drawing and data for the system layout. Assume $C = 0.3$ for pervious areas and $C = 0.9$ for impervious areas.

    a) Using the StormCAD program's Automatic Design feature, size the system using the following design data. Use concrete pipe ($n = 0.013$) and the 25-year intensity-duration-frequency data provided in problem 6 (Hint: StormCAD can mix SI and U.S. customary units). The top of bank elevation at the outfall ditch is 846.1 ft. The outfall pipe invert must be located at or above elevation 838.0 ft. Assume that the water surface elevation at the outfall is 842.0 ft, and that the pipes should have matching soffit (crown) elevations at every structure. Present your design in tabular form and provide a profile plot of your design.

    b) During agency review, the county engineer requests that the water utility and the county work cooperatively to accommodate the planned construction of an elementary school nearby by increasing the size of the proposed storm system so that it can handle the design runoff from the school. The county engineer performs his own calculations and asks that you increase the size of pipes P-3 and P-4 to handle an external CA of 9.5 acres with a time of concentration of 12 min. Using StormCAD, introduce the additional flow at inlet I-3 and revise the facility design using the Automatic Design functionality of the program. Are all the design constraints met? What can you say about the flow conditions in pipe P-3 and pipe P-4? In the rest of the pipes?

    c) If necessary, manually fine-tune and revise the design to meet all design criteria. Document your design as in part (a).

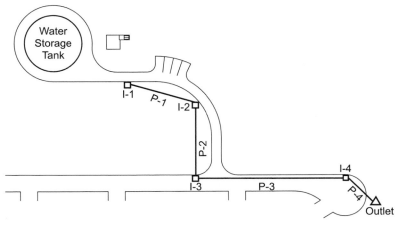

CAD Drawing for Problem 7

Inlet Information for Problem 7

Inlet	Ground Elevation (ft)	Impervious Area (ac)	Pervious Area (ac)	Time of Concentration (min)
I-1	848.9	0.25	0.25	6.0
I-2	848.3	0.09	--	5.0
I-3	847.0	0.20	0.49	5.0
I-4	846.5	0.18	0.5	7.5

Design Constraints for Problem 7

Constraint	Minimum	Maximum
Velocity	2 ft/s	15 ft/s
Cover	4 ft*	--
Pipe Slope	0.005 ft/ft	0.100 ft/ft

Cover constraints may be relaxed at the outfall, where invert elevation requirements will typically govern.

8. An inlet with a ground elevation of 260 m is connected to an outlet with a ground elevation of 259 m and a tailwater elevation of 256 m. The pipe connecting the inlet and outlet is a 20-m long, concrete, circular pipe with a diameter of 525 mm and an upstream invert/sump elevation of 257 m. Print and compare pipe slope, average velocity, pipe flow time, capacity, energy slope, hydraulic grade line upstream, and flow profiles for each of the following conditions.

   a) Scenario 1:
      Inlet inflow = 0.3 m³/s
      Downstream invert/sump elevation = 256.9 m

   b) Scenario 2:
      Inlet inflow = 0.5 m³/s
      Downstream invert/sump elevation = 256.9 m

   c) Scenario 3:
      Inlet inflow = 0.5 m³/s
      Downstream invert/sump elevation = 256.7 m

   d) Scenario 4:
      Inlet inflow = 0.5 m³/s
      Downstream invert/sump elevation = 256.2 m

   What are the differences between the four scenarios, and why do they occur?

9. The system described below drains into a river. Because the water surface elevation of the river varies, analyze the following system with different tailwater elevations. Use the Darcy-Weisbach equation because it is more appropriate for pressure flow than Manning's equation. All pipes are concrete (roughness = 0.122 mm), circular pipes. The pipe and inlet data follow. The ground elevation at the outlet is 312.0 m.

What is the hydraulic grade at the entrance of inlet I-2 under the following tailwater conditions for the 10-year storm event?

a) Tailwater elevation = 310.0 m

b) Tailwater elevation = 311.0 m

c) Tailwater elevation = 313.0 m

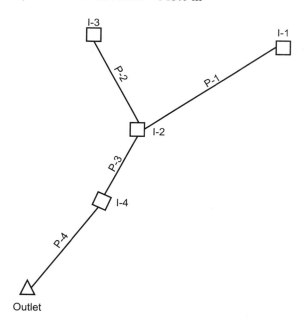

Outlet

Schematic for Problem 9

Rainfall Data for Problem 9

Duration	Rainfall Intensity (mm/hr)		
(min)	2 year	10 year	100 year
5	80	130	210
15	65	97	145
30	45	68	100
60	25	37.5	55

Pipe Information for Problem 9

Pipe	Length (m)	Diameter (mm)	Upstream Invert Elevation (m)	Downstream Invert Elevation (m)
P-1	23	300	312.4	311.5
P-2	25	300	311.5	311.0
P-3	32	525	311.0	310.5
P-4	17	525	310.5	310.4

Inlet Information for Problem 9

Inlet	Area$_1$ (ha)	C_1	Area$_2$ (ha)	C_2	t_c (min)	Ground Elev. (m)	Head Loss Coefficient (Standard Method)	Sump Elev. (m)
I-1	0.2	0.7	0.35	0.6	5.0	315.0	0.5	312.4
I-2	0.3	0.8	0.18	0.6	5.0	314.5	0.7	311.0
I-3	0.8	0.4	0.3	0.7	6.0	314.3	0.5	311.5
I-4	0.9	0.4	0.3	0.5	8.0	313.0	0.5	310.5

10. A schematic of an existing storm system for a residential subdivision is shown below. The rainfall, pipe, inlet, and hydrologic information are provided in the data tables. All pipes are circular, PVC pipes with Manning's $n = 0.010$.

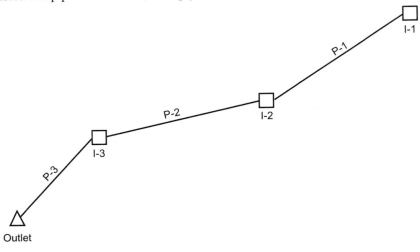

Schematic for Problem 10

a) Analyze the system for a 25-year storm event. Assume a free outfall (critical depth) condition. Provide output tables summarizing pipe flow, velocity, and hydraulic grade at the upstream end of each pipe. How is this system performing?

b) If the existing system were constructed using CMP ($n = 0.024$) instead of PVC, how would the system perform in a 25-year storm event?

c) If the outfall were discharging to a pond that had a water surface elevation equal to that of the ground (using the original PVC pipes), how would the system perform in a 25-year storm? A 50-year storm?

d) Using the tailwater conditions specified in part (a), if the park were paved (with a $C = 0.9$ and time of concentration $= 8$ min), how would the system perform in a 25-year storm? In a 50-year storm?

Rainfall Data for Problem 10

Duration	Rainfall Intensity (in/hr)	
(min)	25 year	50 year
5	4.00	4.60
15	2.80	3.20
30	1.80	2.00
60	0.75	0.90
100	0.55	0.65

Pipe Information for Problem 10

Pipe	Length (ft)	Diameter (in)	Upstream Invert Elevation (ft)	Downstream Invert Elevation (ft)
Pipe-1	70	18	166.70	165.30
Pipe-2	40	18	165.20	164.80
Pipe-3	53	24	164.80	164.40

Inlet Information for Problem 10

Inlet	Ground Elevation (ft)	Rim Elevation (ft)	Sump Elevation (ft)	Head Loss Coefficient (Standard Method)
1	172.00	172.00	166.50	0.5
2	172.00	172.00	165.00	0.5
3	168.00	168.00	164.50	0.5
Outfall	166.50	166.50	164.40	--

Inlet Hydrologic Information for Problem 10

Inlet	Area (ac)	Area Type	Description	C	t_c (min)
1	8	Residential	Single Family	0.5	12
	1	Pavement	Asphalt/Concrete	0.7	
	0.04	Misc.	Playground	0.2	
2	1.2	Pavement	Asphalt/Concrete	0.7	5
3	10	Misc.	Park	0.2	15

11. Use the same network and data provided in part (a) of Problem 10. During a 25-year storm, it was determined that inlet 1 is not capable of capturing all of the flow produced by the runoff for its catch basin. A flow of 5 cfs is bypassed to inlet 2, which is in sag (all gutter flow is captured). Hint: You can apply negative and positive additional carryovers to inlets I-1 and I-2 under the **Catchment** tab.

a) What is the gutter flow captured by inlet 1?

b) What is the gutter flow captured by inlet 2?

c) How is the system performing?

d) A flow monitoring study was performed and the following data was collected:

Pipe	25-Year Storm (cfs)	50-Year Storm (cfs)
Pipe-1	10	11.5
Pipe-2	17.3	19.9
Pipe-3	21.0	25.0

Analyze the system using these known flow values for both the 25- and 50-year storms. How is the system performing? Report the flows, upstream velocities, and hydraulic grade lines for each pipe.

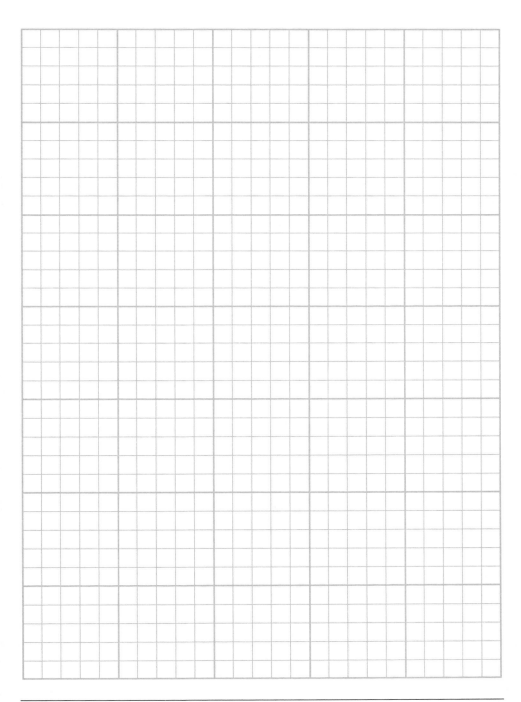

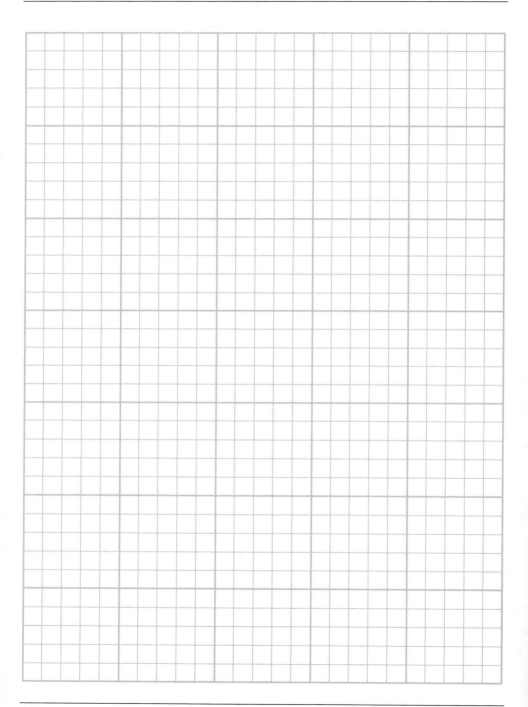

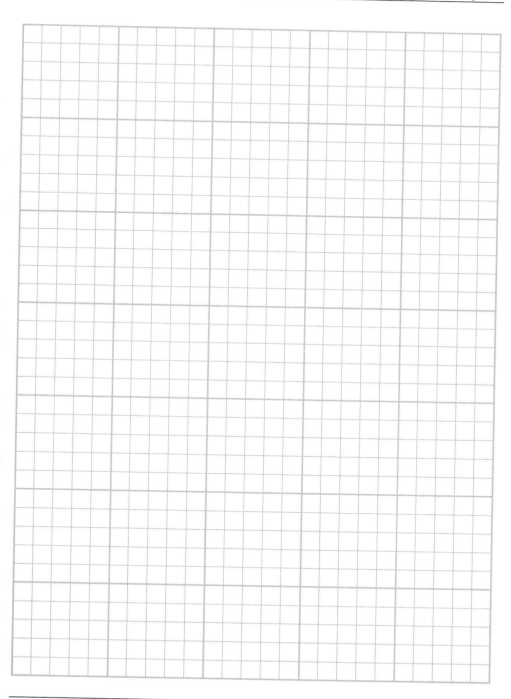

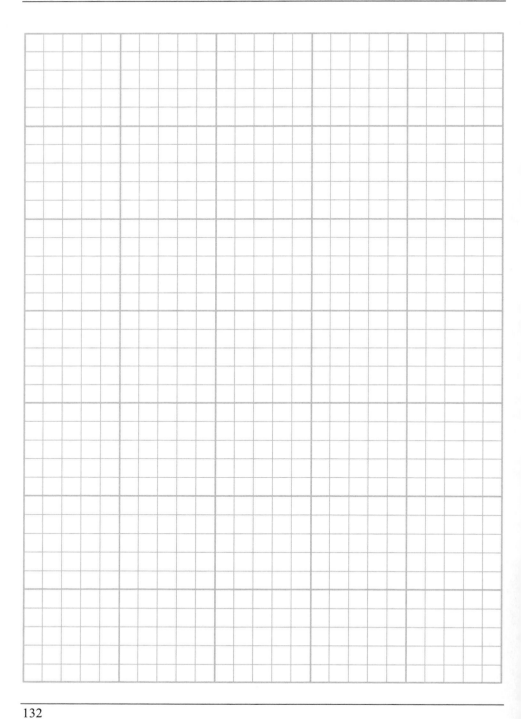

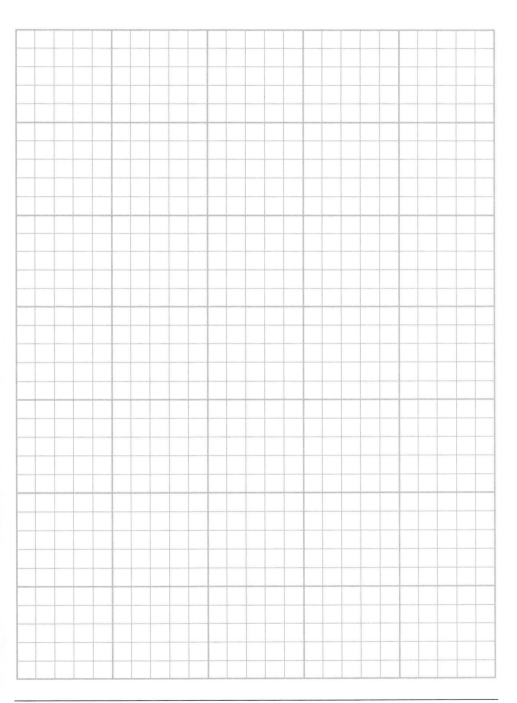

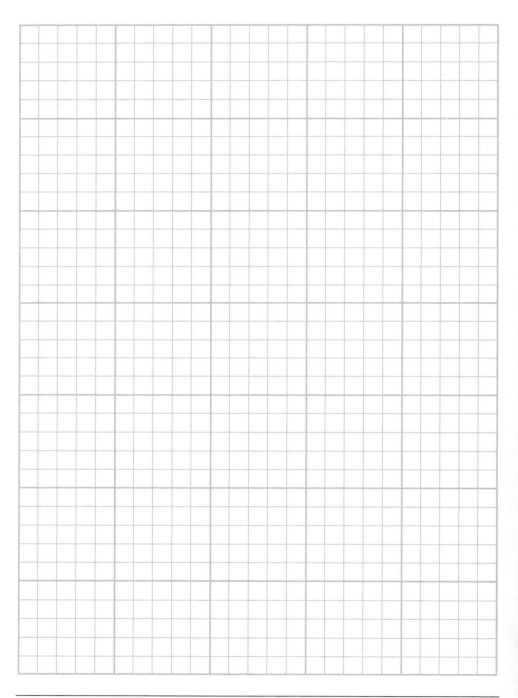

Culvert Hydraulics

4.1 Culvert Systems

Culverts are commonplace in practical hydraulic design, including applications such as roadway crossings and detention pond outlets. A roadway cross-drainage culvert is typically designed to carry flows from one side of the road the other, without allowing the *headwater* (water surface elevation just upstream of the culvert) to exceed safe levels. When engineers analyze these culvert systems, they are usually trying to solve for one or more of the following:

- The size, shape, and number of new or additional culverts required to pass a design discharge

- The hydraulic capacity of an existing culvert system under an allowable headwater constraint

- The upstream flood level at an existing culvert system resulting from a discharge rate of special interest

- Hydraulic performance curves for a culvert system, which are used to assess hydraulic risk at a crossing or as input for another hydraulic or hydrologic model

Similar to a storm sewer system, a culvert system consists of a hydrologic component, a culvert component, and a tailwater component. Although the watershed hydrology and tailwater conditions are almost identical to those that you would normally use in analyzing a storm sewer or other open channel transport system, there are additional hydraulic computations typically reserved for culvert analysis only.

In this chapter, procedures for designing culverts using CulvertMaster are presented. The use of nomographs as aids to hand calculations is described in detail in the *Hydraulic Design of Highway Culverts* manual (Norman et. al, 1985). Further discussion on hydraulic theory, end treatments, alignments, and roadway overtopping is presented by Durrans, 2002.

Culvert Hydraulics

Obtaining accurate solutions in culvert hydraulics can be a formidable computational task. Culverts act as a significant constriction to flow and are subject to a range of flow types, including both gradually varied and rapidly varied flows.

It is this mix of flow conditions and the highly transitional nature of culvert hydraulics that makes the hydraulic solutions so difficult. For this reason, the documented approach is to simplify the hydraulics problem and analyze the culvert system using two different assumptions of flow control:

- *Outlet control* assumption — Computes the upstream headwater depth using conventional hydraulic methodologies that consider the predominant losses due to the culvert barrel friction, as well as the minor entrance and exit losses. The tailwater condition during the design storm has an important effect on the culvert system.

- *Inlet control* assumption — Computes the upstream headwater depth resulting from the constriction at the culvert entrance, while neglecting the culvert barrel friction, tailwater elevation, and other minor losses.

The controlling headwater depth is the larger value of the computed inlet control and outlet control headwater depths. Because the culvert system may operate under inlet control conditions for a range of flow rates and under outlet control conditions for another range, calculations must be performed for both control conditions.

4.2 Outlet Control Hydraulics

Calculations for outlet control headwater depths are similar to those performed for storm sewer analysis. The headwater depth is found by summing the tailwater depth, entrance minor loss, exit minor loss, and friction losses along the culvert barrel. The energy basis for solving the outlet control headwater (HW) for a culvert is given by the basic energy equation and is presented graphically in Figure 4-1.

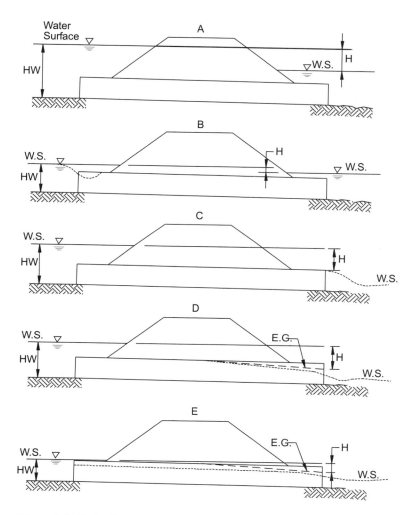

Figure 4-1: Outlet Control Flow Conditions

Full flow conditions (Cases A , B, and C in Figure 4-1) result in the same velocity (and therefore the same velocity head) throughout the length of the culvert; therefore, the energy grade line and hydraulic grade line are parallel throughout the length of the barrel. At the culvert entrance, there is a slight increase in velocity and dip in the HGL caused by the flow contraction that occurs there.

The energy equation can be rewritten specifically for culvert terms, which results in the following form:

$$HW_o + \frac{V_u{}^2}{2g} = TW + \frac{V_d{}^2}{2g} + H_L$$

where HW_O =   headwater depth above the outlet invert (m, ft)
        V_u =   approach velocity (m/s, ft/s)
        TW =   tailwater depth above the outlet invert (m, ft)
        V_d =   exit velocity (m/s, ft/s)
        H_L =   sum of all losses, including the entrance minor loss (H_E), barrel friction losses (H_F), the exit loss (H_O), and other losses (m, ft)

Culverts often connect ponds or other bodies of water with negligible velocities, so the approach velocity and the velocity downstream of the culvert are often neglected, resulting in the following equation:

$$HW_o = TW + H_L$$

where HW_O =   headwater depth above the outlet invert (m, ft)
        TW =   tailwater depth above the outlet invert (m, ft)
        H_L =   sum of all losses as listed above (m, ft)

Friction Losses

Culverts are frequently hydraulically short (entrance and exit losses exceed pipe friction losses), and uniform flow depths are not always achieved. For this reason, gradually varied flow methods are well suited to the analysis. For a more detailed description of gradually varied flow, see Chapter 3.

Entrance Minor Loss

The entrance loss is caused by the contraction of flow as it enters the culvert, and is a function of the barrel velocity head just inside the entrance. It is expressed by the following equation:

$$H_e = k_e \left(\frac{V^2}{2g} \right)$$

where H_e =   entrance loss (m, ft)
        k_e =   entrance loss coefficient
        V =   velocity just inside the barrel entrance (m/s, ft/s)
        g =   gravitational acceleration (m/s², ft/s²)

The entrance loss coefficient varies depending on the type of inlet that is present. The smoother the transition from the channel or pond into the culvert, the lower the loss coefficient. Values for the coefficients are presented in the following table.

Table 4-1: Entrance Loss Coefficients

Culvert Type	Entrance Type and Description	Entrance Loss Coefficient, k_e
Pipe, Concrete	Projecting from fill, socket end (groove-end)	0.2
	Projecting from fill, square cut end	0.5
	Headwall or headwall with wingwalls	
	Socket end of pipe (groove-end)	0.2
	Square-edge	0.5
	Rounded (radius = 1/12D)	0.2
	Mitered to conform to fill slope	0.7
	End-section conforming to fill slope*	0.5
	Beveled edges, 33.7° or 45° bevels	0.2
	Side- or slope-tapered inlet	0.2
Pipe or Pipe Arch, Corrugated Metal	Projecting from fill (no headwall)	0.9
	Headwall or headwall and wingwalls square-edge	0.5
	Mitered to conform to fill slope, paved or unpaved slope	0.7
	End-section conforming to fill slope*	0.5
	Beveled edges, 33.7° or 45° bevels	0.2
	Side- or slope-tapered inlet	0.2
Box, Reinforced Concrete	Headwall parallel to embankment (no wingwalls)	
	Square-edged on 3 edges	0.5
	Rounded on 3 edges to radius of 1/12 barrel dimension, or beveled edges on 3 sides	0.2
	Wingwalls at 30° to 75° to barrel	
	Square-edged at crown	0.4
	Crown edge rounded to radius of 1/12 barrel dimension, or beveled top edge	0.2
	Wingwall at 10° to 25° to barrel	
	Square-edged at crown	0.5
	Wingwalls parallel (extension of sides)	
	Square-edged at crown	0.7
	Side- or slope-tapered inlet	0.2

* Note: "End-section conforming to fill slope," made of either metal or concrete, are the sections commonly available from manufacturers. From limited hydraulic tests, they are equivalent in operation to a headwall in both inlet and outlet control. Some end sections with a closed taper in their design have superior hydraulic performance.

Exit Minor Loss

The exit loss is an expansion loss, which is a function of the change in velocity head that occurs at the discharge end of the culvert. In culvert hydraulics, this sudden expansion loss is expressed as:

$$H_o = 1.0\left[\frac{V^2}{2g} - \frac{V_d^2}{2g}\right]$$

where V_d = velocity of the outfall channel (m/s, ft/s)
V = velocity just inside the end of the culvert barrel (m/s, ft/s)
g = gravitational acceleration (m/s², ft/s²)

When the discharge velocity is negligible (as for a pond or slow-moving channel), the exit loss is equal to the barrel velocity head.

Gradually Varied Flow Analysis

Culverts operating under outlet control with unsubmerged outlets (Cases D and E in Figure 4-1) require an analysis of the hydraulic profile in order to determine the headwater elevation. In Case D, the water surface reaches the crown of the culvert at some point upstream of the barrel. In both cases, the flow passes through critical depth at the outlet end of the barrel. The flow is represented by the M2 profile (see Figure 3-8).

4.3   Inlet Control Hydraulics

When a culvert is operating under inlet control conditions (as in Figure 4-2), the hydraulic control section is the culvert entrance itself. This means that the friction and minor losses within the culvert are not as significant as the losses caused by the entrance constriction.

Because the control section for culverts operating under inlet control conditions is at the upstream end of the culvert barrel, critical depth generally occurs at or near the inlet, and flows downstream of the inlet are supercritical. The hydraulic profile and outlet velocities are determined using frontwater gradually varied flow techniques.

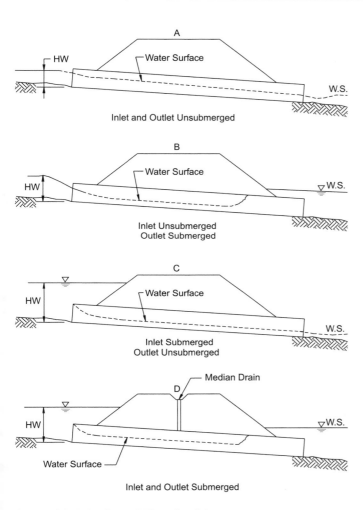

Figure 4-2: Inlet Control Flow Conditions

Three types of inlet control hydraulics are in effect over a range of culvert discharges:

- *Unsubmerged* **(A and B)** – For low discharge conditions, the culvert entrance acts as a weir. The hydraulics of weir flow are governed by empirical working equations developed as a result of model tests.

- *Submerged* **(C)** – When the culvert entrance is fully submerged, it is assumed to be operating as an orifice.

- *Transitional* **(D)** – This flow type occurs in the poorly defined region just above the unsubmerged zone and below the fully submerged zone.

Unsubmerged Flow

There are two equations for unsubmerged (weir) flow. The first is based on the specific head at critical depth (with correction factors), whereas the second equation is more closely related to a weir equation. Although either equation will produce adequate results, the second equation is more commonly used during hand calculations because it is easier to apply.

Note that these equations were developed by the U.S. FHWA and as such are only intended for use in U.S. customary units. SI units should be converted before applying these equations.

Unsubmerged, Form 1

$$\frac{HW_i}{D} = \frac{H_c}{D} + K\left[\frac{Q}{AD^{0.5}}\right]^M - 0.5S$$

Unsubmerged, Form 2

$$\frac{HW_i}{D} = K\left[\frac{Q}{AD^{0.5}}\right]^M$$

where
HW_i = headwater depth above the control section invert (ft)
D = interior height of the culvert barrel (ft)
H_c = specific head at critical depth, $y_c + V_c^2/2g$ (ft), where y_c = Critical depth (ft) and V_c = Velocity at critical depth (ft/s)
Q = culvert discharge (ft³/s)
A = full cross-sectional area of the culvert barrel (ft²)
S = culvert barrel slope (ft/ft)
K, M = constants from Table 4-2

These equations are applicable up to approximately $Q/AD^{0.5} = 3.5$. When using the first equation with mitered inlets, use a slope correction factor (last term of Form 1 equation) of $+0.7S$ instead of $-0.5S$.

Submerged Flow

The equation for submerged (orifice) flow is:

$$\frac{HW_i}{D} = c\left[\frac{Q}{AD^{0.5}}\right]^2 + Y - 0.5S$$

where
HW_i = headwater depth above the control section invert (ft)
D = interior height of the culvert barrel (ft)
H_c = specific head at critical depth, $y_c + V_c^2/2g$ (ft)
Q = culvert discharge (ft³/s)
A = full cross-sectional area of the culvert barrel (ft²)
S = culvert barrel slope (ft/ft)
c, Y = constants from Table 4-2.

This equation for submerged flow is applicable above approximately $Q/AD^{0.5} = 4.0$. When using this equation with mitered inlets, use a slope correction factor (last term of equation) of $+0.7S$ instead of $-0.5S$.

Table 4-2: Coefficients for Inlet Control Design Equations

Shape and Material	Inlet Edge Description	Equation Form	Unsubmerged		Submerged	
			K	M	c	Y
Circular Concrete	Square edge w/headwall	1	.0098	2.0	.0398	0.67
	Groove end w/headwall		.0018	2.0	.0292	.74
	Groove end projecting		.0045	2.0	.0317	.69
Circular CMP	Headwall	1	.0078	2.0	.0379	.69
	Mitered to slope		.0210	1.33	.0463	.75
	Projecting		.0340	1.50	.0553	.54
Circular	Beveled ring, 45° bevels	1	.0018	2.50	.0300	.74
	Beveled ring, 33.7° bevels		.0018	2.50	.0243	.83
Rectangular Box	30° to 75° wingwall flares	1	.026	1.0	.0347	.81
	90° and 15° wingwall flares		.061	0.75	.0400	.80
	0° wingwall flares		.061	0.75	.0423	.82
Rectangular Box	45° wingwall flare d = .043D	2	.510	.667	.0309	.80
	18° to 33.7° wingwall flare d=.083D		.486	.667	.0249	.83
Rectangular Box	90° headwall w/¾" chamfers	2	.515	.667	.0375	.79
	90° headwall w/45° bevels		.495	.667	.0314	.82
	90° headwall w/33.7° bevels		.486	.667	.0252	.865
Rectangular Box	¾" chamfers; 45° skewed headwall	2	.545	.667	.0505	.73
	¾" chamfers; 30° skewed headwall		.533	.667	.0425	.705
	¾" chamfers; 15° skewed headwall		.522	.667	.0402	.68
	45° bevels; 10°-45° skewed headwall		.498	.667	.0327	.75
Rectangular Box ¾" Chamfers	45° non-offset wingwall flares	2	.497	.667	.0339	.803
	18.4° non-offset wingwall flares		.493	.667	.0361	.806
	18.4° non-offset wingwall flares 30° skewed barrel		.495	.667	.0386	.71
Rectangular Box Top Bevels	45° wingwall flares – offset	2	.497	.667	.0302	.835
	33.7° wingwall flares – offset		.495	.667	.0252	.881
	18.4° wingwall flares – offset		.493	.667	.0227	.887
C M Boxes	90° headwall	1	.0083	2.0	.0379	.69
	Thick wall projecting		.0145	1.75	.0419	.64
	Thin wall projecting		.0340	1.5	.0496	.57
Horizontal Ellipse Concrete	Square edge w/headwall	1	.0100	2.0	.0398	.67
	Groove end w/headwall		.0018	2.5	.0292	.74
	Groove end projecting		.0045	2.0	.0317	.69
Vertical Ellipse Concrete	Square edge w/headwall	1	.0100	2.0	.0398	.67
	Groove end w/headwall		.0018	2.5	.0292	.74
	Groove end projecting		.0095	2.0	.0317	.69
Pipe Arch 18" Corner Radius CM	90° headwall	1	.0083	2.0	.0379	.69
	Mitered to slope		.0300	1.0	.0463	.75
	Projecting		.0340	1.5	.0496	.57
Pipe Arch 18" Corner Radius CM	Projecting	1	.0300	1.5	.0496	.57
	No bevels		.0088	2.0	.0368	.68
	33.7° bevels		.0030	2.0	.0269	.77
Pipe Arch 31" Corner Radius CM	Projecting	1	.0300	1.5	.0496	.57
	No bevels		.0088	2.0	.0368	.68
	33.7° bevels		.0030	2.0	.0269	.77
Arch CM	90° headwall	1	.0083	2.0	.0379	.69
	Mitered to slope		.0300	1.0	.0463	.75
	Thin wall projecting		.0340	1.5	.0496	.57
Circular	Smooth tapered inlet throat	2	.534	.555	.0196	.90
	Rough tapered inlet throat		.519	.64	.0210	.90
Elliptical Inlet Face	Tapered inlet-beveled edges	2	.536	.622	.0368	.83
	Tapered inlet-square edges		.5035	.719	.0478	.80
	Tapered inlet-thin edge projecting		.547	.80	.0598	.75
Rectangular	Tapered inlet throat	2	.475	.667	.0179	.97
Rectangular Concrete	Side tapered—less favorable edges	2	.56	.667	.0446	.85
	Side tapered—more favorable edges		.56	.667	.0378	.87
Rectangular Concrete	Slope tapered—less favorable edges	2	.50	.667	.0446	.65
	Slope tapered—more favorable edges		.50	.667	.0378	.71

4.4 CulvertMaster

CulvertMaster is a program that helps civil engineers design and analyze culvert hydraulics. Just click a button to create a new worksheet, enter data in the clearly labeled fields, and click to calculate. You can solve for most hydraulic variables, including culvert size, flow, and headwater. It also allows you to generate and plot rating tables and graphical output showing computed flow characteristics.

CulvertMaster contains options to automatically generate peak discharges, including the Rational Method and SCS Graphical Peak Discharge Method. You have a choice of culvert barrel shapes including circular pipes, arches, boxes, and more. Calculations handle free surface, pressure and varied flow situations including backwater and drawdown curves. CulvertMaster's flexible reporting features allow you to print the results in report format or as a graphical plot.

The theory and background used in CulvertMaster are described in detail in this chapter, as well as in the CulvertMaster online help system.

How Can You Use CulvertMaster?

CulvertMaster can design or analyze culverts and compute headwater for a range of flow rates. For a typical CulvertMaster project, an engineer may be interested in several culvert locations and try several designs for each location. You can use CulvertMaster to:

- Size culverts
- Compute and plot rating tables and curves
- View output in both English and SI units
- Generate professional-looking reports and graphs

4.5 Tutorial Example

The following tutorial provides step-by-step instructions on how to solve the example problem using CulvertMaster's Quick Culvert Calculator (included on the CD that accompanies this textbook).

Problem Statement

Several circular, concrete culverts that have square-edged entrances with headwalls ($n = 0.013$, $k_e = 0.5$) must be used to carry 54 m^3/s. The culverts are 20 m long, on a 5.5 percent slope with upstream and downstream invert elevations of 261.0 m and 259.9 m, respectively. The maximum allowable headwater elevation is 268 m, and the elevation of the tailwater is 257.4 m.

a) How many culverts should be used if the diameter of the culverts is 1950 mm?

b) What is the headwater depth?

c)   Is the system flowing under inlet or outlet control?

d)   What is the velocity at the culvert exit?

e)   Construct a performance curve showing the headwater elevation as a function of discharge. Consider both inlet and outlet control.

PART (a): How many culverts should be used if the diameter of the culverts is 1950 mm?

Solution

- When you start CulvertMaster, you should be prompted with the **Welcome to CulvertMaster** dialog. From this dialog, you can access the tutorials, open existing projects, and create new ones. Select **Create New Project**, provide a filename, and click **Save**.

- If the **Welcome to CulvertMaster** dialog does not appear, CulvertMaster is set to **Hide Welcome Dialog on Startup**. To start a new project, select **New** from the **File** menu, enter a filename, and click **Save**. (You can change from **Hide Welcome Dialog** mode to **Show Welcome Dialog** mode in the **Options** dialog, which is accessible by selecting **Options** from the **Tools** menu.)

- The **Project Setup Wizard** will appear. Add a project title and any appropriate comments, and click **Next**. We will not be defining a rainfall table or a rainfall equation, so select **Next.** We need to check the unit system before creating an element (Quick Culvert Calculator), so select the **None** radio button and **Finished** to exit.

- Because this problem uses SI units, select **Options** from the **Tools** pull-down menu and change the unit system to **System International** if this option is not already selected. Click **OK** to exit the dialog. If you changed unit systems, you may be prompted to confirm the switch. If so, click **Yes**.

- Click the **Quick Culvert Calculator** button on the left hand side of the window.

- Provide a title for the worksheet and click **OK**.

- Select **Discharge** from the **Solve For:** pull-down menu.

- Enter the values for maximum allowable headwater, tailwater elevation, upstream and downstream invert elevations, length, culvert shape and material, Manning's *n,* and the culvert entrance coefficient. If you want to change the units or precision of any of the variables entered, you can do so by double-clicking the units next to the variable.

- Run the model by clicking the **Solve** button. Run the model several times, increasing the number of culvert barrels until the discharge is greater than or equal to the designated flow rate of 54 m^3/s. As you will see, three culverts with 1950-mm diameters will carry 61 m^3/s. Your dialog should match Figure 4-3.

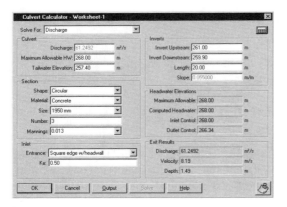

Figure 4-3: CulvertMaster Dialog for the Circular, Concrete Culverts

PART (b): What is the headwater depth?

Solution

The headwater depth is equal to the difference between the **Computed Headwater** and the **Invert Upstream**:

$$268.0 \text{ m} - 261.0 \text{ m} = 7.0 \text{ m}$$

PART (c): Is the system flowing under inlet or outlet control?

Solution

The system is flowing under inlet control, because the inlet control elevation is greater than the outlet control.

PART (d): What is the velocity at the culvert exit?

Solution

Taken from the exit results section of the **Culvert Calculator,** the exit velocity is 8.19 m/s.

Part (e): Construct a performance curve showing the headwater elevation as a function of discharge. Consider both inlet and outlet control.

Solution

- Click the **Output** button and select the **Plot Curves** button.
- Under the **Compute** heading in the dialog, select **Inlet Control HW Elev** and **Outlet Control Elev,** and then click the **Refresh** button.
- The graph in Figure 4-4 shows the performance curve for the three-barrel culvert set.

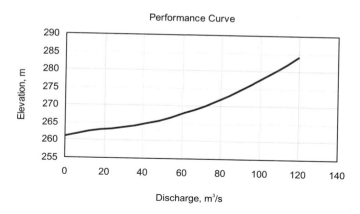

Figure 4-4: Performance Curve for Three Circular Concrete Culverts in Tutorial Example

4.6 Problems

Solve the following problems using CulvertMaster's Quick Culvert Calculator.

1. A culvert is 11 m long and has upstream and downstream inverts of 263.4 m and 263.1 m, respectively. The downstream tailwater elevation is below the downstream pipe invert.

    For a K_e of 0.5 and a Manning's n value of 0.013, what minimum diameter concrete circular culvert (in mm) is required to pass 1.4 m³/s under a roadway with a maximum allowable headwater elevation of 265.2 m?

    What is the headwater elevation for the selected culvert?

2. An existing 9.73-m-long, 560 × 420-mm steel and aluminum var CR arch ($n = 0.025$) has a 90-degree headwall. The inverts are 33.11 m and 33.09 m. Assuming no tailwater effects, what is the maximum discharge that can pass through this culvert before the maximum allowable water surface elevation of 34.25 m is exceeded?

3. Twin 1220 × 910-mm box culverts ($n = 0.013$, entrance has 90-degree and 15-degree wingwall flares) carry 8.5 m³/s along a 31-m length of pipe constructed at a 1.0% slope. The tailwater depth is 0.61 m.

    a) What is the headwater depth?

    b) Are the culverts flowing under inlet or outlet control conditions?

    c) What would the headwater depth and flow regime be if the flow rate were 380 cfs?

4. A 100-ft horizontal concrete ellipse pipe ($n = 0.013$, $K_e = 0.5$) on a 3.5% slope is required to carry 65 cfs. Assume there is a free outfall. The maximum allowable headwater is 4.7 feet.

    a) What is the minimum pipe size (in inches) required?

    b) What would be the minimum size for a vertical concrete ellipse pipe?

5. A 12.2-m-long, 920 × 570-mm concrete arch pipe ($n = 0.013$, groove-end with headwall entrance) constructed at a 0.8% slope carries 1.84 m³/s.

    a) If there is a constant tailwater depth of 0.3 m, what is the headwater depth for both inlet and outlet control conditions?

    b) Is the culvert flowing under inlet or outlet control conditions?

    c) What would be the result if the tailwater were 0.5 m deeper?

6. Triple 3050 × 1830-mm, 200-m-long, concrete box culverts ($n = 0.013$, $K_e = 0.5$) carry 110 m³/min. The culverts are constructed on a 1.4% slope and discharge into a pond with a depth 0.8 m above the downstream culvert invert. What is the exit velocity of the culverts?

7. Twin culverts are proposed to discharge 6.5 m³/s. The culverts will be 36.6 m long and have inverts of 20.1 m and 19.8 m. The design engineer analyzed the three culvert systems described below. The tailwater elevation is free outfall. Which of the following proposed culverts will result in the highest headwater elevation? The lowest?

    a) 1200-mm circular concrete pipes ($n = 0.013$ and $K_e = 0.5$)

    b) 1220 × 910-mm concrete box culverts ($n = 0.013$, 90° and 15° wingwall flares at entrance)

    c) 1630 × 1120mm steel and aluminum var CR arches ($n = 0.025$ and $K_e = 0.5$)

8. A 40-ft-long elliptical pipe ($n = 0.013$ and $K_e = 0.5$) will be constructed to carry 80 cfs with inverts of 22.6 ft and 22.1 ft. The tailwater is constant at an elevation of 24.0 ft. Which pipe will provide a lower headwater elevation: a 38 × 60-in. horizontal ellipse or a 60 × 38-in. vertical ellipse?

9. A circular concrete culvert has a free outfall. The culvert is 60 ft long on a 2% slope and is 30 inches in diameter. The culvert entrance will project from the embankment. Create a rating table that correlates the culvert discharge to the depth of the headwater, from 0 ft to 6 ft in 0.5-ft increments.

10. A detention pond drains through a circular concrete culvert that has a square-edge inlet with a headwall ($n = 0.013$, $K_e = 0.5$). The peak discharge of the pond is 4 m³/s, and the headwater elevation is 15.5 m. The culvert is 10 m long on a 5% slope. The depth of the headwater is 4 m, and the tailwater elevation is below the elevation of the downstream invert. What is the elevation of the upstream invert? What size culvert is required?

11. A stream flows under a road through a 48-in. concrete circular culvert that has a square-edge inlet with a headwall ($n = 0.013$, $k_e = 0.5$). The culvert is on a 5% slope with a length of 31.2 ft, a downstream invert elevation of 92.5 ft, and a free tailwater outfall. The surface of the road is at an elevation of 108.3 ft, and the stream has a base flow rate of 176.57 cfs.

   a) If the runoff from a rainstorm adds another 176.57 cfs of flow to the stream, will the road be flooded?

   b) What is the maximum flow rate that will not flood the road?

12. A 15-m-long culvert that has a projecting groove end inlet is needed on a 2% slope with a free outfall. The elevation of the upstream invert is 100 m, and the maximum headwater depth is 5 m.

   a) What size concrete arch culvert ($n = 0.013$, $K_e = 0.5$) is needed to carry 6 m³/s of water?

   b) Is the culvert operating under inlet or outlet control?

   c) If the tailwater depth changes to 0.3 m, what is the flow control?

   d) If the tailwater depth changes to 3.3 m, what is the flow control?

   e) Why does the flow control change or not change?

13. A 15-m-long concrete vertical ellipse culvert that has a square-edge inlet with a headwall (860×550 mm, $n = 0.013$, $K_e = 0.5$) has upstream and downstream invert elevations of 2.00 m and 1.46 m, respectively. If the tailwater elevation is 3.02 m, at what flow rate (greater than 0.1 m³/s) are inlet and outlet control headwater elevations equal? (Hint: Use rating curves.) Is this free-surface flow or pressurized flow?

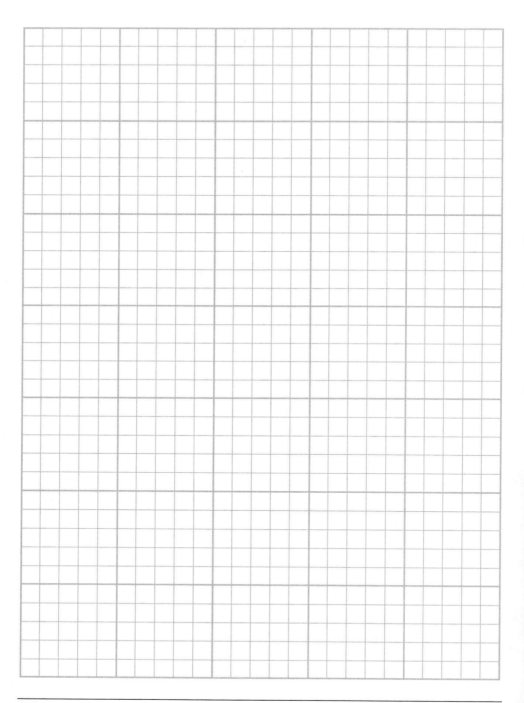

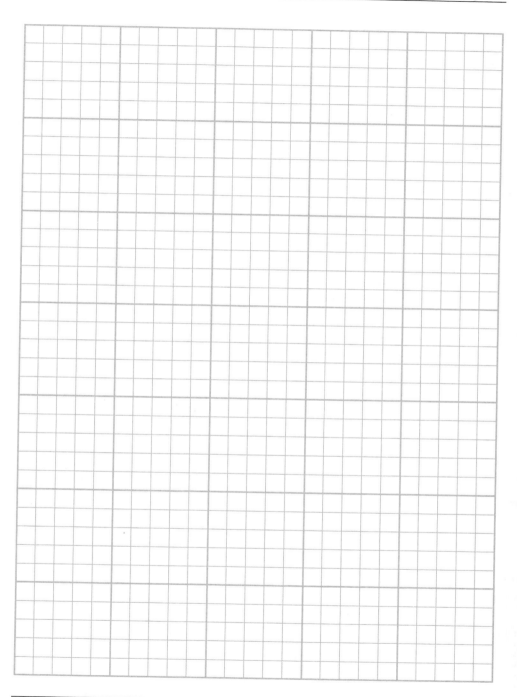

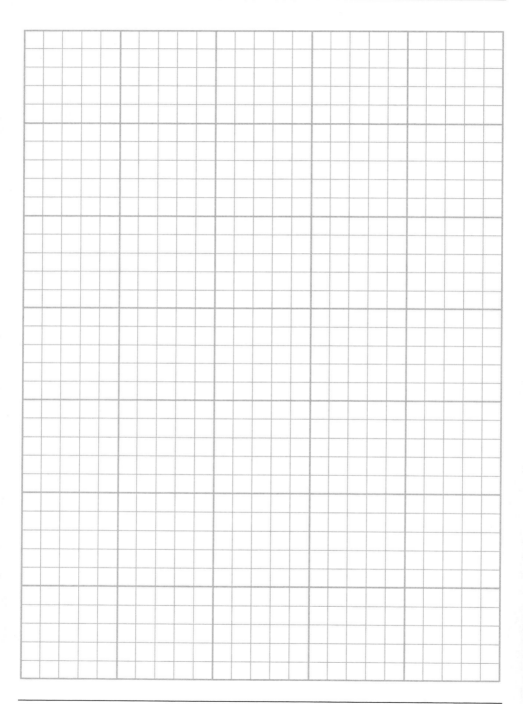

Detention Pond Design

5.1 Overview of Stormwater Detention

Stormwater detention is the temporary storage of runoff in basins, underground containers, or on rooftops. Wet or dry *detention basins* (also called *detention ponds*) are the most commonly used structures and are the subject of this chapter. Once runoff has been collected in a detention basin it can be released to downstream properties or conveyances in a controlled manner such that downstream flooding and other adverse impacts are prevented or alleviated. The construction of stormwater detention facilities is typically associated with new developments, as these usually result in increased stormwater runoff rates and volumes.

Figure 5-1 demonstrates the basic principles of detention pond analysis. An inflow runoff hydrograph (see Chapter 2) from one or more contributing drainage areas is directed to a storage facility (in this case, a graded detention pond). Runoff is then released from the facility at a controlled rate through a properly sized outlet structure such as a culvert. The result is a pond outflow hydrograph that is substantially flatter (that is, has a lower peak flow) than the inflow hydrograph.

This chapter provides basic information on stormwater detention design and analysis concepts. The topics covered include basic detention facility types, pond volume calculations, outlet structure types, and the storage-indication method of pond routing. For more in-depth coverage of stormwater detention, the reader is referred to the Haestad Press book *Stormwater Modeling and Detention Design*.

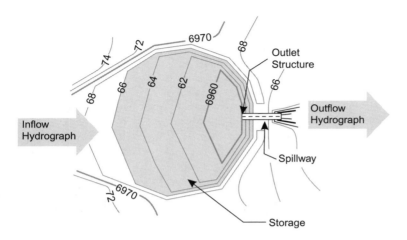

Figure 5-1: Conceptual Drawing of a Detention Pond

5.2   Basic Design Considerations

Design criteria for detention ponds vary widely. In the United States, detention regulations are typically adopted at the municipal or county level, so local regulations and guidelines must be consulted before the stormwater detention facility can be designed. Despite the wide variation in design practices, the underlying philosophy of most regulations is that peak runoff rates discharged from the undeveloped site for one or more design storm events should not be exceeded after the site development.

Several basic categories of detention facilities exist. Ponds may be wet or dry between storm events; detention may occur on the surface or underground; and a facility may lie in a main drainage path or be removed from it. The type of facility may be dictated by regulations or by the needs and limitations of the individual site or drainage area.

Pre-Development versus Post-Development Criteria and Recurrence Frequency

As a watershed is developed, the peak discharge rate and the amount of runoff will tend to increase, whereas the time to peak will typically decrease. The intent of stormwater detention is typically to limit post-development peak discharges from a site to discharge rates no greater than those that occurred prior to development. Thus, the conveyance capacities of existing downstream structures will still be sufficient if these structures were adequately sized prior to development.

Sometimes allowable detention facility discharges may be based on criteria other than pre-development flows. For instance, if a structure downstream of the property is undersized, the developer may be required to actually lower peak discharge rates below pre-development values so as not to exceed its capacity. It is important to note, however, that even if peak discharge objectives are met, detention ponds typically do not mitigate the increase in runoff *volume* caused by land development. Although the peak flow rate from a site for a given storm event may be the same as it was prior to development, the duration of the discharge can be substantially longer.

The criteria described previously must be met for one or more specified design storm events. For most localities, these design events will be specified in their regulations. For example, the regulations may specify that post-development peak flows be less than pre-development peaks for 24-hour, synthetic storms having return frequencies of 2, 5, and 10 years. (It is advisable, however, to check the design for storms of different durations.) The regulations may further state that an emergency overflow structure capable of handling flows from the 100-year storm be constructed. The magnitude of the largest storm that the facility must be designed to accommodate sometimes depends on factors such as site area and land use.

Types and Configurations of Stormwater Detention Facilities

A *dry pond* has an outlet that is positioned at or below the lowest elevation in the pond, such that the pond drains completely between storm events. A *wet pond,* on the other hand, is one whose outlet is at an elevation above the pond bottom. Water remains in the pond during dry-weather periods between storm events and this water can only be depleted by infiltration into the soils and by evaporation from the water surface. A *retention pond* is a type of wet pond in which no outlet structure exists; infiltration and evaporation are the only means by which water can escape.

Detention ponds can be designed in an almost unlimited number of shapes and sizes. An *aboveground pond* usually consists of a depressed or excavated area with an earthen berm. In cases where there is not ample surface area available to meet storage requirements, *underground detention* may be necessary. Underground detention may consist of a series of large pipes or prefabricated custom chambers manufactured specifically for underground detention.

On-line and off-line ponds are distinguished from one another based on whether they are positioned along the alignment of the main stormwater drainage path. An *on-line pond,* as its name suggests, is positioned along the pathway and all runoff must pass through it. An *off-line pond* is located outside of the main drainage pathway, and only a portion of the total contributing stormwater runoff is diverted through it.

Multiple ponds may be necessary to achieve detention requirements under certain site conditions. Ponds can be connected in series such that the outflow hydrograph from one pond is also the inflow hydrograph for the next pond downstream. In some cases, particularly where the topography is flatter, the ponds may be close enough in elevation that the downstream pond stage has tailwater effects on the rating curve for the upstream pond. This type of calculation is called interconnected pond modeling and is beyond the scope of this chapter.

5.3 Detention Pond Modeling Concepts

Stormwater detention design requires estimation of a complete runoff hydrograph, as opposed to the single peak discharge typically used in storm sewer design. Procedures for inflow hydrograph estimation were presented in Chapter 2. This section provides a conceptual review of stormwater runoff hydrographs and discusses how they are shaped and altered by added detention facilities.

Figure 5-2 serves as a definition sketch for the basic hydrograph concepts associated with detention. The *inflow hydrograph* represents the runoff from a watershed. Its principal attributes are the peak discharge rate (in ft^3/s or m^3/s) and the time from the beginning of the storm to the peak discharge. The area under this curve represents the total volume of runoff resulting from this storm event.

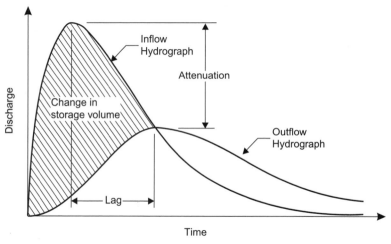

Figure 5-2: Detention Pond Inflow and Outflow Hydrographs

The *outflow hydrograph* represents the discharge from a detention facility. The outflow hydrograph is obtained by performing a *routing analysis* (discussed later in this chapter) for a given detention pond, outlet configuration, and inflow hydrograph. The reduction in the peak discharge seen in the outflow hydrograph is referred to as *attenuation,* and the increase in the time to peak discharge is the referred to as the *lag.*

If the infiltration and evaporation occurring in the pond during the storm event are negligible, the areas under the two curves (that is, the runoff volumes) must be equal. The area between the inflow and outflow hydrographs represents the maximum volume of water present in the pond during the storm event. If this volume is greater than the storage capacity of the pond, the pond will overflow.

The following three scenarios summarize the relationship of a pond's inflow rate, outflow rate, storage, and water surface elevation for any given time interval within a stormwater runoff event:

- If the average inflow rate is greater than average outflow rate during a time interval, the volume of stored water in the pond increases during the time interval, and the water surface elevation in the pond increases.
- If the average inflow rate is equal to the average outflow rate during a time interval, the volume of stored water does not change during the interval, and the water surface elevation remains constant.
- If the average outflow rate is greater than the average inflow rate during a time interval, the volume of stored water decreases during the time interval, and the water surface elevation in the pond decreases.

Most detention ponds have ***uncontrolled outlets*** (that is, their outlets have no valves or gates that can be opened or closed). For a pond with an uncontrolled outlet into a free outfall, the peak of the outflow hydrograph from the pond will occur at the point where the outflow hydrograph intersects the receding limb of the inflow hydrograph (see Figure 5-2).

This concept can be used as a check on the validity of a set of routing calculations, and can be reasoned as follows. Prior to the time of the intersection point, the inflow rate is larger than the outflow rate and the volume of water in the pond is increasing. After that intersection time, the volume is decreasing because the outflow rate is greater than the inflow rate. Thus, the maximum stored volume of water in the pond occurs at the time where the two hydrographs intersect. Because the outflow rate from a pond increases as the headwater depth in the pond increases, it follows that the maximum outflow rate must occur at the maximum depth, which also corresponds to the maximum storage during the event. Finally, at the point of intersection, the outflow is equal to the inflow rate, resulting in a zero rate of change of stored volume at the moment in time when the water surface crests in the pond.

5.4   Components of Detention Facilities

Detention facilities usually consist of an aboveground pond that is excavated and graded into the land surface, or they may consist of shallow collection areas in parking lots. In areas where available space is at a premium, it may be economically advantageous to use underground storage consisting of pipes and/or vaults. Thus, the physical components of individual detention facilities can be quite variable, but some general observations can be made. The following subsections provide descriptions of the most common elements of detention facilities.

Dam Embankments

In many cases, detention facilities are formed by excavating and grading a depression in the land surface, and the resulting pond has no dam embankment per se. In other cases, a stream or localized depression is dammed to create a detention pond. Most typically, a combination of these two approaches is used in which an existing depression is enlarged and dammed. The design of the dam should conform to accepted geotechnical engineering practices. Governmental dam safety and permitting requirements may be applicable if the embankment height or storage exceeds a regulatory limit.

Freeboard

Freeboard for a storm event is defined as the vertical distance from the maximum water surface elevation (stage) to the top of the dam. The storage available within the freeboard elevation range adds a "safety" volume to the required detention storage volumes that exist below this elevation. Some jurisdictions and reviewing agencies mandate freeboard requirements for the maximum design event.

Pond Bottoms and Side Slopes

Side slopes of ponds, especially for wet ponds that become attractions for people, should be gentle. Barrier vegetation, such as cattails, can also be installed along the perimeters of wet ponds to limit access to the water's edge.

Detention pond bottoms should have a slope sufficient to ensure complete drainage between storm events in dry ponds, and to facilitate pond drainage for maintenance in the case of wet ponds. For dry ponds, the engineer should consider providing a riprap or concrete low-flow channel from the inlet to the outlet structure to assist in draining the pond bottom.

Outlet Structures

The detention pond outlet structure allows flow to discharge from the pond at a controlled rate. Early detention ponds were usually designed to control only a single runoff event having a specified recurrence interval; thus, these ponds had very simple outlet structures. This practice provided little to no benefit with smaller or larger storm events.

Modern detention design typically focuses on control of multiple storm events and often requires several outlet openings at different pond stages. These multiple openings can consist of multiple pipe outlets with differing diameters or invert elevations, orifices at various levels, overflow weirs, or any combination of these elements. Figure 5-3 depicts a profile view of an outlet structure configuration consisting of several structural components.

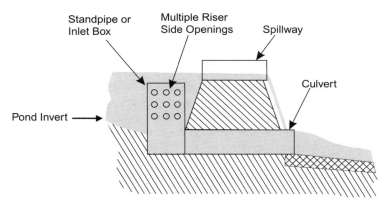

Figure 5-3: Composite Detention Outlet Structure

Overflow Spillways

All detention ponds, regardless of the type, should be fitted with *overflow spillway* facilities to convey flows in excess of those for which the detention facility was designed. The overflow spillway may be an extension of a normal weir outlet, or it may be completely separate. To prevent undue damages downstream, consideration must be given to the paths that pond overflows will take. These outflow pathways are part of the major drainage system referred to in previous chapters.

5.5 Routing Data: Storage and Hydraulic Relationships

Hydrograph routing through a detention facility is the process of computing an outflow hydrograph and water surface elevation data based on a specified inflow hydrograph. Pond routing requires two key types of data in order to describe the pond's storage and hydraulic characteristics:

- *Stage versus storage volume data* to describe the pond's shape and size
- *Stage versus discharge data* to describe the pond outlet hydraulics

The following subsections describe these relationships.

Stage versus Storage Volume

The *stage versus storage relationship* for a pond relates pond water surface elevation (the *stage*) or water depth (h) to the volume of water stored (S). The relationship may be given in a table or graphed as in Figure 5-4. Precision of the curve or table increases as the incremental elevation between the points decreases. The designer must judge the appropriate degree of storage approximation when setting the elevation increment size for the rating curve.

Figure 5-4 demonstrates how stage-storage data is used in routing to determine the relative rise or fall in water surface for a given change in volume. In this example, h_1 and S_1 are, respectively, the elevation and volume at the beginning of the time step, and ΔS is the change in volume during the time step calculated from the difference between the integrated inflow and outflow hydrographs. At the end of the time step, volume $S_2 = S_1 + \Delta S$. Elevation h_2 at the end of the time step can be found from the curve based on S_2. In this example, the net change in storage is positive; thus, the change in water surface elevation is also positive (the water is rising).

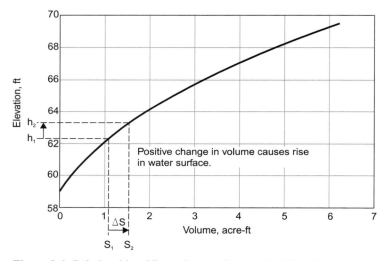

Figure 5-4: Relationship of Stage-Storage Data to Pond Routing

If a detention facility has a regular geometric shape (for example, it is a cylindrical tank), a geometric equation can be applied to describe the stage-storage volume relationship. In most cases, however, the engineer must first determine a detention basin's surface area (A) at incremental elevations or depths, and then use this information to develop stage-storage data. Two methods for determining the stage-storage relationship—the ***average-end-area method*** and the ***conic method***—are presented in this section. Numerical integration may also be used in some cases, although this technique is beyond the scope of this text.

Average-End-Area Method

The average-end-area method uses the same concept frequently seen in computations for estimating earthwork volumes. In this method, the incremental storage volume available between two water surface elevations is computed as:

$$\Delta S = \frac{A_1 + A_2}{2}(h_2 - h_1)$$

where h_1 = water surface elevation 1
        h_2 = water surface elevation 2 ($h_2 > h_1$)
        A_1 = available water surface area corresponding to stage h_1
        A_2 = available water surface area corresponding to stage h_2
        ΔS = incremental storage volume available between h_1 and h_2

Computation of incremental storage amounts for a series of known stages and surface areas, followed by summing of the incremental storages, yields the desired relationship between h and S.

One limitation of the average-end-area method is that it applies a linear averaging technique to describe area, whereas the change in area is actually a second-order function of height for a pond with sloped sides. However, the error associated with numerical volume integration is well within the error bounds of other key design assumptions, such as the selected design storm and watershed homogeneity.

Example 5-1: Computing Storage Volume Using the Average-End-Area Method

An underground storage vault is to be constructed to serve as a detention pond for a heavily urbanized area. The walls of the vault will be vertical, but the floor will be sloped along its length to promote drainage. In plan view, the vault is rectangular with a length of 75 feet and a width of 40 feet. The slope of the floor, along the 75-ft dimension, is 2%. The invert of the lower end of the vault is at an elevation of 123.00 ft.

Determine the elevation vs. surface area relationship for the vault and use this information to calculate and graph the elevation-storage relationship. Use the average-end-area method.

Solution

The difference in elevation along the length of the floor of the vault is

    $75(0.02) = 1.50$ ft

Because the floor elevation at its lower end is at an elevation (stage) of 123.00 ft, the elevation at its high end is 124.50 ft. For any stage between these elevations, the rectangular water surface area is equal to the width of the vault ($W = 40$ ft) times the length of the water surface area. That length depends on the depth of water in the vault and can be expressed in terms of the elevation, h, as

    $L = (h - 123.00)/0.02$

The corresponding water surface area is:

$A_s = WL = 40(h - 123.00)/0.02$

These expressions apply to values of h ranging from 123.00 ft to 124.50 ft. For stages above 124.50 ft, the surface area is constant because of the vertical walls and is equal to

$A_s = 40(75) = 3000$ ft^2

The first two columns of Table 5-1 give the elevation vs. surface area relationship for elevations from 123.00 ft to 130.00 ft.

To compute the elevation-storage relationship using the average-end-area method, adjacent area values in column 2 are added, and then divided by the stage increment for those areas. The steps are described next, and results are reported in Table 5-1. The relationship is plotted in Figure 5-5.

- Column 3 = [Column 2 (current row)] + [Column 2 (previous row)]
- Column 4 = [Column 1 (current row)] – [Column 1 (previous row)]
- Column 5 = [Column 3 (current row) ÷ 2] × [Column 4 (current row)]
- Column 6 = [Column 5 (current row)] + [Column 6 (previous row)]

Table 5-1: Calculation of Detention Volume using the Average-End-Area Method

(1)	(2)	(3)	(4)	(5)	(6)
Elevation (ft)	**Area (ft^2)**	**$A_s(h_1) + A_s(h_2)$ (ft^2)**	**$h_1 - h_2$ (ft)**	**ΔS (ft^3)**	**Cumulative S (ft^3)**
123.0	0	0	0.0	0	0
123.25	500	500	0.25	62.5	62.5
123.5	1000	1500	0.25	187.5	250
123.75	1500	300	0.25	375	625
124.0	2000	500	0.25	625	1,250
124.25	2500	7500	0.25	937.5	2,187
124.5	3000	10,500	0.25	1312.5	3,500
125.0	3000	13,500	0.5	3375	6,875
130.0	3000	16,500	5.0	41,250	48,125

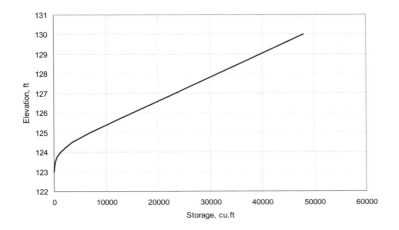

Figure 5-5: Plot of Elevation-Storage Relationship for Example 5-1

Conic Method

This method applies a conic geometry to each stage increment to approximate the nonlinear relationship between stage and water surface area, as illustrated in Figure 5-6. The incremental storage volume between two stages h_1 and h_2 ($h_2 > h_1$) is defined as:

$$\Delta S = \left(\frac{h_2 - h_1}{3}\right)(A_1 + A_2 + \sqrt{A_1 A_2})$$

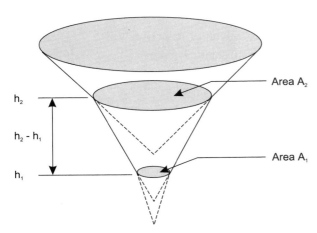

Figure 5-6: Illustration of Conic Method for Computing Pond Volume

Use the conic method to calculate and graph the elevation vs. storage relationship for a pond with an elevation vs. surface area relationship as given in Table 5-2.

Table 5-2: Elevation-Area Data for Example 5-2

Elevation (ft)	Area (acre)
100.00	0.158
100.50	0.170
101.00	0.182
101.50	0.194
102.00	0.207
102.50	0.221
103.00	0.234
103.50	0.248
104.00	0.263
104.50	0.278
105.00	0.293
105.50	0.309
106.00	0.325
106.50	0.342
107.00	0.359

Solution

Table 5-3 is used to determine the cumulative volume at each elevation. Each column represents a step in the calculations used for the conic method. A plot of the elevation-storage relationship is given in Figure 5-7.

- Columns 1 and 2 are the elevation vs. surface area relationship, and are taken from Table 5-2.
- Column 3 = {[Column 1 (current row)] – [Column 1 (previous row)]} / 3
- Column 4 = [(Column 2 (current row)] + [Column 2 (previous row)] + {[Column 2 (current row)] × [Column 2 (previous row)]}$^{0.5}$
- Column 5 = (Column 3) × (Column 4)
- Column 6 = [Column 6 (previous row)] + [Column 5 (current row)]

Table 5-3: Calculations for Example 5-2

(1)	(2)	(3)	(4)	(5)	(6)
Elevation (ft)	Area (ac)	$(h_2 - h_1)/3$ (ft)	$A_1 + A_2 + \sqrt{A_1 A_2}$ (ac)	ΔS (ac-ft)	Cumulative S (ac-ft)
100.00	0.158	0.000	0.000	0.000	0.000
100.50	0.170	0.167	0.492	0.082	0.082
101.00	0.182	0.167	0.528	0.088	0.170
101.50	0.194	0.167	0.564	0.094	0.264
102.00	0.207	0.167	0.602	0.100	0.364
102.50	0.221	0.167	0.641	0.107	0.471
103.00	0.234	0.167	0.682	0.114	0.585
103.50	0.248	0.167	0.723	0.121	0.705
104.00	0.263	0.167	0.766	0.128	0.833
104.50	0.278	0.167	0.811	0.135	0.968
105.00	0.293	0.167	0.856	0.143	1.111
105.50	0.309	0.167	0.903	0.150	1.262
106.00	0.325	0.167	0.951	0.158	1.420
106.50	0.342	0.167	1.000	0.167	1.587
107.00	0.359	0.167	1.051	0.175	1.762

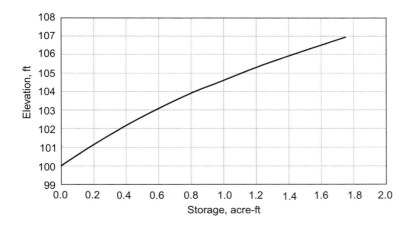

Figure 5-7: Stage-Storage Relationship for Example 5-2

Stage versus Discharge

The discharge Q from a detention facility depends on the stage h of the pond, on the geometric and hydraulic characteristics of the outlet(s), and possibly on tailwater effects that may influence the outlet hydraulics. In cases where interconnected ponds are to be routed, the discharge from one pond to another depends on the stages in the ponds, and on the hydraulic characteristics of the channel or conduit connecting them.

The hydraulic characteristics for a pond outlet structure are described by a *stage vs. discharge* rating table which is applied during routing to determine the relative increase or decrease in outflow, given a change in the stage (water surface elevation). Figure 5-8 demonstrates how elevation vs. discharge data is related to routing. The rating curve is calculated by computing the flow for various stage elevations. Precision of the curve increases as the incremental elevation between points decreases. The designer must judge the appropriate degree of flow approximation when setting the elevation increment size for the rating curve.

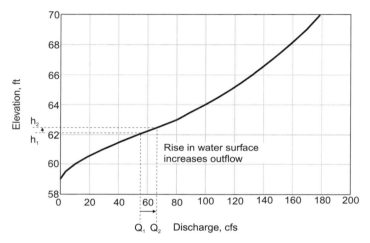

Figure 5-8: Relationship of Elevation-Discharge Data to Detention Routing

In Figure 5-8, h_1 and Q_1 are the elevation and outflow at the beginning of the time step, respectively. Elevation h_2 at the end of the time step is determined from the stage vs. storage curve based on the change in volume. From h_2, Q_2 can be found using the stage versus discharge curve. Thus, for this example the net change in elevation is positive (rising), so the change in outflow is positive (increasing).

Most dry detention facilities have both *low-* and *high-level outlets.* The low-level outlet may consist of a pipe or culvert, i.e., culvert one or more orifices or a weir positioned at or near one or more orifices, or a weir. The high-level outlet is usually an overflow spillway, and is expected to function only during extreme runoff events with recurrence intervals that exceed the pond's design constraints. Where ponds are designed to control runoff rates for several different recurrence intervals, intermediate outlets are usually also provided. They are similar to low-level outlets in practice and design, but are installed at higher elevations.

The stage vs. discharge relationship for a pond is developed using hydraulic relationships depending on the number and types of individual outlets. The relationships for various types of pond outlets are discussed next.

Pipe or Culvert Outlets

The stage versus discharge relationship for a pipe or culvert outlet can be developed using culvert design procedures described in Chapter 4. The outlet may perform under either inlet or outlet control, depending on downstream effects. A culvert performance curve delineating discharge as a function of the headwater depth (or stage) is the desired stage vs. discharge relationship.

For small diameter pipes ($D < 12$ in), culvert hydraulics can be adequately represented using the orifice equation (discussed in Section 1.3). This assumption holds true if the ratio of headwater depth to pipe diameter is at least 1.5, and if tailwater (outlet control) effects are negligible (Brown et al., 1996).

Orifices and Weirs

The hydraulic properties of orifices and weirs are discussed in Section 1.3.

Overflow Spillways

An overflow spillway has the purpose of safely conveying discharges when the design storage capacity of a detention pond is exceeded during large storm events. Overflow spillways are commonly referred to as *emergency spillways* because they are designed to operate under extreme rainfall conditions to prevent dam overtopping.

The storm recurrence interval for which an overflow spillway should be designed is an issue that requires exercise of professional judgment, as well as consideration of the adverse effects of downstream flooding or damages. In areas where the major drainage system is evaluated for a designated storm recurrence interval, the same recurrence interval might be used for overflow spillway design. On the other hand, if failure of a dam embankment could cause considerable damages or loss of life downstream, regulatory requirements pertaining to dams may be appropriate.

Detailed coverage of spillway hydraulics is beyond the scope of this book. For more advanced discussion on spillway and outlet design, refer to the Haestad Press book *Stormwater Modeling and Detention Design*.

Composite Stage versus Discharge Relationships

The overall, or composite, stage vs. discharge relationship for a detention pond represents the total discharge from a pond, possibly occurring through several outlets, as a function of the water surface elevation (or depth). Assembly of a composite relationship involves computation and summing of the discharges through each outlet for each stage of interest. Example 5.3 demonstrates the development of the stage-discharge relationship.

Structures in Parallel

The most basic type of composite outlet structure is one that has different outlet devices working independently of one another. In this situation, the hydraulic rating characteristics for each device are simply summed at each elevation to compute the total outflow. Figure

5-9 displays a composite set of outlet structures working in parallel, and Figure 5-10 shows the rating curve resulting from this outlet configuration.

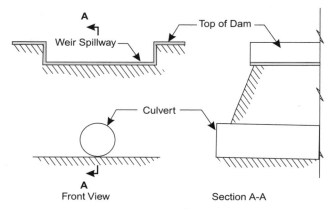

Figure 5-9: Composite Outlet with Outlet Structures Discharging in Parallel

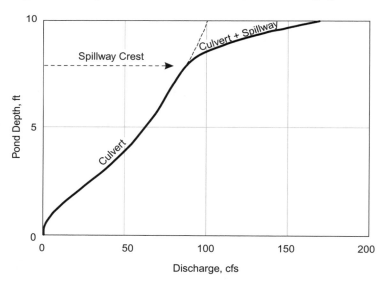

Figure 5-10: Depth versus Discharge for a Composite Outlet with Outlet Structures Discharging in Parallel

Example 5-3: Stage versus Discharge for a Composite Structure

A simple composite outlet structure is being designed with an orifice and a weir operating in parallel. The orifice is a 6-in diameter orifice plate with an invert elevation of 100.00 ft and an orifice coefficient of 0.60. The orifice discharges into the top section of a large culvert; under maximum head conditions in the pond, the water within the culvert will not rise above the orifice invert (that is, the orifice controls throughout). The concrete rectangular contracted weir has a weir coefficient approximated as 2.6 for the entire range of headwaters, a weir length of 15 ft, and a crest elevation at 105.00 ft. It operates under free outfall conditions.

Calculate and graph the elevation vs. discharge rating curve from elevations 100.00 ft to 107.00 ft for each 0.50 ft increment. (Note that a smaller increment would yield a smoother, more precise rating curve.)

Solution

Table 5-4 shows the stage-storage calculation results described by the following steps. Figure 5-11 is a plot of the composite structure rating curve.

- Orifice Centroid Elevation = 100.00 ft + (1/2 × 0.5 ft) = 100.25 ft
- Orifice Area = $\pi D^2/4$ = 0.196 ft^2
- Column 1 is the range of rating table elevations (100.0 ft to 107.0 ft, in 0.5-ft increments)
- Column 2 is the head on the orifice = (Column 1) – (Orifice Centroid Elevation)
- Column 3 is the orifice discharge = Solution to orifice equation for C = 0.60, A = 0.196, h = Column 2 (The orifice equation is $Q = CA(2gH)^{0.5}$, as introduced in Chapter 1.)
- Column 4 is the head on the weir = (Column 1) – (Weir Crest Elevation)
- Column 5 is the weir discharge = Solution to rectangular weir equation for C = 2.6, L = 15.0, h = Column 4 (The weir equation is $Q = CLH^{3/2}$, as introduced in Chapter 1.)
- Column 6 is the composite structure discharge = (Column 3) + (Column 5)

Table 5-4: Stage-Discharge Calculations for Example 5-3

(1)	(2)	(3)	(4)	(5)	(6)
Elevation (ft)	Centroid = 100.25 ft		Crest = 105.00 ft		Total Flow (cfs)
	Head (ft)	Flow (cfs)	Head (ft)	Flow (cfs)	
100.00	0.00	0.00	0.00	0.00	0.00
100.50	0.25	0.47	0.00	0.00	0.47
101.00	0.75	0.82	0.00	0.00	0.82
101.50	1.25	1.06	0.00	0.00	1.06
102.00	1.75	1.25	0.00	0.00	1.25
102.50	2.25	1.42	0.00	0.00	1.42
103.00	2.75	1.57	0.00	0.00	1.57
103.50	3.25	1.70	0.00	0.00	1.70
104.00	3.75	1.83	0.00	0.00	1.83
104.50	4.25	1.95	0.00	0.00	1.95
105.00	4.75	2.06	0.00	0.00	2.06
105.50	5.25	2.16	0.50	13.79	15.95
106.00	5.75	2.26	1.00	39.00	41.27
106.50	6.25	2.36	1.50	71.65	74.01
107.00	6.75	2.45	2.00	110.31	112.76

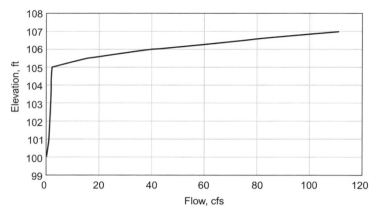

Figure 5-11: Rating Curve for Outlet Structure in Example 5-3

Structures in Series

When outlet structures are in series, it is possible that backwater effects caused by hydraulic controls at downstream structures will affect the discharges through connecting upstream structures. In these cases, hydraulic grade line calculations are required to determine the interactions between individual structure components.

Figure 5-12 illustrates a pond outlet with structures in series. In this example, as the stage rises, the culvert eventually throttles (controls) the combined flow through the v-notch weir and the inlet box, causing the inlet box riser to be fully submerged. This phenomenon is shown graphically near the center portion of the stage vs. discharge relationship in Figure 5-13.

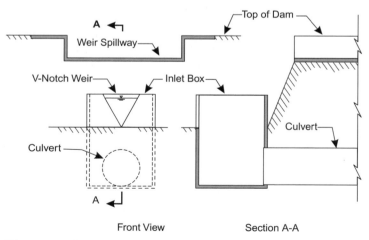

Figure 5-12: Composite Outlet with Outlet Structures Discharging in Parallel and in Series

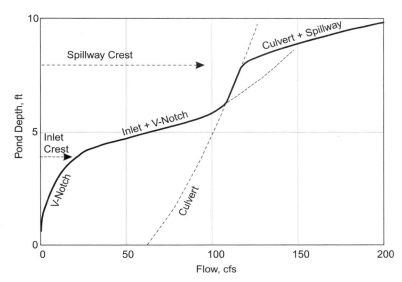

Figure 5-13: Rating Curve for a Composite Outlet with Outlet Structures Discharging in Parallel and in Series

This text provides only an introduction to basic outlet hydraulics. For more detailed explanations on analyzing complex outlet structures such as outlets in series, refer to Haestad Press' *Stormwater Modeling and Detention Design*.

5.6 Storage Indication Method

Routing of a detention pond is the process by which a given inflow hydrograph to the pond is transformed into the corresponding outflow hydrograph. In addition to the inflow hydrograph, the outflow hydrograph also depends on the storage and hydraulic relationships of the pond (described in the previous sections) and on the initial water surface elevation in the pond when the inflow hydrograph begins.

Fundamentally, routing of a pond amounts to a solution of the conservation of mass equation:

$$\frac{dS}{dt} = I(t) - O(t)$$

where S = the volume of water in the pond $(\text{ft}^3, \text{m}^3)$
$I(t)$ = specified inflow at time t (cfs, m^3/s)
$O(t)$ = the outflow at time t (cfs, m^3/s)

This equation states that the change in storage during a time period is equal to the difference between the inflow and the outflow. There are two unknowns in this equation (S and O); thus, information on both storage characteristics and hydraulic characteristics is required to solve it. Various routing methods are available, but the most commonly used method in simple stormwater detention is the ***storage indication method***, which is based on a finite-difference approximation of the conservation of mass equation.

Figure 5-14 shows the inflow and outflow hydrographs for a pond. The graph magnifies a time slice (step) for which the inflow is greater than the outflow. The x-axis of the slice has units of time (t), and the y-axis of the slice, which represents flow rate, has units of volume (L^3) per time, or L^3/t. Thus, the bounded area of the slice has units of $T \times (L^3/t) = L^3$, or volume. Because the inflow is greater than the outflow for this time slice, the change in volume is positive, which means the pond water surface (stage) is rising during this time step.

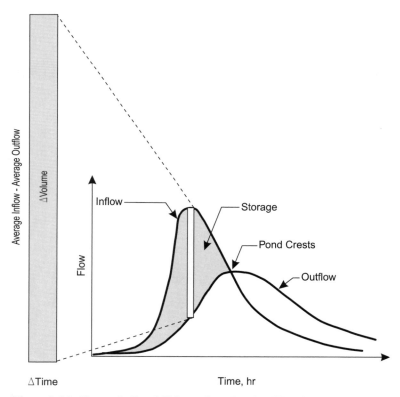

Figure 5-14: Change in Pond Volume for a Routing Time Step

At the point where the inflow equals the outflow, the change in storage is zero, the water surface elevation (stage) is constant, and the pond is cresting. After the pond has crested, the outflow rate is greater than the inflow rate, resulting in a net loss in volume that causes the water surface (stage) to fall during the time step.

Because the shaded area of Figure 5-14 represents the bounded area for which inflow is greater than outflow before the pond crests, this area represents the total volume stored while the pond is filling. As stated previously, the shaded area represents the maximum storage volume.

Figure 5-15 shows a portion of the inflow and outflow hydrographs for a pond. The graph illustrates a time period in which the inflow rate is greater than the outflow rate, but the relationships that follow are applicable for any time period, regardless of the relative magnitudes of the inflow and outflow rates. Over a time interval $\Delta t = t_{n+1} - t_n$, the inflow rate varies from I_n to I_{n+1}, and therefore the average inflow rate over the time interval can be approximated as $(I_n + I_{n+1})/2$. Over the same time interval, the average outflow rate can be approximated as $(O_n + O_{n+1})/2$. The change in storage over the time interval is $\Delta S = S_{n+1} - S_n$, whereas the time rate of change of storage may be approximated as $\Delta S/\Delta t = (S_{n+1} - S_n)/\Delta t$. Substitution of the average inflow and outflow rates and the approximate rate of change of storage, into the conservation of mass equation yields:

$$\frac{S_{n+1} - S_n}{\Delta t} = \frac{I_n + I_{n+1}}{2} - \frac{O_n + O_{n+1}}{2}$$

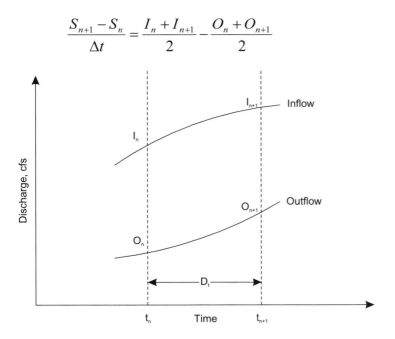

Figure 5-15: Definition Sketch for Terms in Finite Difference Approximation

Because the inflow hydrograph is a known quantity in detention pond routing, the terms I_n and I_{n+1} are known for every time interval in the routing process. For the first time interval, at the beginning of a pond inflow event, the terms O_n and S_n are also initially known. Note that O_n and S_n are related as for each pond stage h_n there is a corresponding S_n and a corresponding O_n. Rearranging the finite difference approximation with unknown quantities on the left and known quantities on the right yields the storage indication equation:

$$\left(\frac{2S_{n+1}}{\Delta t} + O_{n+1} \right) = \left(\frac{2S_n}{\Delta t} - O_n \right) + (I_n + I_{n+1})$$

Thus, knowledge of the quantities S_n, O_n, and I_n at the beginning of a time interval (at time t_n), as well as knowledge of the inflow rate I_{n+1} at the end of the time interval, can be used to compute the value of the left side of the equation. However, there are two unknowns on the left side (O_{n+1} and S_{n+1}). Additional information must be established to expose the relationship between O_{n+1} and S_{n+1} so that these two values can be determined.

A *storage indication curve* is a graph delineating the relationship between O and $(2S/\Delta t + O)$. Such a graph can be constructed by realizing that for any stage h in a pond, there are corresponding values of O and S; hence, there are corresponding values of O and $(2S/\Delta t + O)$.

In performing storage indication calculations for a specified time interval $n + 1$, the storage indication equation is applied to compute the numerical value of the quantity $(2S_{n+1}/\Delta t + O_{n+1})$. Next, the value of $(2S_{n+1}/\Delta t - O_{n+1})$ for the time interval $n + 1$ must be found. Because the value of $(2S_{n+1}/\Delta t + O_{n+1})$ is known, and because this value can be used with the storage-indication curve to find O_{n+1}, $(2S_{n+1}/\Delta t - O_{n+1})$ can be computed as

$$(2S_{n+1}/\Delta t - O_{n+1}) = (2S_{n+1}/\Delta t + O_{n+1}) - 2O_{n+1}$$

The term on the left side of the equation can now be used in the next time step $(n + 2)$ to compute $(2S_{n+2}/\Delta t + O_{n+2})$, and the process repeats through every time step.

Section 5.7 describes the full procedure used in storage indication routing and presents an example problem.

5.7 Stormwater Detention Analysis Procedure

This chapter introduced each of the basic components required for modeling how a pond functions during a rainfall event. In order to apply pond routing techniques to model a pond, the various components of hydrographs, storage volume, and outlet structures are used in the following steps:

1. Calculate the post-developed inflow hydrograph discharging into the pond. Methods for calculating hydrographs are covered in Chapter 2.

2. Calculate the storage volume rating curve (stage vs. storage) for the given pond design. The rating curve should start at the dry invert of the pond and extend to the top of the dam.

3. Calculate the outflow rating curve (stage vs. outflow) for the given pond outlet structure. The rating curve should match the range of elevations of the physical pond design, i.e., match the storage rating curve range of elevations. This holds true even if lower elevations will have zero discharge within a wet pond.

4. Establish the relationship between stage, storage, and discharge by creating a storage indication curve for $(2S/\Delta t + O)$ versus outflow.

5. Use the hydrograph from Step 1 and the storage indication curve from Step 4 to route the inflow hydrograph through the storage and discharge relationship to obtain a pond outflow hydrograph.

Example 5-4: Detention Pond Routing Example

Route the inflow hydrograph given in Table 5-5 through the pond described by the stage versus storage data computed in Example 5-2 and the stage versus discharge data computed in Example 5-3. Determine the maximum water surface elevation for the detention basin, the maximum storage volume, maximum outflow rate, and peak lag resulting from detention.

Table 5-5: Inflow Hydrograph for Example 5-4

Time (minutes)	Inflow (cfs)
0	0.00
10	0.58
20	5.94
30	15.44
40	20.75
50	20.27
60	17.44
70	14.19
80	11.42
90	9.44
100	8.12
110	7.27
120	6.61
130	5.49
140	3.32
150	1.52
160	0.66
170	0.29
180	0.12
190	0.05
200	0.02
210	0.00

Solution

The results from Examples 5-2 and 5-3 are combined in Table 5-6. Note the importance of calculating the same elevations for storage and discharge in order to directly correlate flow and storage at each elevation.

Table 5-6: Elevation-Volume-Flow Data for Example 5-4

Elevation (ft)	Total Volume (ac-ft)	Total Flow (cfs)
100.00	0.000	0.00
100.50	0.082	0.47
101.00	0.170	0.82
101.50	0.264	1.06
102.00	0.364	1.25
102.50	0.471	1.42
103.00	0.585	1.57
103.50	0.705	1.70
104.00	0.833	1.83
104.50	0.968	1.95
105.00	1.111	2.06
105.50	1.262	15.95
106.00	1.420	41.27
106.50	1.587	74.01
107.00	1.762	112.76

Follow the five steps outlined for storage indication pond routing:

1. Compute the post-developed pond inflow hydrograph using the procedures presented in Chapter 2 or another method. In this example, the final inflow hydrograph is given.

2. Calculate the stage versus storage curve from the pond grading plan or storage structure geometry. This information was calculated in Example 5-2 (no calculations are necessary for this example).

3. Calculate the stage versus outflow curve for the pond outlet structure. This information was calculated in Example 5-3.

4. Calculate and graph the storage indication curve that correlates $2S/\Delta t + O$ and Outflow. To calculate this curve, the rating elevations for the stage vs. storage curve must be identical to those used for the stage vs. outflow curve. Use a 10-minute time step in this example.

Step 4 results for $2S/\Delta t + O$ are given in Table 5-7. Column 4 values were computed using:

Column 4 = {2.0 × [(Column 2) × 43,560 ft^2/ac] ÷ (10 min × 60 s/min)} + (Column 3)

Table 5-7: Relationship Between Elevation and $2S/\Delta t + O$ for Example 5-4

(1) Elevation (ft)	(2) Volume (ac-ft)	(3) Flow (cfs)	(4) $2S/\Delta t + O$ (cfs)
100.00	0.000	0.00	0.00
100.50	0.082	0.47	12.38
101.00	0.170	0.82	25.50
101.50	0.264	1.06	39.39
102.00	0.364	1.25	54.10
102.50	0.471	1.42	69.81
103.00	0.585	1.57	86.51
103.50	0.705	1.70	104.07
104.00	0.833	1.83	122.78
104.50	0.968	1.95	142.50
105.00	1.111	2.06	163.38
105.50	1.262	15.95	199.19
106.00	1.420	41.27	247.45
106.50	1.587	74.01	304.44
107.00	1.762	112.76	368.60

Because the maximum inflow is about 20 cfs, we already know that the maximum outflow value should be equal to or less than 20 cfs. The storage indication curve shown in Figure 5-16 is an expanded view for the outflow range below 20 cfs, which makes it easier to read the smaller flow values during the routing tabulation.

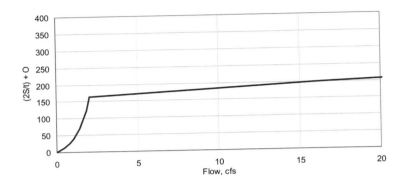

Figure 5-16: Storage Indication Curve for Example 5-4

5. Use the inflow hydrograph from Step 1 and the storage indication curve from Step 4 to route the hydrograph using a systematic worksheet approach as shown in Table 5-8.

- Columns 1 and 2 represent the given inflow hydrograph.
- Under initial conditions, columns 3 through 6 have values of 0. Because the pond is initially empty, the initial elevation (column 6) is 100.00 ft.
- For subsequent time steps,

  [Column 3 (current row)]= [Column 2 (previous row)]+ [Column 2 (current row)]

  [Column 5 (current row)] = [Column 3 (current row)] + [Column 4 (previous row)]

- Determine column 6 values by using the column 5 values and solving for the associated outflow from the storage indication curve calculated in step 4.
- Solve column 7 (current row) using stage vs. outflow curve created in step 3.
- Finally, to complete the current row, solve

  [Column 4 (current row)] = [Column 5 (current row)] – 2 × [Column 6 (current row)].

- The tabulated results shown stop at $t = 300$ minutes into the routing. To complete the routing, the calculations need to be continued until the pond is fully drained (the routed outflow in column 6 recedes to zero). The graph for the inflow and outflow hydrographs displays the entire routing time.

Table 5-8: Routing Results from Example 5-4

(1) Time (min)	(2) Inflow (cfs)	(3) $I_1 + I_2$ (cfs)	(4) $2S/\Delta t - O$ (cfs)	(5) $2S/\Delta t + O$ (cfs)	(6) Outflow (cfs)	(7) Elevation (ft)
0	0	0	0.00	0.00	0.00	100.00
10	0.58	0.58	0.54	0.58	0.02	100.02
20	5.94	6.52	6.52	7.06	0.27	100.28
30	15.44	21.38	26.18	27.90	0.86	101.09
40	20.75	36.19	59.69	62.37	1.34	102.26
50	20.27	41.02	97.36	100.71	1.68	103.40
60	17.44	37.71	131.26	135.07	1.90	104.31
70	14.19	31.63	158.77	162.89	2.06	104.99
80	11.42	25.61	163.97	184.38	10.21	105.29
90	9.44	20.86	164.07	184.83	10.38	105.30
100	8.12	17.56	163.35	181.63	9.14	105.25
110	7.27	15.39	162.70	178.74	8.02	105.21
120	6.61	13.88	162.22	176.58	7.18	105.18
130	5.49	12.1	161.71	174.32	6.30	105.15
140	3.32	8.81	160.86	170.52	4.83	105.10
150	1.52	4.84	159.78	165.70	2.96	105.03
160	0.66	2.18	157.86	161.96	2.05	104.97
170	0.29	0.95	154.73	158.81	2.04	104.89
180	0.12	0.41	151.11	155.14	2.02	104.80
190	0.05	0.17	147.29	151.28	2.00	104.71
200	0.02	0.07	143.41	147.36	1.98	104.62
210	0	0.02	139.52	143.43	1.95	104.52
220	0	0	135.65	139.52	1.93	104.42
230	0	0	131.84	135.65	1.91	104.33
240	0	0	128.07	131.84	1.89	104.23
250	0	0	124.34	128.07	1.86	104.13
260	0	0	120.66	124.34	1.84	104.04
270	0	0	117.03	120.66	1.82	103.94
280	0	0	113.45	117.03	1.79	103.85
290	0	0	109.92	113.45	1.77	103.75
300	0	0	106.44	109.92	1.74	103.66

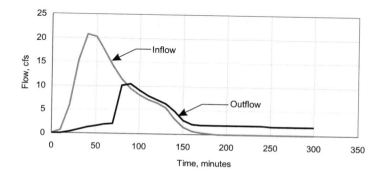

Figure 5-17: Pond Inflow and Outflow Hydrographs

From the routing table:

- Maximum stage = 105.30 ft, which is above spillway crest
- Maximum storage = 1.2 ac-ft (determined from the stage vs. storage data for an elevation of 105.30 ft)
- Maximum flow = 10.38 cfs
- Outflow peak time = 90 min
- Peak flow was delayed 50 min from inflow peak time of 40 min

5.8   PondPack

What Is PondPack?

PondPack is a stormwater modeling program capable of analyzing a wide range of situations, from simple sites to complex networked watersheds. The program analyzes pre- and post-developed watershed conditions and sizes ponds.

PondPack also computes outlet structure rating curves with tailwater effects, pond infiltration, pond detention times, and channel routing effects. It includes the capability to model interconnected ponds with divergent (multiple) outfalls.

The program can use any rainfall duration or distribution to compute hydrographs for multiple events. Hydrographs can be added at junctions and routed through multiple reaches and ponds. PondPack helps automate almost every aspect of drainage design computations.

PondPack graphically displays such items as watershed diagrams, hydrographs, rainfall curves, I-D-F curves, outlet rating curves, volume curves, time versus elevation curves, time versus volume curves, cross-sections, channel rating curves, and a wide variety of other output diagrams.

PondPack builds customized reports organized by categories and automatically creates section and page numbers, tables of contents, and indexes. You can display a short results summary for an entire watershed, or build a comprehensive drainage report showing any or all report items. Additional information on the options available in PondPack are presented in Appendix A.

How Can You Use PondPack for Windows?

You can apply this software to all phases of a stormwater detention project, from feasibility studies to analysis of the final design. This product can be used to:

- Create full drainage reports with table of contents and index

- Compute pre- and post-developed flows using popular methods such as SCS or Rational Method
- Estimate storage requirements
- Size ponds
- Model multi-stage outlets with tailwater considerations
- Analyze culverts with inlet/outlet control checking
- Model simple pond sites
- Solve complex watershed networks with interconnected ponds
- Model unlimited diversions
- Review tidal outfall effects on pond outlets
- Analyze channel capacity
- Check outflow rates against pre-developed conditions
- Compute water quality parameters such as minimum drain time and detention time
- Model any rainfall duration or time distribution
- Simulate gauged rainfall events and synthetic rainfall distribution events

5.9 Tutorial Example

This tutorial provides step-by-step instructions for solving Examples 5-2, 5-3, and 5-4 using PondPack software (included on the CD-ROM that accompanies this textbook). Additionally, the hydrograph given in Example 5-4 will be generated within PondPack from rainfall distribution data and basin characteristics instead of being entered manually.

Problem Statement

In this example, an inflow hydrograph will be routed through a detention pond and outlet structure. The drainage area entering the pond consists of 10 acres with a runoff curve number (CN) of 80 and a time of concentration of 30 minutes.

The stage-surface area data to be used in computing the pond volume is repeated in Table 5-9. The detention pond outlet consists of an orifice and a weir operating in parallel. The orifice consists of a 6-inch diameter orifice plate with an invert elevation of 100.00 ft. and an orifice coefficient of 0.6. The rectangular, contracted weir has a weir coefficient of approximately 2.6 for the applicable headwater range. It is 15.0 ft wide and has a crest elevation of 105.00 ft. Both the orifice and the weir operate under free outfall conditions.

The system will be analyzed for a 10-year, 2-hour storm event with a total rainfall depth of 4.5 in. Synthetic distribution data from the Illinois State Water Survey Bulletin 70/71 will be used. Specifically, the design storm will utilize the first-quartile distribution for events having recurrence intervals of 10 years or less.

This example includes the following tasks:

a) Open PondPack and set up a new project using the Setup Wizard. Set up the 10-year, 2-hour design storm described in the problem.

b) Lay out the schematic hydrologic network.

c) Enter the watershed data and compute the pond inflow hydrograph.

d) Enter the stage-area data for the pond and compute and graph the stage-volume data.

e) Enter the information on the orifice and weir, and compute and graph the discharge-rating curve for the composite outlet.

f) Route the hydrograph through the detention system and view the results. Determine the maximum water surface elevation and storage volume for the detention pond, the maximum pond outflow rate, and the peak lag resulting from detention.

Solution

PART (a)   *Open PondPack and set up a new project using the Setup Wizard. Set up the 10-year, 2-hour design storm described in the problem.*

- Double-click the PondPack icon to open the software. Click the button to **Create a New Project**. Name the file **Tutorial.ppw** and click **Save**.

- In the Project Setup Wizard, assign the project the title "**CAiHE Tutorial**," enter your name as the Project Engineer, and click **Next**.

- Make sure that the Hydrograph Method is set to Unit Hydrograph, the Unit Hydrograph Simulation is set to Default Method, and the Unit System is set to English Units. Click **Next**.

- To set up the design storm, click the ellipsis ⬚ button by the **Select Network Storm Collection** field. Click the **New** ⬚ button and name the Storm List "**Tutorial**." Click **OK**.

- Under the **Rainfall Collection** tab, click the **New** button, highlight **Synthetic Curve**, and click **OK**.

- Enter a **Return Frequency** of 10 yrs, a **HYG Storm Tag** of "10yr," a **Rain Depth** of 4.5 in., and a **Duration Multiplier** of 2.00 (for a 2-hour storm).

- From the **Rainfall Curve** selection box, select the "00-10 1stQ 50%" storm distribution, and then click **OK**. Click **Close** to exit the Storm Collection Library.

- In the **Select Network Storm Collection** list box, select **Tutorial**, the storm collection you just created, from the pull down menu. Make sure that under **General Settings** the **Minimum Tc** is less than or equal to 0.5 hr, and change the **Output Increment** to 0.1667 hrs (10 min). Click **Next**.

- The **Report Filter** list allows you to specify only the items that you want to include in a report. In addition to the items already checked, check the box for **Pond Route Calcs**. Click **Finished**. The project setup is now complete.

PART (b)   *Lay out the schematic hydrologic network.*

- In the PondPack drawing pane, right-click and select **Subarea** from the pop-up menu. Position the pointer in the upper-left quadrant of the drawing pane and left-click once to insert the subarea node.

- Right-click in the drawing pane again and select **Links\Hydrograph Link** from the pop-up menu. Left-click once on the subarea that you just created, move the pointer slightly down and to the right, and right-click the mouse.

- In the pop-up menu, select **Pond**, and then left-click once to insert the pond node.

- Move the mouse further down and to the right of the drawing pane, right-click, select **Outfall**, and left-click once to insert the outfall node. You have now completed the schematic network layout, which should look similar to Figure 5-18.

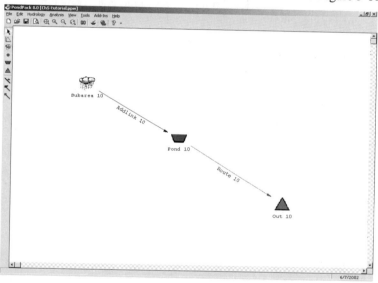

Figure 5-18: PondPack Drawing Pane with Network Layout

PART (c)   *Enter the watershed data and compute the pond inflow hydrograph.*

- If the output hydrograph time step was not set during the Project Setup, select **Options** from the **Tools** pull-down menu on the top toolbar. Under the **Project Options** tab, set the **Default Output HYG Increment** to 0.1667 hrs (10 min). This change is to ensure that the hydrograph as reported by PondPack will match that given in Example 5-4. Click **Close**.

- Double left-click the subarea node to open its element dialog editor. Under the **Subarea Data** tab, the **Infiltration and Area** list box should be set to **CN, Area**. In the table on this same tab, type **Example Subarea** as the **Description** and enter a **CN** of 80 and an **Area** of 10.0 acres. Leave the other columns blank.

- Go to the Tc & UH Setup tab. The Unit Hydrograph Method should be set to SCS Method.

- Click the **New** button under **Time of Concentration**. Select **User Defined** from the list and click **OK**. Enter a **User Defined** value of 0.5 hrs (30 min).

- Go to the **Graph** tab. Click the **Report Builder** [icon] button to compute the hydrograph for the subarea and generate the report list. If you receive warning messages, click **OK** to close the warning dialog.

- In the Report Builder, highlight **Runoff Hydrographs SUBAREA 10 10yr Unit Hyd. (HYG output)** and click the **Preview** button on the right side. The output data should match the hydrograph given in Example 5-4.

- Close the Print Preview window and the Report Builder. Notice that a plot of the hydrograph now appears under the **Graph** tab of the **Subarea** dialog. Click **OK** to close the **Subarea** dialog and return to the drawing pane.

PART (d)   *Enter the stage-area data for the pond and compute and graph the stage-volume data.*

- With the left mouse button, double-click the **Pond** node to open its dialog editor. Under the **Pond Volume** tab, select **Elevation-Area** from the **Volume** list box.

- Enter the elevation-area data from Table 5-9 into the table in the dialog. (This data is the same as that used in Example 5-2.)

Table 5-9: Elevation-Area Data for Determining Pond Volume

Elevation (ft)	Area (ac)
100.00	0.158
100.50	0.170
101.00	0.182
101.50	0.194
102.00	0.207
102.50	0.221
103.00	0.234
103.50	0.248
104.00	0.263
104.50	0.278
105.00	0.293
105.50	0.309
106.00	0.325
106.50	0.342
107.00	0.359

- Under the **Graph** tab, click the **Report Builder** button. Highlight **Pond Volumes POND 10 Vol: Elev-Area** in the Report Builder and click Preview. The output should match the data from Example 5-2.

- Close the Print Preview window and the Report Builder. Notice that a graph of Elevation vs. Volume is now displayed under the **Graph** tab of the **Pond** dialog. Click **OK** to close the dialog and return to the drawing pane.

PART (e) *Enter the information for the orifice and weir, and compute and graph the discharge rating curve for the composite outlet.*

- Double left-click the middle of the red arrow representing the pond outlet structure to open its dialog. The list box for **Link Type** should be set to **Level Pool Route**.
- Click the ellipsis button for the **Outlet Structure**. Select **Add** to insert a new structure and click **OK** to accept the default structure name **Outlet 1**.
- In the Outlet Structure Editor, click the **Insert** button to insert the first component of the outlet structure. Highlight **Orifice** in the list and click **OK**.
- In the **Orifice Structure** dialog under **IDs and Direction**, enter **OR** for the Outlet ID. Leave the flow direction set to **Forward Flow Only. The Downstream ID** should be **TW** (for tailwater).
- The orifice type is **Circular**. Enter **1** for the # **Openings**, an **Orifice Coefficient** of 0.6, an **Invert Elevation** of 100.00 ft, and a **Diameter** of 0.5 ft. Click **OK**.
- In the **Outlet Structure Editor**, click the **Insert** button again. Select **Weir** from the list and click **OK**.
- In the editor dialog for the weir, assign the weir the Outlet ID **WR**, leave the direction as **Forward Flow Only**, and set the Downstream ID to **TW**.
- The list box for weir type should be set to **Rectangular**. Set the **Weir Elevation** to 105.00 ft, the **Weir Coefficient** to 2.6, and the **Weir Length** to 15 ft. Change the list box under **Rectangular Weir** type to **Contracted**. Click **OK** to close the editor.
- Under the **Headwater** tab of the **Outlet Structure Editor**, enter a **Step** of 0.5 ft. Under the **Tailwater** tab, make sure the list box is set to **Free Outfall**.
- Go to the **Graph** tab of the **Outlet Structure Editor** and click the **Report Builder** button. Click the **Create** button to generate a report with individual and composite structure rating curves. Page through the report and compare the rating curves to those generated in Example 5-3 to make sure the results match.
- Close the Print Preview and the Report Builder. Notice the rating curve plot under the **Graph** tab of the outlet editor. Click **OK** to close the editor dialog, and close the Composite Outlet Structure Manager. Select your newly created "Outlet 1" under the **Outlet Structure** list box and click **OK** to return to the drawing pane.

PART (f) *Route the hydrograph through the detention system and view the results. Determine the maximum water surface elevation and storage volume for the detention pond, the maximum pond outflow rate, and the peak lag resulting from detention.*

- Click the **GO** button at the top of the drawing pane to open the Compute Network dialog. Verify that the **Network Storms** list box is set to **Tutorial** and the **Output Increment** is 10.00 min (0.1667 hrs).
- Click **GO** to solve the entire network, including the pond routing calculations. If you receive warning messages, click **OK** to close the dialog.
- Click the **Report Builder** button. Scroll down the report list to **Pond Routing   POND 10   OUT 10yr   Pond Routing Calcs (Total Out)**, highlight it, and click **Preview**. The routing calculations should be similar to those generated in Example 5-4.
- Close the Print Preview window to return to the Report Builder. In the report list, highlight **Master Summary   Watershed   Master Network Summary** and click **Preview**.
- From the Master Summary Report, the following results can be obtained or derived (in the case of peak lag time):

  Maximum pond water surface elevation = 105.3 ft

  Maximum pond storage volume = 1.20 ac-ft

  Maximum pond outflow rate = 10.38 cfs

  Peak lag = (Time of peak flow) – (Time of concentration) = 1.5 hr – 0.5 hr = 1 hr

This example provided instructions on using PondPack's most basic features. The user is encouraged to further explore features such as graphing and pond volume estimation. It should also be noted that the reporting that occurred in each portion of this tutorial is not required to compute the entire network. Computations initiated using the **GO** button include pond volume calculations, rating curve calculations, and so forth.

5.10 Problems

The following problems can be solved with the PondPack computer program that is on the CD accompanying this book.

1. A detention pond has the shape of a trapezoidal basin. The specifications are:

Top elevation	120 ft
Top length	400 ft
Top width	300 ft
Bottom elevation	100 ft
Bottom length	280 ft
Bottom width	180 ft

Construct an elevation versus volume graph for the basin. What is the volume at an elevation of 120 ft?

2. Given the elevation-area data for a detention pond, construct an elevation versus volume graph for the pond. What is the volume of the pond at an elevation of 205 m?

Elevation –Volume Data for Problem 2

Elevation (m)	Area (m²)
200.0	1,700
200.5	2,500
201.0	2,900
201.5	3,700
202.0	4,300
202.5	4,800
203.0	5,500
203.5	6,900
204.0	8,100
204.5	12,300
205.0	15,000

3. An outlet structure for a pond consists of a riser pipe with 2 orifices. The riser is a 3-ft diameter pipe with a rim elevation of 105 ft. A 1-ft diameter orifice has an invert of 101 ft and a 0.5-ft orifice has an invert of 100 ft. Use 3.33 for the weir coefficient and 0.614 for the orifice coefficient. Construct an elevation versus flow diagram for a headwater range of 100 to 120 ft, with a increment of 1 ft. What is the discharge at a headwater elevation of 120 ft?

4. A composite outlet has a 4-m broad crested weir at an elevation of 203.5 m and a 50-cm diameter orifice at an elevation of 200 m. The weir coefficient is 1.84 and the orifice coefficient is 0.614. Construct an elevation versus discharge curve for the structure over a headwater range of 200 to 205 m with a step of 1 m. What is the discharge at a headwater elevation of 205 m?

5. Use the detention pond described in problem 5-2 and the outlet structure described in problem 5-4 to route the following hydrograph. What is the peak discharge from the pond? What is the maximum elevation in the pond?

Inflow Hydrograph Data for Problem 5

Time (hr)	Flow (m³/s)	Time (hr)	Flow (m³/s)
0.0	0.00	3.6	3.12
0.2	0.24	3.8	2.64
0.4	0.80	4.0	2.24
0.6	1.52	4.2	1.84
0.8	2.48	4.4	1.66
1.0	3.76	4.6	1.44
1.2	5.28	4.8	1.18
1.4	6.56	5.0	0.90
1.6	7.44	5.2	0.86
1.8	7.92	5.4	0.70
2.0	8.00	5.6	0.62
2.2	7.92	5.8	0.53
2.4	7.44	6.0	0.44
2.6	6.88	6.2	0.26
2.8	6.24	6.4	0.14
3.0	5.44	6.6	0.08
3.2	4.48	6.8	0.00
3.4	3.68	7.0	0.00

6. A proposed development will consist of single-family homes and a small park on a 25-acre site. Local regulations require that on-site detention be used to maintain peak runoff rates at predevelopment levels for a 25-year storm. Design a detention facility to meet this requirement.

Use the SCS 24-hour Type II storm with a total depth of 6.5 in. and the SCS Unit Hydrograph Method to compute the runoff hydrograph. The pond is to be a trapezoidal basin with a total depth of 5 ft and 3H:1V side slopes. For the outlet structure, use a 1-ft diameter orifice with an invert at the bottom of the basin together with a rectangular weir. Size and place the weir such that the predevelopment peak flow is not exceeded and a minimum of 1 ft of freeboard is maintained. Document your design by filling in the table.

Land Cover Data for Problem 6

Stage	Land cover	Area (acres)	CN	t_c (min)
Pre-Development	Wooded	15	58	45
	Meadow	10	65	
Post-Development	0.5-ac residential lots	21	75	
	Roads	0.3	98	30
	Park	3.7	79	

Proposed Design for Problem 6

Predevelopment peak runoff flow rate/allowable outflow rate	
Estimated storage volume required	
Dimensions of bottom of pond	
Dimensions of top of pond	
Computed pond volume below freeboard elevation	
Weir length	
Height of weir above bottom of pond	
Maximum water surface elevation	
Peak pond outflow rate	

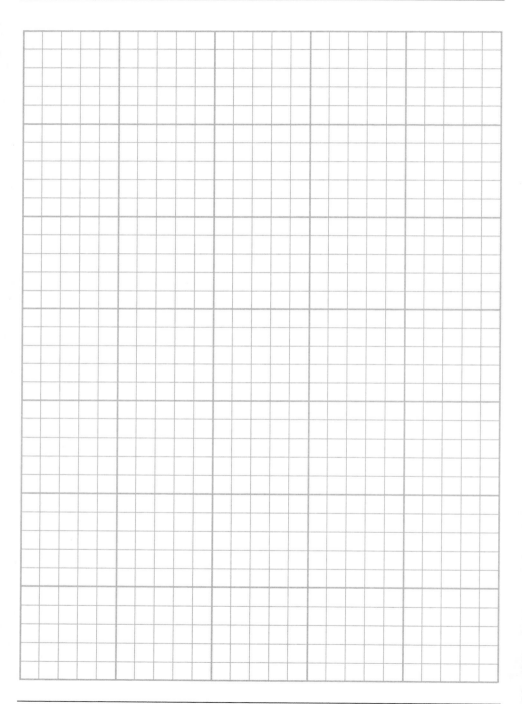

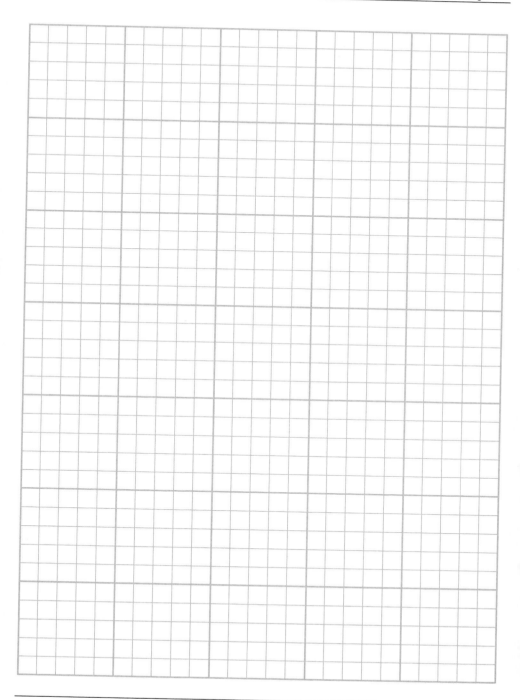

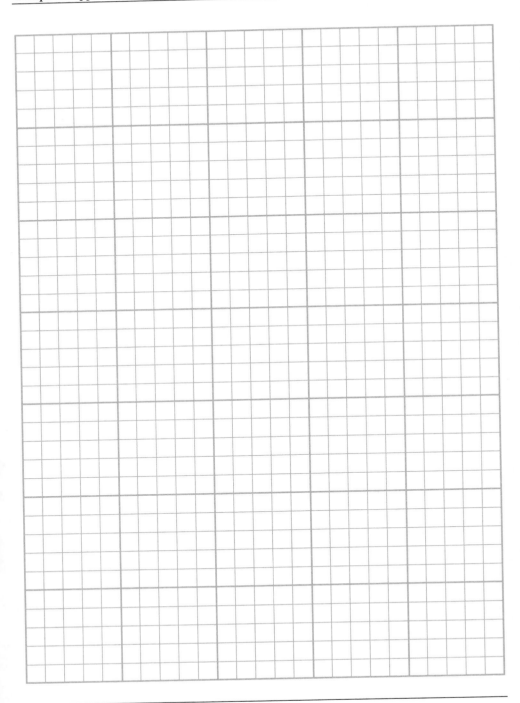

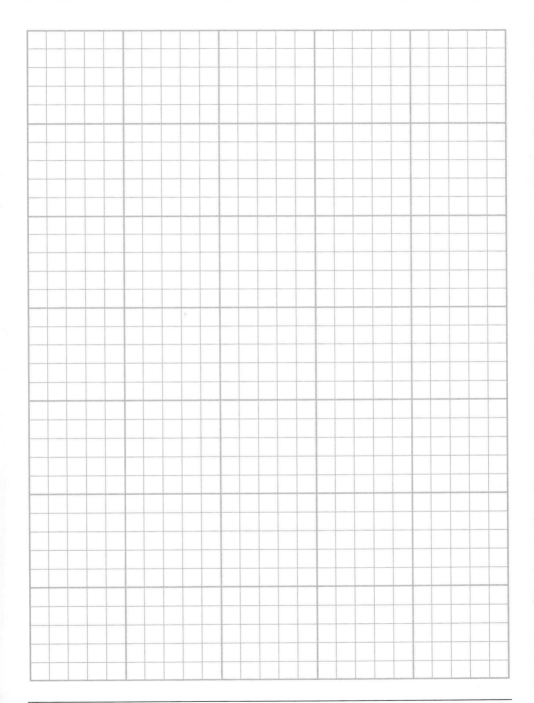

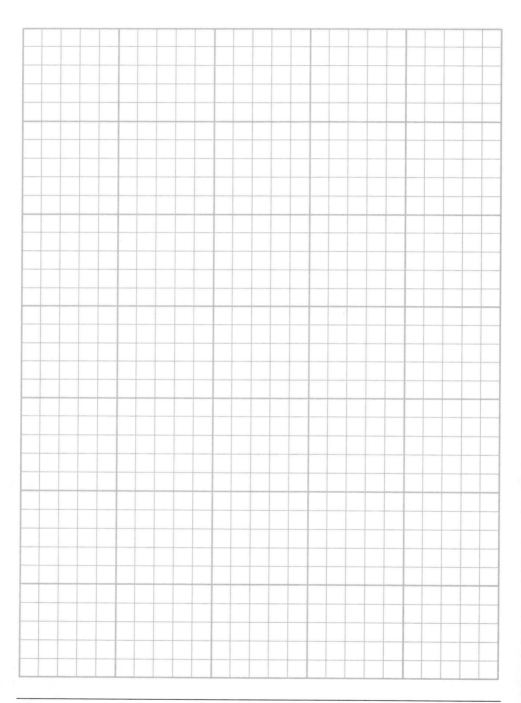

Pressure Piping Systems and Water Quality Analysis

6.1 Pressure Systems

Pressure piping network analysis has many applications, including well pumping systems and heating and cooling systems. This chapter deals primarily with the topic of pressure piping as it relates to potable water distribution systems.

The main purpose of a water distribution system is to meet demands for potable water. People use water for drinking, cleaning, gardening, and any number of other uses, and this water needs to be delivered in some fashion. A secondary purpose of many distribution systems is to provide water for fire protection.

If designed correctly, the network of interconnected pipes, storage tanks, pumps, and regulating valves provides adequate pressure, adequate supply, and good water quality throughout the system. If incorrectly designed, some areas may have low pressures, poor fire protection, and even present health risks.

Water Demands

Just as storm sewer analysis is driven by the watershed runoff flow rate, water distribution system analysis is driven by customer demand. Water usage rates and patterns vary greatly from system to system and are highly dependent on climate, culture, and local industry. Every system is different, so the best source of information for estimating demands is directly recorded system data.

Metered Demand

Metered demands are often a modeler's best tool, and can be used to calculate average demands, minimum demands, peak demands, and so forth. This data can also be compiled into daily, weekly, monthly, and annual reports that show how the demands are influenced by weather, special events, and other factors.

Unfortunately, many systems still do not have complete system metering. For these systems, the modeler is often forced to use other estimation tools (including good engineering judgment) to obtain realistic demands.

Demand Patterns

A *pattern* is a function relating water use to time of day. Patterns allow the user to apply automatic time-variable changes within the system. Different categories of users, such as residential or industrial customers, will typically be assigned different patterns to accurately reflect their particular demand variations. A *diurnal curve* is a type of pattern that describes changes in demand over the course of a daily cycle, reflecting times when people are using more or less water than average. Most patterns are based on a multiplication factor versus time relationship, whereby a multiplication factor of 1.0 represents the base value (often the average value). In equation form, this relationship is written as:

$$Q_t = A_t \times Q_{base}$$

where Q_t =   demand at time t
              A_t =   multiplier for time t
             Q_{base} =   baseline demand

Using a representative diurnal curve for a residence (Figure 6-1), we see that there is a peak in the diurnal curve in the morning as people take showers and prepare breakfast, another slight peak around noon, and a third peak in the evening as people arrive home from work and prepare dinner. Throughout the night, the pattern reflects the relative inactivity of the system, with very low flows compared to the average. (Note that this curve is conceptual and should not be construed as representative of any particular network.)

There are two basic forms for representing a pattern: stepwise and continuous. A *stepwise pattern* is one that assumes a constant level of usage over a period of time, and then jumps instantaneously to another level where it again remains steady until the next jump. A *continuous pattern* is one for which several points in the pattern are known and sections in between are transitional, resulting in a smoother pattern. Notice that, for the continuous pattern in Figure 6-1, the magnitude and slope of the pattern at the start and end times are the same — a continuity that is recommended for patterns that repeat.

Because of the finite time steps used in the calculations, most computer programs convert continuous patterns into stepwise patterns for use by the algorithms, with the duration of each step equal to the time step of the analysis.

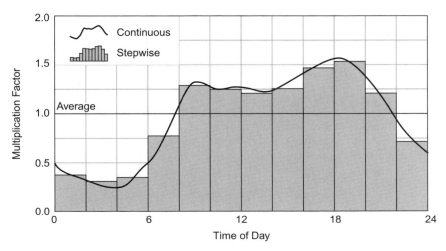

Figure 6-1: Typical Diurnal Curve

6.2 Energy Losses

Friction Losses

The hydraulic theory behind friction losses is the same for pressure piping as it is for open channel hydraulics. The most commonly used methods for determining head losses in pressure piping systems are the Hazen-Williams equation and the Darcy-Weisbach equation, both discussed in Chapter 1. Many of the general friction loss equations can be simplified and revised because of the following assumptions that can be made for a pressure pipe system:

- Pressure piping is almost always circular, so the flow area, wetted perimeter, and hydraulic radius can be directly related to diameter.
- Pressure systems flow full (by definition) throughout the length of a given pipe, so the friction slope is constant for a given flow rate. This means that the energy grade and hydraulic grade drop linearly in the direction of flow.
- Because the flow rate and cross-sectional area are constant, the velocity must also be constant. By definition, then, the energy grade line and hydraulic grade line are parallel, separated by the constant velocity head.

These simplifications allow for pressure pipe networks to be analyzed much more quickly than systems of open channels or partially full gravity piping. Several hydraulic components that are unique to pressure piping systems, such as regulating valves and pumps, add complexity to the analysis.

Minor Losses

Localized areas of increased turbulence cause energy losses within a pipe, creating a drop in the energy and hydraulic grades at that point in the system. These disruptions are often caused by valves, meters, or fittings (such as the pipe entrance in Figure 6-2), and are generally called *minor losses*. These minor losses are often negligible relative to friction losses and may be ignored during analysis.

Although the term "minor" is a reasonable generalization for most large-scale water distribution models, these losses may not always be as minor as the name implies. In piping systems that contain numerous fittings relative to the total length of pipe, such as heating or cooling systems, the minor losses may actually have a significant impact on the energy loss.

The equation most commonly used for determining the loss in a fitting, valve, meter, or other localized component is:

$$H_m = K \frac{V^2}{2g}$$

where H_m =   minor loss (m, ft)
        K =   minor loss coefficient for the specific fitting
        V =   velocity (m/s, ft/s)
        g =   gravitational acceleration (m/s^2, ft/s^2)

Typical values for the fitting loss coefficient are included in Table 6-1. As can be seen with similar fitting types, the K-value is highly dependent on bend radius, contraction ratios, and so forth. Gradual transitions create smoother flow lines and smaller head losses than sharp transitions because of the increased turbulence and eddies that form near a sharp change in the flow pattern. Figure 6-2 shows flow lines for a pipe entrance with and without rounding.

Table 6-1: Typical Fitting K Coefficients

Fitting	K-value
Pipe Entrance	
Bellmouth	0.03 - 0.05
Rounded	0.12 - 0.25
Sharp Edged	0.50
Projecting	0.80
Contraction – Sudden	
$D_2/D_1 = 0.80$	0.18
$D_2/D_1 = 0.50$	0.37
$D_2/D_1 = 0.20$	0.49
Contraction – Conical	
$D_2/D_1 = 0.80$	0.05
$D_2/D_1 = 0.50$	0.07
$D_2/D_1 = 0.20$	0.08
Expansion – Sudden	
$D_2/D_1 = 0.80$	0.16
$D_2/D_1 = 0.50$	0.57
$D_2/D_1 = 0.20$	0.92
Expansion – Conical	
$D_2/D_1 = 0.80$	0.03
$D_2/D_1 = 0.50$	0.08
$D_2/D_1 = 0.20$	0.13

Fitting	K-value
90° Smooth Bend	
Bend radius / D = 4	0.16 - 0.18
Bend radius / D = 2	0.19 - 0.25
Bend radius / D = 1	0.35 - 0.40
Mitered Bend	
$\theta = 15°$	0.05
$\theta = 30°$	0.10
$\theta = 45°$	0.20
$\theta = 60°$	0.35
$\theta = 90°$	0.80
Tee	
Line Flow	0.30 - 0.40
Branch Flow	0.75 - 1.80
Cross	
Line Flow	0.50
Branch Flow	0.75
45° Wye	
Line Flow	0.30
Branch Flow	0.50

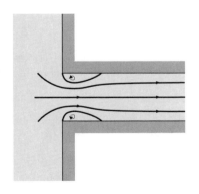
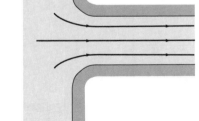

Sharp Entrance: K=0.50   Rounded Entrance: K=0.03

Figure 6-2: Flow Lines in Minor Losses

199

6.3 Energy Gains — Pumps

Pumps are an integral part of many pressure systems and are an important part of modeling head change in a network. Pumps add energy (head gains) to the flow to counteract head losses and hydraulic grade differentials within the system. There are several types of pumps that are used for various purposes; pressurized water systems typically have centrifugal pumps.

A centrifugal pump is defined by its ***characteristic curve***, which relates the pump head (head added to the system) to the flow rate. To model the behavior of the pump system, additional information is needed to ascertain the actual point at which the pump will be operating.

The ***system operating point*** is the point at which the pump curve crosses the ***system curve*** – the curve representing the static lift (H_s) and head losses (H_L) due to friction and minor losses. When these curves are superimposed (as in Figure 6-3), the operating point is easily located.

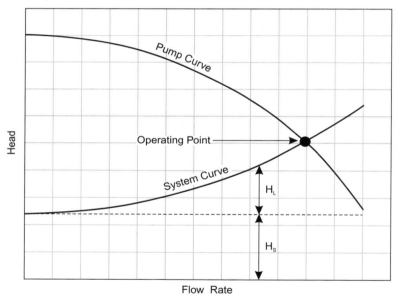

Figure 6-3: System Operating Point

As water surface elevations and demands throughout the system change, the static head (H_S) and head losses (H_L) vary. These changes cause the system curve to move around, whereas the pump characteristic curve remains constant. These shifts in the system curve result in a shifting operating point over time.

Variable-Speed Pumps

A centrifugal pump's characteristic curve is fixed for a given motor speed and impeller diameter, but can be determined for any speed and any diameter by applying the affinity laws. For variable-speed pumps, these affinity laws are presented as:

$$\frac{Q_1}{Q_2} = \frac{n_1}{n_2} \quad \text{and} \quad \frac{H_1}{H_2} = \left(\frac{n_1}{n_2}\right)^2$$

where Q = pump flow rate $(m^3/s, ft^3/s)$
H = pump head (m, ft)
n = pump speed (rpm)

Thus, pump discharge rate is proportional to pump speed, and the pump discharge head is proportional to the square of the speed. Using this relationship, once the pump curve is known, the curve at another speed can be predicted. Figure 6-4 illustrates the affinity laws applied to a variable-speed pump. The line labeled "Best Efficiency Point" indicates how the best efficiency point changes at various speeds.

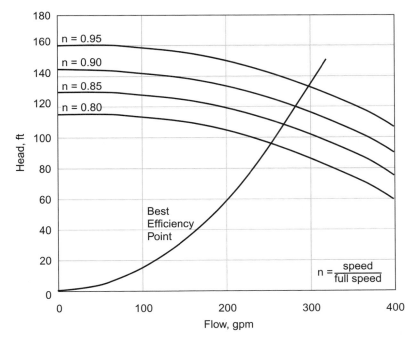

Figure 6-4: Relative speed factors for variable-speed pumps

Constant Horsepower Pumps

During preliminary studies, the exact characteristics of the pump may not be known. In these cases, the assumption is often made that the pump is adding energy to the water at a constant rate. Horsepower is input as the actual power added to the system, and not the rated horsepower of the motor (because there is a loss of efficiency in the motor, and motors usually run at less than their rated capacity). Specifying a pump as a constant horsepower pump means that the pump will add the same power to the water at any flow rate. Although this assumption is useful for some applications, a constant horsepower pump should only be used for preliminary studies.

6.4 Control Valves

There are several types of valves that may be present in a typical pressurized pipe system. These valves have different behaviors and different applications, but all valves are used to automatically control parts of the system, opening, closing, or throttling to achieve the desired result.

Check Valves (CVs)

Check valves are used to maintain flow in one direction only by closing when the flow begins to reverse. When the flow is in the same direction as the specified direction of the check valve, the valve is considered to be fully open.

Flow Control Valves (FCVs)

A *flow control valve* limits the flow rate through the valve to a specified value in a specified direction. A flow rate is used to control the operation of a flow control valve. These valves are commonly found in areas where a water district has contracted with another district or a private developer to limit the maximum demand to a value that will not adversely affect the provider's system.

Pressure Reducing Valves (PRVs)

Pressure reducing valves are often used to separate pressure zones in water distribution networks. These valves prevent the pressure downstream from exceeding a specified level, in order to avoid pressures and flows that could otherwise have undesirable effects on the system. A pressure or a hydraulic grade is used to control the operation of a PRV.

Pressure Sustaining Valves (PSVs)

Pressure sustaining valves maintain a specified pressure upstream of the valve. Similar to the other regulating valves, PSVs are often used to ensure that pressures in the system (upstream, in this case) will not drop to unacceptable levels. A pressure or a hydraulic grade is used to control the operation of a pressure sustaining valve.

Pressure Breaker Valves (PBVs)

Pressure breaker valves create a specified head loss across the valve and are often used to model components that cannot be easily modeled using standard minor loss elements.

Throttle Control Valves (TCVs)

Throttle control valves simulate minor loss elements whose head loss characteristics change over time. With a throttle control valve, the minor loss K is adjusted based on some other system flow or head.

6.5 Pipe Networks

In practice, pipe networks consist not only of pipes, but also of miscellaneous fittings, services, storage tanks, reservoirs, meters, regulating valves, pumps, and electronic and mechanical controls. For modeling purposes, these system elements can be organized into four fundamental categories:

- *Junction nodes*: Junctions are specific points (nodes) in the system where an event of interest is occurring. Junctions include points where pipes intersect, points where major demands on the system (such as a large industry, a cluster of houses, or a fire hydrant) are located, or critical points in the system where pressures are important for analysis purposes.

- *Boundary nodes*: Boundaries are nodes in the system where the hydraulic grade is known, and they define the initial hydraulic grades for any computational cycle. They set the hydraulic grade line used to determine the condition of all other nodes during system operation. Boundary nodes are elements such as tanks, reservoirs, and pressure sources. A model must contain at least one boundary node for the hydraulic grade lines and pressures to be calculated.

- *Links*: Links are system components such as pipes that connect to junctions or boundaries and control the flow rates and energy losses (or gains) between nodes.

- *Pumps and valves:* Pumps and valves are similar to nodes in that they occupy a single point in space, but they also have link properties because head changes occur across them.

An event or condition at one point in the system can affect all other locations in the system. Although this fact complicates the approach that the engineer must take to find a solution, there are some governing principles that drive the behavior of the network, such as the Conservation of Mass and the Conservation of Energy.

Conservation of Mass — Flows and Demands

This principle is a simple one. At any node in the system under incompressible flow conditions, the total volumetric or mass flow entering must equal the mass flow leaving (plus the change in storage).

Separating the total volumetric flow into flows from connecting pipes, demands, and storage, we obtain the following equation:

$$\sum Q_{in}\Delta t = \sum Q_{out}\Delta t + \Delta\forall_S$$

where ΣQ_{in} = total flow into the node
ΣQ_{out}= total flow out of the node
$\Delta\forall_S$ = change in storage volume
Δt = change in time

Conservation of Energy

Chapter 1 introduced the application of the energy equation to hydraulic analysis. The principle of conservation of energy dictates that the head losses through the system must balance at each point (Figure 6-5). For pressure networks, this means that the total head loss between any two nodes in the system must be the same regardless of the path taken between the two points. The head loss must be "sign consistent" with the assumed flow direction (that is, head loss occurs in the direction of flow, and head gain occurs in the direction opposite that of the flow).

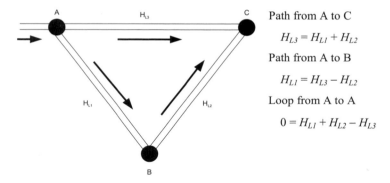

Path from A to C

$$H_{L3} = H_{L1} + H_{L2}$$

Path from A to B

$$H_{L1} = H_{L3} - H_{L2}$$

Loop from A to A

$$0 = H_{L1} + H_{L2} - H_{L3}$$

Figure 6-5: Conservation of Energy

Although the equality can become more complicated with minor losses and controlling valves, the same basic principle can be applied to any path between two points. As shown in Figure 6-5, the combined head loss around a loop must equal zero in order to compute the same hydraulic grade for a given point.

6.6 Network Analysis

Steady-State Network Hydraulics

Steady-state analysis is used to determine the operating behavior of a system at a specific point in time, or under steady-state conditions. This type of analysis can be useful in discovering the short-term effect of fire flows or average demand conditions on the system.

For this type of analysis, the network equations are determined and solved with tanks being treated as fixed-grade boundaries. The results that are obtained from this type of analysis are instantaneous values, and may not be representative of the values of the system a few hours — or even a few minutes — later in time.

Extended-Period Simulation

An extended-period simulation is used to determine the behavior of the system over time. This type of analysis allows the user to model tanks filling and draining, regulating valves opening and closing, and pressures and flow rates changing throughout the system in response to varying demand conditions and automatic control strategies formulated by the modeler.

Whereas a steady-state model may tell the user whether the system has the capability to meet a specific demand, an extended-period simulation indicates whether the system has the ability to provide acceptable levels of service over a period of minutes, hours, or days. Extended-period simulations can also be used for energy consumption and cost studies, as well as for water quality modeling.

Data requirements for an extended-period simulation go beyond what is needed for a steady-state analysis. The user must determine water usage patterns, provide more detailed tank information, and enter operational rules for pumps and valves.

6.7 Water Quality Analysis

In the past, water distribution systems were designed and operated with little consideration of water quality, due in part to the difficulty and expense of analyzing a dynamic system. The cost of extensive sampling and the complex interaction between fluids and constituents makes numeric modeling the ideal method for predicting water quality.

To predict water quality parameters, an assumption is made that there is complete mixing across finite distances, such as at a junction node or in a short segment of pipe. Complete mixing is essentially a mass balance given by:

$$C_a = \frac{\Sigma Q_i C_i}{\Sigma Q_i}$$

where C_a =   average (mixed) constituent concentration
        Q_i =   inflow rates
        C_i =   constituent concentrations of the inflows

Age

Water age provides a general indication of the overall water quality at any given point in the system. Age is typically measured from the time that the water enters the system from a tank or reservoir until it reaches a junction.

Along a given link, water age is computed as:

$$A_j = A_{j-1} + \frac{x}{V}$$

where A_j =   age of water at j-th node
        x =   distance from node j-1 to node j
        V =   velocity from node j-1 to node j

If there are several paths for water to travel to the j-th node, the water age is computed as a weighted average using the equation:

$$AA_j = \frac{\sum Q_i \left[AA_i + \left(\frac{x}{V} \right)_i \right]}{\sum Q_i}$$

where AA_j =   average age at the node immediately upstream of node j
        Q_i =   flow rate to the j-th node from the i-th node

Trace

Identifying the origin of flow at a point in the system is referred to as *flow tracking* or *trace modeling*. In systems that receive water from more than one source, trace studies can be used to determine the percentage of flow from each source at each point in the system. These studies can be very useful in delineating the area influenced by an individual source, observing the degree of mixing of water from several sources, and viewing changes in origins over time.

Constituents

Reactions can occur within pipes that cause the concentration of substances to change as the water travels through the system. Based on conservation of mass for a substance within a link (for extended-period simulations only):

$$\frac{\partial c}{\partial t} = V \frac{\partial \mathbf{c}}{\partial x} + \theta(c)$$

where c =   substance concentration as a function of distance and time
         t =   time increment
         V =   velocity
         x =   distance along the link
         $\theta(c)$ =   substance rate of reaction within the link

In some applications, there is an additional term for dispersion, but this term is usually negligible (plug flow is assumed through the system).

Assuming that complete and instantaneous mixing occurs at all junction nodes, additional equations can be written for each junction node with the following conservation of mass equation:

$$C_k\big|_{x=0} = \frac{\sum Q_j C_j\big|_{x=L} + Q_e C_e}{\sum Q_j + Q_e}$$

where C_k =   concentration at node k
         j =   pipe flowing into node k
         L =   length of pipe j
         Q_j =   flow in pipe j
         C_j =   concentration in pipe j
         Q_e =   external source flow into node k
         C_e =   external source concentration into node k

Once the hydraulic model has solved the network, the velocities and the mixing at the nodes are known. Using this information, the water quality behavior can be derived using a numerical method.

Initial Conditions

Just as a hydraulic simulation starts with some amount of water in each storage tank, initial conditions must be set for a water age, trace, or constituent concentration analysis. These initial water quality conditions are usually unknown, so the modeler must estimate these values from field data, a previous water quality model, or some other source of information.

To overcome the problem of unknown initial conditions at the vast majority of locations within the water distribution model, the duration of the analysis must be long enough for the system to reach equilibrium conditions. Note that a constant value does not have to be reached for equilibrium to be achieved; rather, equilibrium conditions are reached when a repeating pattern in age, trace, or constituent concentration is established.

Pipes usually reach equilibrium conditions in a short time, but storage tanks are much slower to show a repeating pattern. For this reason, extra care must be taken when setting a tank's initial conditions, in order to ensure the model's accuracy.

Numerical Methods

There are several theoretical approaches available for solving water quality models. These methods can generally be grouped as either Eulerian or Lagrangian in nature, depending on the volumetric control approach that is taken. Eulerian models divide the system into fixed pipe segments, and then track the changes that occur as water flows through these segments. Lagrangian models also break the system into control volumes, but then track these water volumes as they travel through the system. This chapter presents two alternative approaches for performing water quality constituent analyses.

Discrete Volume Method

The Discrete Volume Method (DVM) is an Eulerian approach that divides each pipe into equal segments with completely mixed volumes (Figure 6-6). Reactions are calculated within each segment, and the constituents are then transferred to the adjacent downstream segment. At nodes, mass and flow entering from all connecting pipes are combined (assuming total mixing). The resulting concentration is then transported to all adjacent downstream pipe segments. This process is repeated for each water quality time step until a different hydraulic condition is encountered. When this occurs, the pipes are divided again under the new hydraulic conditions, and the process continues.

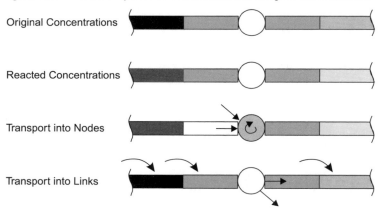

Figure 6-6: Eulerian DVM

Time-Driven Method

The Time-Driven Method (TDM) is an example of a Lagrangian approach (Figure 6-7). This method also breaks the system into segments, but rather than using fixed control volumes as in Eulerian methods, the concentration and size of water parcels are tracked as they travel through the pipes. With each time step, the farthest upstream parcel of each pipe elongates as water travels into the pipe, and the farthest downstream parcel shortens as water exits the pipe.

Similar to the Discrete Volume Method, the reactions of a constituent within each parcel are calculated, and the mass and flow entering each node are summed to determine the resulting concentration. If the resulting nodal concentration is significantly different from the concentration of a downstream parcel, a new parcel will be created rather than elongating the existing one. These calculations are repeated for each water quality time step until the next hydraulic change is encountered and the procedure begins again.

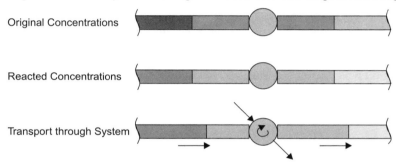

Figure 6-7: Lagrangian TDM

6.8 WaterCAD

What Does WaterCAD Do?

WaterCAD is a powerful, easy-to-use program that helps civil engineers design and analyze water distribution systems. It is also used by water utility managers to as a tool for the efficient operation of distribution systems. WaterCAD provides intuitive access to the tools you need to model complex hydraulic situations. WaterCAD's sophisticated modeling capabilities can:

- Perform steady-state, extended-period, and water quality simulations
- Analyze multiple time-variable demands at any junction node
- Model flow control valves, pressure reducing valves, pressure sustaining valves, pressure breaking valves, and throttle control valves
- Model cylindrical and non-cylindrical tanks and constant hydraulic grade source nodes
- Track conservative and non-conservative chemical constituents
- Determine water source and age at any element in the system
- Estimate construction costs

- Simulate the operating cycles of constant- or variable-speed pumps
- Estimate the cost of pumping over any time period

WaterCAD can be used as a stand-alone program, integrated with AutoCAD, or linked to a Geographical Information System (GIS) via the GEMS component. The theory and background used in WaterCAD are presented in this chapter and in the WaterCAD online help system. Additional information on features contained in the professional version and available options are presented in Appendix A.

How Can You Use WaterCAD?

WaterCAD can analyze complex distribution systems under a variety of conditions. For a typical WaterCAD project, you may be interested in determining system pressures and flow rates under average loading, peak loading, or fire flow conditions. Extended-period analysis tools also allow you to model the system's response to varying supply and demand schedules over a period of time; you can even track chlorine residuals or determine the source of the water at any point in the distribution system.

In summary, you can use WaterCAD for:

- Pipe sizing
- Pump sizing
- Master planning
- Operational studies
- Rehabilitation studies
- Vulnerability studies
- Water quality studies

WaterCAD is a state-of-the-art software tool primarily for use in the modeling and analysis of water distribution systems. Although the emphasis is on water distribution systems, the methodology is applicable to any fluid system with the following characteristics:

- Steady or slowly changing turbulent flow
- Incompressible, Newtonian, single phase fluid
- Full, closed conduits (pressure system)

Examples of systems with these characteristics include potable water systems, sewage force mains, fire protection systems, well pumps, and raw water pumping.

6.9 Tutorial Example

The following tutorial gives step-by-step instructions on how to solve an example problem using WaterCAD (included on the CD that accompanies this textbook).

Tutorial 1 – Three Pumps in Parallel

Problem Statement

A pump station is designed to supply water to a small linen factory. The factory, at an elevation of 58 m, draws from a circular, constant-area tank at a base elevation of 90 m with a minimum water elevation of 99 m, an initial water elevation of 105.5 m, a maximum water elevation of 106 m, and a diameter of 10 m.

Three main parallel pumps draw water from a source with a water surface elevation of 58 m. Two pumps are set aside for everyday usage, and the third is set aside for emergencies. Each pump has a set of controls that ensure it will run only when the water level in the tank reaches a certain level. Use the Hazen-Williams equation to determine friction losses in the system. The network layout is given in Figure 6-8; the pump and pipe data are given in the tables below.

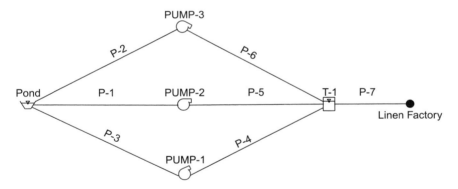

Figure 6-8: Schematic of Example Problem

a)   Can the pumping station support the factory's 20 l/s demand for a 24-hour period?

b)   If there were a fire at the factory that required an additional 108 l/s of water for hours 0 through 6, would the system with the pump controls given in the problem statement be adequate? Supply the Extended Period Simulation report describing the system at each time step.

c)   How might the system be operated so that the fire flow requirement in part (b) is met?

Pipe Information for Tutorial Problem

Pipe	Length (m)	Diameter (mm)	Material	Roughness
P-1	6	150	Cast Iron	90
P-2	6	150	Cast Iron	90
P-3	6	150	Cast Iron	90
P-4	71	150	Cast Iron	90
P-5	72	150	Cast Iron	90
P-6	73	150	Cast Iron	90
P-7	18	200	Cast Iron	90

Pump Information for Tutorial Problem

Pump	Elevation (m)	Pump Curve Head (m)	Flow (l/s)	Controls
PUMP-1	58	78 58.5 0	0 32 63	On when T-1 is below 105.50 meters Off when T-1 is above 106.00 meters
PUMP-2	58	78 58.5 0	0 32 63	On when T-1 is below 105.20 meters Off when T-1 is above 106.00 meters
PUMP-3	58	67 50.3 0	0 32 63	On when T-1 is below 99.25 meters Off when T-1 is above 103.00 meters

PART (a):   *Can the pumping station support the factory's 20 l/s demand for a 24-hour period?*

Solution

Project Setup Wizard

- When you start WaterCAD, you should be prompted with the **Welcome to WaterCAD** dialog. From this dialog, you can access the tutorials, open existing projects, and create new ones. Select **Create New Project**, provide a filename, and click **Save**.

- If the **Welcome to WaterCAD** dialog does not appear, WaterCAD is set to **Hide Welcome Dialog on startup**. To start a new project, select **New** from the **File** menu, enter a filename, and click **Save**. (You can change from **Hide Welcome Dialog** mode to **Show Welcome Dialog** mode in the **Global Options** dialog, which is accessible by selecting **Options** from the **Tools** menu.)

- Once you have provided a filename, the **Project Setup Wizard** will appear. Add a project title and any comments, and then click **Next**.

- In the second screen of the **Project Setup Wizard**, select the **Hazen-Williams Formula** from the pull-down menu in the **Friction Method** field and click **Next**.

- In the third screen of the **Project Setup Wizard** dialog, select **Schematic** from the **Drawing Scale** field. This option will allow you to define the pipe lengths and node locations without having to worry about scale and spatial placement on the x-y plane. Click **Next**.

  Note: If the units on this screen are not SI, then you need to cancel out of the Project Setup Wizard and reset the unit system. You can simplify data entry by specifying a global unit system for the model. Select **Options** from the **Tools** drop down menu. On the select **Global Options** tab, select **System International** from the pull-down menu in the **Unit System** field if it is not already selected. Once this has been done, you will need to select **New** from the **File** menu, enter a filename, and click **Save**. This should open the **Project Setup Wizard.** Begin working by returning to the second bullet.

- If you look at the pipe data in the problem statement, you will see that in terms of diameter, material, and roughness, the pipes are the same except for pipe P-7. Therefore, we can set up a prototype pipe that will create default physical data for all the pipes throughout the project. Any of the data can be changed later on a pipe-by-pipe basis.

- To set up a prototype pipe, click the **Pressure Pipe** button in the fourth screen of the **Project Setup Wizard**. The Pipe Defaults dialog appears. Change the diameter to **150 mm.** Scroll through the list in the **Materials** field and select **Cast Iron**. Finally, change the Hazen-Williams roughness value to 90. Click **OK**, and then click **Finished** to exit the wizard.

- Once you have reached the main screen you may want to use the **Auto Prompting** option. Select **Options** from the **Tools** drop down menu. On the **Global Options** tab check the Auto Prompting box. This option causes a dialog to appear every time you create a new element in your schematic. The dialog, which gives you the option of labeling the elements yourself, allows you to easily match your model data to the data given in the problem. Auto Prompting is not required; however, it will help you input the data correctly. Click **OK**.

Laying Out the System

- Begin with the pipeline running horizontally through the center of the system. Because you selected **Schematic** in the **Project Setup Wizard** dialog, you do not have to lay out the system exactly as shown in the problem statement. You can roughly sketch the schematic by following the instructions here.

- Click the **Pipe Layout** button ⊞ on the vertical toolbar on the left side of the screen.

- Move the cursor to the work area and right-click the mouse. Select **Reservoir**. To place the reservoir, simply click the left mouse button. In the **Auto Prompt** dialog, change the label R-1 to "Pond." Click **OK**.

- Move your mouse horizontally to the right and place Pump-2. Right-click and select **Pump** from the pop-up menu. Left-click to place the pump. Label the pump and pipe appropriately in the **Auto Prompt** dialog.

- Repeat the process for tank T-1, selecting **Tank** from the pop-up menu.

- Now, place the junction node "Linen Factory." After placing the junction, right-click and select **Done**.

- Now, continue by entering the remaining two pumps and four pipes in the same way as described previously.

- Except for the scale, your schematic should look roughly like the one given in the problem statement.

Data Entry

- Double-click the reservoir node Pond to open its dialog editor. Enter 58 m in the **Elevation** field. Click **OK**.

- Double-click tank T-1. Click the **Section** tab at the top of the dialog. Enter the given diameter for the circular section and the appropriate elevations from the problem statement. Disregard the inactive volume field. Be sure that **Elevations** is selected in the **Operating Range** field. Click **OK**.

- Double-click **PUMP-1**. Enter the appropriate elevation from the pump data table in the problem statement into the **Elevation** field. Select **Standard (3 Point)** from the **Pump Type** field. Notice that the units for the pump curve discharges given in the problem statement are in l/s. To change the units in the model, move the cursor to the design discharge field and right-click. Select **Design Properties** to enter the **Set Field Options** dialog. Then select l/s from the **Units** field and click **OK**. This action changes the units for all pump discharge fields throughout the project. Enter the pump curve data given for **PUMP-1**.

- Next, enter the pump controls given in the problem statement. These controls dictate the conditions under which a pump is on or off. Click the **Controls** tab at the top of the dialog for Pump-1.

- Click **Add**. Select **Status** from the **Control Type** field of the **Control** dialog.

- Select **On** from the **Status** field. By doing so, **PUMP-1** will be on for the condition you select in the next step.

- Select **Node** from the **Condition** field, and then select **T-1** from the **Node** field.

- Select **Below** from the **Comparison** field and enter an elevation of 105.5 m. Make sure that you have designated an **Elevation** and not a **Level**. Click **OK**.
- The **Controls** field should now read: "On if node T-1 below 105.5 m."
- Click **Add** and enter the second control. The status should be set to off when the node T-1 is above 106 m.
- Enter the data and controls for the other two pumps in the same way.
- Double-click the junction for the Linen Factory. Enter 58 m in the **Elevation** field. Click the **Demands** tab at the top of the dialog. Enter in a fixed demand of 20 l/s in the **Demand** field. Click **OK**.
- For the pipes, you can edit the data as you have been by clicking each element individually and then entering in the appropriate data. However, this method can be time consuming, especially as the number of pipe elements increase. It is often easier to edit the data in a tabular format.

- Click the **Tabular Reports** button in the toolbar at the top of the screen. Select **Pipe Report** from the **Available Tables** list and click **OK**.
- The fields highlighted in the **Pipe Report** table are output fields. The fields in white are input fields and can be edited like you would edit data in a spreadsheet.
- **Warning:** The pipes may not be listed in the table in numerical order. You may want to sort the pipe labels in ascending order. To do this, move the cursor to the top of the table and place it on the **Label** column. Right-click, select **Sort**, and then select **Ascending**. The pipes should then be listed in numerical order.
- Enter the correct pipe lengths from the problem statement and change the diameter for pipe P-7 to 200 mm. Close the **Pipe Report**.

  Note: You can customize which columns appear in the **Pipe Report** table by clicking the **Tabular Reports** button in the toolbar, clicking **Table Management,** and then selecting **Edit**. After you select and open a table, you can also click the **Options** button and choose **Customize** to customize the table you have active.

Running the Model

- To run the model, first click the **GO** button on the top toolbar. To examine the flow through the system over a 24-hour period, select **Extended Period**. Set the start time to 12:00:00 a.m. and the duration to 24 hours. The **Hydraulic Time Step** of 1 hour will provide sufficient output for the purpose of this tutorial. Click the **GO** button.
- There are a couple of ways to determine whether your model meets the target demand:

Scroll through the results and check to see if there are any disconnected node warnings. When the level in Tank T-1 drops to the minimum tank elevation of 99 m (tank level of 9 m), the tank closes off, preventing any more water from leaving. This closure will cause the linen factory to be disconnected from the rest of the system (that is, it will not get the required 20 l/s).

-OR-

Double-click the junction Linen Factory and click the Messages tab on top of Junction dialog. The messages in the box will warn you if the node ever becomes disconnected.

Answer

As you will see for this problem, all the pressures at the linen factory hover around 465 kPa, and no disconnected nodes are detected. Therefore, the pumping station can support the factory's 20 l/s demand for a 24-hour period.

PART (b): *If there were a fire at the factory that required an additional 108 l/s water for hours 0 through 6, would the system with the pump controls given in the problem statement be adequate? Supply the Extended Period Simulation report describing the system at each time step.*

Solution

- Add another demand to the Linen Factory node. Double-click the Linen Factory junction, and select the **Demands** tab. In the row below the 20 l/s demand, enter 108 l/s. Click **OK**.
- Click the **GO** button in the toolbar. You only need to run this model for six hours, so change 24 to 6 in the **Duration** field. Click **GO** to run the model.
- As you scroll through the results, you will see that at 3.42 hours (time 3:25:27) the water level in Tank T-1 reaches the minimum level of 9 m. If you scroll through the results, you will see warning messages (yellow folders instead of green) indicating a disconnected node at the linen factory at 3:25:27 and hours 4, 5, and 6.

Answer

If there were a fire at the factory, the existing system would NOT be adequate.

PART (c): *How might the system be operated so that the fire flow requirement in Part (b) is met?*

Answer

PUMP-3 could be manually switched on at the beginning of the fire to supply the flow necessary to fight the fire at the linen factory.

Tutorial 2 – Water Quality

This tutorial example demonstrates the use of WaterCAD to simulate water quality in a water distribution system. Scenario Manager is used to facilitate different types of analyses on the same network (within the same project file).

Problem Statement

A local water company is concerned with the water quality in its water distribution network. The company wishes to determine the age and the chlorine concentration of the water as it exits the system at different junctions. The water surface at the reservoir is 70 m.

Chlorine is injected into the system at the source of flow, R-1, at a concentration of 1 mg/l. It has been determined through a series of bottle tests that the average bulk reaction rate of the chlorine in the system (including all pipes and tanks) is approximately –0.5 /day.

The network model may be entered in WaterCAD using the layout in Figure 6-9 and the data that follows.

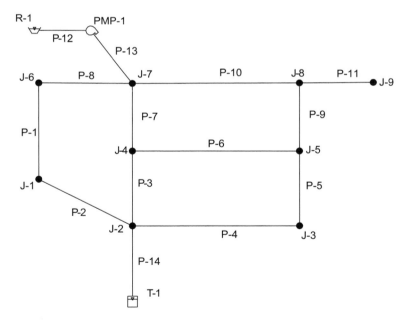

Figure 6-9: Schematic for Water Quality Tutorial

The tank has a circular diameter of 15 m. The minimum elevation is 99 m. The maximum elevation is 104 m, and the initial elevation is 103.4 m. The base elevation is 98 m, and the inactive volume is 10 m^3. The elevation of the pump is 70 m.

Pump Information for Water Quality Tutorial

Head (m)	Discharge (l/min)	Controls
40	0	Off if node T-1 above 103.5 m
35	3,000	On if node T-1 below 99.5 m
24	6,000	

Stepwise Demand Pattern Data for Water Quality Tutorial

Time from Start (hr)	Multiplier	Time from Start (hr)	Multiplier
0	0.80	13	1.30
1	0.60	14	1.40
2	0.50	15	1.50
3	0.50	16	1.60
4	0.55	17	1.80
5	0.60	18	1.80
6	0.80	19	1.40
7	1.10	20	1.20
8	1.50	21	1.00
9	1.40	22	0.90
10	1.30	23	0.80
11	1.40	24	0.80
12	1.40		

Junction Data for Water Quality Tutorial

Junction	Elevation (m)	Demand (l/min)
J-1	73	151
J-2	67	227
J-3	85	229
J-4	61	212
J-5	82	208
J-6	56	219
J-7	67	215
J-8	73	219
J-9	55	215

Pipe Data for Water Quality Tutorial

Pipe	Length (m)	Diameter (mm)	Roughness
P-1	300	200	130
P-2	305	200	130
P-3	225	200	130
P-4	301	200	130
P-5	225	200	130
P-6	301	200	130
P-7	225	200	130
P-8	301	200	130
P-9	200	200	130
P-10	301	200	130
P-11	300	200	130
P-12	1	250	130
P-13	3,000	300	130
P-14	300	300	130

a) Perform an age analysis on the system using a duration of seven days and a time step of one hour. Determine the youngest and oldest water in the distribution system and the storage tank. Explain why water age varies.

b) Perform a constituent analysis using the same duration and time step as in part (a). Determine the range of concentrations in the system and the storage tank. Explain the behavior of the system with regard to chlorine.

c) Are the simulation results consistent with the known behavior of chlorine?

d) Why is it necessary to run the model for such a long period of time? Do you feel seven days is too long or too short a time period to test the model? Why?

Base Scenario

- After the network model is loaded (or entered), run the model by clicking the **GO** button on the top toolbar. The Scenario: Base dialog opens. On the **Calculation** tab, select **Extended Period** and click the **GO** button. WaterCAD calculates the system parameters for a 24-hour simulation period. Details of the calculation can be viewed on the **Results** tab.

- Close the Scenario: Base dialog. Play the 24-hour simulation by clicking the **Play** button to the right of the **Arrow** button on the left side of the window. The flow in the pipes is indicated by the arrows. Note that that there is no flow in pipes P-12 and P-13 when the pump is not operating. The flow direction reverses in pipes P-1, P-2, P-3, P-4, P-5, P-7, and P-9 over the 24-hour period. The volume of the water in tank T-1 is indicated by the **% Full** annotation next to the tank label.

Age Analysis

- The analysis of the age of water within the network may be performed by defining and running an age analysis scenario. From the **Analysis** drop-down **menu**, select **Scenarios**.

- Click the Scenario Wizard.

- Enter Age Analysis as the name of the scenario. Click **Next**.

- Select **Base** as the scenario on which the new scenario is based. Click **Next**.

- The type of simulation is **Extended Period**. The duration is 168 hours (7 days). Check the **Water Quality Analysis** check box and select **Age**. Click **Next**.

- Select **Age** as the alternative to change. Click **Next**.

- Click the **Create New Age Alternative** radio button. Click **Next**.

- The dialog should indicate that the Age Alternative is varied for the new scenario. All other alternatives are the same as those in the Base Scenario. Click **Finish**.

- Check that the scenario is set to **Age Analysis** by highlighting the scenario, right-clicking and selecting **Edit.** Make sure that the **Water Quality Analysis** box is checked and the **Age** radio button is selected. Close out of this window and click the

Go Batch Run button. Select the **Age Analysis** check box (the other boxes should not be checked) and then click **Batch**. Confirm that 1 batch run is to be performed.

- Close the Scenarios dialog to view the results.

Results: The oldest water in the network will be found in tank T-1. Double-click on the tank symbol in the network. Select **Report** and then **Graph** on the bottom of the dialog. Select **T-1** on the **Elements** tab. The dependent variable is calculated age. Click on **OK** to view the graph of age as a function of time. This graph is shown below.

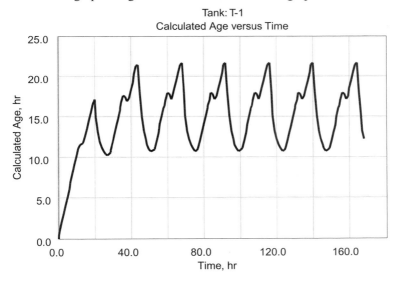

Figure 6-10: Age of water in Tank T-1

Note that the water distribution network reaches dynamic equilibrium during the second day of the simulation. After 36 hrs, at T-1, the maximum age is 21.7 hrs and the minimum age is 10.7 hrs.

To view the variation in age in the network, close the graph and the tank dialog, and return to the network view. Double-click any junction and select the **Report** tab at the bottom of the junction dialog. Select the **Graph** option. On the **Graph** setup dialog, click the **Elements** tab. Check the boxes for J-2, J-3, J-7, and J-9 and then click **OK**.

The values that are plotted can be viewed by selecting the **Data** tab. Note that after 36 hrs, the maximum age in the network is 17.0 hrs at J-7.

Water Quality Analysis

In order to analyze the behavior of chlorine in the network, the properties of chlorine must be defined in the engineering library.

- From the **Tools** menu, select **Engineering Library.** Highlight **Constituent** and select **Edit.**

- Insert a new constituent. This constituent will appear as "unlabeled" in the table. Highlight the "unlabeled" constituent and select **Edit**. Change the label to "Chlorine." Use the default diffusivity and select the **Reaction Rates** tab.

- Enter the **Bulk Reaction Order** as 1 and the **Bulk Reaction Rate** as -0.5 $(\text{mg/l})^{1-n}$/day. Because $n = 1$, the units of the rate constant are day^{-1}. If these units are not displayed, you must use the FlexUnits tool to set the units. Click **OK**.

- Close the Constituent Library and the Engineering Library.

- On the **Analysis** menu, select **Scenarios**.

- Click the **Scenario Wizard.**

- Enter *Chlorine Analysis* as the name of the scenario. Click **Next**.

- Select **Base** as the scenario on which the new scenario is based. Click **Next**.

- The type of simulation is **Extended Period**. The duration is 168 hrs (7 days). Check the **Water Quality Analysis** check box and select **Constituent**. Click **Next**.

- Select **Constituent** as the alternative to change. Click **Next**.

- Click the **Create New Constituent Alternative** radio button. Click **Next**.

- The dialog should indicate that the **Constituent Alternative** is varied for the new scenario. All other alternatives are the same as those in the base scenario. Click **Finish** and close the Scenario dialog.

- Make sure that the "Chlorine Analysis" scenario is the active scenario from the scenario drop-down menu and double-click the reservoir to define the loading of chlorine. Select the **Quality** tab. Check the **Is Constituent Source** box. The Constituent Source Type is concentration and the baseline concentration is 1.0 mg/L. The constituent source pattern is fixed. Click **OK**.

- The bulk reaction rate in the pipes can be set using the **Table Manager** tool. Click on the **Table Manager** icon, highlight the **Pipe Report** and click **OK**. Add the Bulk Reaction Rate to the table by selecting **Options** and **Customize.** Select **Bulk Reaction Rate** from the available columns and use the first **Add** button to add it to the selected columns. Select **OK** to exit. Scroll to the **Bulk Reaction Rate** column and use the **Global Edit** tool to set the value to -0.5 /day for each pipe. Close the Pipe Report.

- Double-click tank T-1 and select the **Quality** tab. Set the initial chlorine concentration to 0.0 and the bulk reaction rate to -0.5 /day. Click **OK**.

- Run the scenario by clicking the **GO** button in the top row. The Scenario dialog indicates that the Chlorine Analysis will be calculated. Click **GO,** and the **Results** summary appears. Close the scenario to view the results.

- Step through the animation using the arrows next to the hour field to hour 2. Select the **Contour Map Manager** tool. Set the Minimum to 0.0, Maximum to 1.0, Increment to 0.02 and Index to 0.1 mg/L. Click **OK**.

- The chlorine concentrations for each time step can be viewed using the arrow tools next to the hour field to step through time.

Results: The lowest chlorine concentration will be found in tank T-1. Double-click the tank symbol in the network. Select **Report** and then **Graph**. The dependent variable is calculated concentration. Click **OK** to view the graph of chlorine concentration as a function of time. This graph is shown in Figure 6-11.

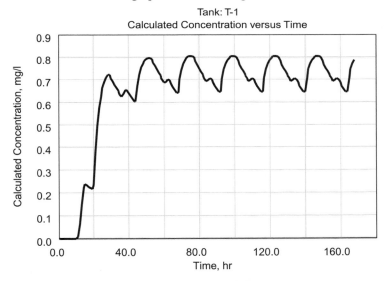

Figure 6-11: Chlorine Concentration in Tank T-1

Note that the water distribution network reaches dynamic equilibrium during the third day of the simulation. After 48 hrs, the maximum age at tank T-1 is 0.81 hrs, and the minimum age is 0.64 hrs.

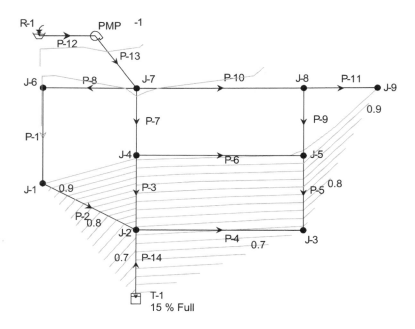

Figure 6-12: Contours of Chlorine Concentration at 42 Hours

To view the variation in chlorine concentration in the network, close the graph and the tank dialog and return to the network view. Double-click any junction and select the **Report** tab at the bottom of the junction dialog. Select the **Graph** option. On the **Graph** setup dialog, click the **Elements** tab. Check the boxes for **J-2, J-3, J-7,** and **J-9,** and then click **OK**.

To compare age against chlorine concentration at a selected junction, set the scenario to **Age Analysis** and double-click on **J-3**. Select **Report \ Graph** and **OK**. Do not close the graph. Move the mouse to the network window and set the scenario to **Chlorine Analysis**. Double-click **J-3**. Select **Report \ Graph** and **OK**. The graphs of age versus time and chlorine concentration should now be open on the desktop. Move the graphs so that both are visible and the axes are aligned. Comparison of the two graphs suggests an inverse correlation between age and chlorine concentration.

Answers

a) The oldest water is found in the storage tank. It is the farthest from the source and incoming water is always mixed with the tank's contents. In the distribution system, the oldest water is found at J-3. The youngest water is found at J-7 when the pump PMP-1 is running.

b) The lowest chlorine concentration is in Tank T-1 when it is nearly empty. In the distribution system, the lowest chlorine concentration is found at J-3 when T-1 is emptying. The highest concentration is found at J-7 when pump PMP-1 is running.

c) These results are consistent with the fact that chlorine concentration declines over time. For example, during the third day of operation, the minimum chlorine concentration at Junction J-3 is coincident with the maximum age (17 hours), and the maximum chlorine concentration (0.95 mg/l) is coincident with the minimum age (2.17 hours).

d) Inspection of the graph of chlorine concentration in tank T-1 suggests that the system stabilizes into a daily pattern on the third day. However, if the initial tank level or the demands are changed stabilization may take longer. It appears that the seven-day simulation period is adequate for this network.

Tutorial 3 – Pumping Costs

This tutorial demonstrates the use of WaterCAD to calculate the energy costs associated with pumping.

Problem Statement

Calculate the daily electrical costs for the network in Tutorial 2 using the following data:

Energy price	$0.10/kWh
Motor efficiency	90%
Pump efficiency	50% at 2,000 l/m
	60% at 2,500 l/m
	55% at 3,000 l/m

Solution

- The first step is to add the pump and motor efficiency data to PMP-1. On the network view, double-click **PMP-1** and select the **Energy** tab.

- On the **Efficiency Type** field select the **Multiple Efficiency Points** option. In the **Efficiency Points** table, add the efficiencies for the three discharges in the problem statement.

- In the **Motor Efficiency** section, enter 90%

- Click **OK** to close the PMP-1 dialog.

Next, the Energy Cost tool is used to calculate energy costs.

- From the **Analysis** drop-down menu, select **Energy Costs**.
- Click the **Prices** button to open the Energy Cost Manager.

- Edit Energy Pricing-1 to enter the electricity cost. Enter one line in the cost table. The Time From Start is 0.0, and the Energy Price is 0.10. Click **OK** twice to return to the **Energy Cost** window.

- Set the alternative to **Chlorine Analysis** and click **Go.**

Results: On the left panel of the Energy Cost window, highlight the Chlorine Analysis line. On the right panel, select the **Summary** tab. For the seven-day simulation, the following data were calculated:

Pump energy used	4,030 kWh
Volume pumped	21,220 m³
Pump cost	$403
Daily cost	$58

Tutorial 4 – Capital Cost Estimating

WaterCAD has many tools for preparing project cost estimates. See Appendix C for a detailed discussion of Capital Cost Analysis with Haestad Methods software. In this exercise, the Unit Cost function and the Cost Table features will be demonstrated.

Problem Statement

Prepare a cost estimate for materials and installation portion of the project in Tutorial 2. Use the following cost data:

Pipe Cost Function	
Unit Cost	$/m
Unit Cost Function Attribute	Diameter (mm)
Function Coefficients for Unit Cost $= d + a(x - c)^b$	
a	0.15
b	0.3
c	150
d	55
Pump Station	
Pump	$15,000
Installation	$4,000
Valves and Piping	$750
Structure	$50,000
Storage	
Tank installation	$100,000
Site preparation	$15,000
SCADA	$20,000
Pipe Junction	$1000/ea.

Do not consider the cost of the reservoir or intake structure.

Solution

- From the **Analysis** pull-down menu, select **Capital Costs\Unit Cost Functions**.

- Click the **Add** button and select **Formula Unit Cost Function** as the Unit Cost Function Type and Diameter as the **Unit Cost Function Attribute.** Click **OK**. Enter the data for circular pipe from the problem statement above. To view a plot of the function, click on the **Initialize Range** button and then on **Plot**. Close the Plot viewer. Click **OK** and **Close** to close the Cost Function dialog to return to the Network layout view.

- Click the **Tabular Reports** button in the toolbar at the top of the screen. Select the **Pipe Cost Report** from the **Available Tables** list and click **OK**.

- Right-click the header of the **Include in Capital Cost Calculation?** column. Select the **Global Edit** option. Check the box next to **Include in Capital Cost Calculation?** and then click **OK.**

- Right-click the header of the **Element Costs** column. Select the **Global Edit** option. Enter "Materials and Installation" in the first line of the label column. Click the **Advanced** button. Check the box next to **Set Quantity Equal to Pipe Length,** and then select **Diameter Cost Function** for the Unit Cost Function. Click **OK** to close the Capital Costs window.

- Click the **Options** button and select **Table Manager**. Highlight the Node Cost Report, and click **OK.**

- Right click the Include in **Capital Cost Calculation** option and then select **Global Edit**. Check the box for **Include in Capital Cost Calculation.**

- Right-click the header of the **Element Costs** column. Select the **Global Edit** option. Enter "Materials and Installation" in the first line of the label column, a quantity of 1, a unit of each, and 1,000 in the Unit Cost column. Click **OK** to close the cost window.

- On the T-1 row, click the field in the **Element Costs** column. It should turn into a button. Click the button. Enter the data in the following table. WaterCAD will calculate the last column. Click **OK** to exit the capital cost window.

Element Costs

Label	Quantity	Unit	Unit Cost ($)	Cost ($)
Materials and Installation	1	each	100,000	
Site Preparation	1	each	15,000	
SCADA	1	each	20,000	

- On the PMP-1 row, click the field in the **Element Costs** column. The field turns into a button. Click the button. Check the **Include in Capital Cost Calculation** box. Enter the data in the following table. WaterCAD will calculate the last column. Click **OK** to exit the capital cost window.

Capital Costs for Pump Station

Label	Quantity	Unit	Unit Cost ($)	Cost ($)
Pump	1	each	15,000	
Installation	1	each	4,000	
Valves & piping	1	each	750	
Structure	1	each	50,000	

- Select the **Element Costs** field for R-1 and it should turn into a button. Click the button to access the capital costs. Since the R-1 will not be included in capital costs, highlight the **Material and Installation** row and select the **Delete** button. Select **OK** to exit capital costs. Uncheck the box to include R-1 in the capital cost calculation. Select **Close** to exit the tabular reports.

- You are now ready to calculate the total project costs. On the **Analysis** drop-down menu, select **Capital Costs** to open the Cost Manager. The cost is calculated for the base scenario. Click the **Cost Reports** button and select **Detailed** from the drop-down menu. The Detailed Cost Report table opens. To obtain a hard copy, select **Print Review** and then click **Print**.

Solution

From the **Analysis** drop-down menu, select **Capital Costs.** Note that costs may be calculated for any scenario. In this example, the physical layout for all three scenarios is identical. Click the **Report** button next to **Scenario Costs** and the pie chart button. A report with the following table is produced.

	Base		
Label	Construction Costs ($)	Non-Construction Costs ($)	Total Cost ($)
Pump	69,750	0	69,750
Tank	135,000	0	135,000
Reservoir	1,000	0	1,000
Pressure Junction	9,000	0	9,000
Pressure Pipe	751,932	0	751,932
		Total	966,682

6.10 Problems

Solve the following problems using the WaterCAD computer program.

1. The ductile iron pipe network shown below carries water at 20°C. Assume that the junctions all have an elevation of 0 m and the reservoir is at 30 m. Use the Hazen-

Williams formula ($C = 130$) and the pipe and demand data below to perform a steady-state analysis and answer the following questions:

a) Which pipe has the lowest discharge? What is the discharge (in l/min)?

b) Which pipe has the highest velocity? What is the velocity (in m/s)?

c) Calculate the problem using the Darcy-Weisbach equation ($k = 0.26$ mm) and compare the results.

d) What effect would raising the reservoir by 20 m have on the pipe flow rates? What effect would it have on the hydraulic grade lines at the junctions?

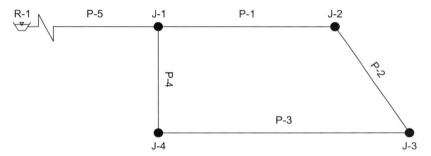

Schematic for Problem 1

Pipe and Junction Information for Problem 1

Pipe	Diameter (mm)	Length (m)		Junction	Demand (l/min)
P-1	150	50		J-1	570
P-2	100	25		J-2	660
P-3	100	60		J-3	550
P-4	100	20		J-4	550
P-5	250	760			

2. A pressure gage reading of 288 kPa was taken at J-5 in the pipe network shown below. Assuming a reservoir elevation of 100 m, find the appropriate Darcy-Weisbach roughness height (to the hundredths place) to bring the model into agreement with these field records. Use the same roughness value for all pipes. The pipe and junction data are shown below.

a) What roughness factor yields the best results?

b) What is the calculated pressure at J-5 using this factor?

c) Other than the pipe roughnesses, what other factors could cause the model to disagree with field-recorded values for flow and pressure?

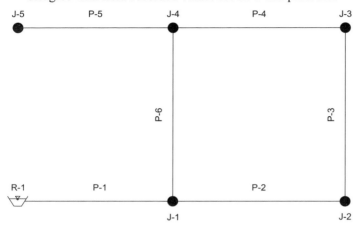

Schematic for Problem 2

Pipe and Junction Information for Problem 2

Pipe	Diameter (mm)	Length (m)
P-1	250	1,525
P-2	150	300
P-3	150	240
P-4	150	275
P-5	150	245
P-6	200	230

Junction	Elevation (m)	Demand (l/min)
J-1	55	950
J-2	49	1,060
J-3	58	1,440
J-4	46	1,175
J-5	44	980

3. A distribution system is needed to supply water to a resort development for normal usage and emergency purposes (such as fighting a fire). The proposed system layout is shown in the following figure:

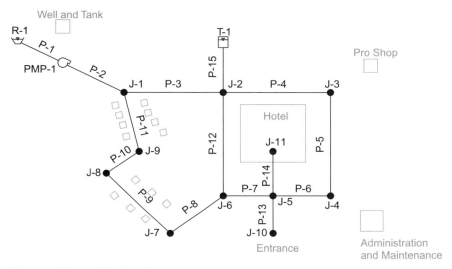

Proposed Network for Problem 3

The source of water for the system is a pumped well. The water is treated and placed in a ground-level tank (shown above as a reservoir because of its plentiful supply), which is maintained at a water surface elevation of 210 ft. The water is then pumped from this tank into the rest of the system.

The well system alone cannot efficiently provide the amount of water needed for fire protection, so an elevated storage tank is also needed. The bottom of the tank is at 376 ft (high enough to produce 35 psi at the highest node), and the top is approximately 20 ft higher. To avoid the cost of an elevated tank, this 80-ft diameter tank is located on a hillside, 2,000 ft away from the main system. Assume that the tank starts with a water surface elevation of 380 ft.

The pump was originally sized to deliver 300 gpm with enough head to pump against the tank when it is full. Three defining points on the pump curve are as follows: 0 gpm at 200 ft of head; 300 gpm at 180 ft of head; and 600 gpm at 150 ft of head. The pump elevation is assumed to be the same as the elevation at J-1, although the precise pump elevation isn't crucial to the analysis.

The system is to be analyzed under several demand conditions with minimum and maximum pressure constraints. During normal operations, the junction pressures should be between 35 psi and 80 psi. Under fire flow conditions, however, the minimum pressure is allowed to drop to 20 psi. Fire protection is being considered both with and without a sprinkler system.

Demand Alternatives: WaterCAD enables you to store multiple demand alternatives corresponding to various conditions (such as average day, peak hour, etc.). This feature allows you run different scenarios that incorporate various demand conditions within a single project file without losing any input data. For an introduction and more information about scenarios and alternatives, see WaterCAD's online help system and Appendices A and B.

Junction Information for Problem 3

Junction	Elevation (ft)	Average Day (gpm)	Peak Hour (gpm)	Minimum Hour (gpm)	Fire with Sprinkler (gpm)	Fire without Sprinkler (gpm)
J-1	250	0	0	0	0	0
J-2	260	0	0	0	0	0
J-3	262	20	50	2	520	800
J-4	262	20	50	2	520	800
J-5	270	0	0	0	0	800
J-6	280	0	0	0	0	800
J-7	295	40	100	2	40	40
J-8	290	40	100	2	40	40
J-9	285	0	0	0	0	0
J-10	280	0	0	0	360	160
J-11	270	160	400	30	160	160

Pipe Network: The pipe network consists of the pipes listed in the following tables. The diameters shown are based on the preliminary design, and may not be adequate for the final design. For all pipes, use ductile iron as the material and a Hazen-Williams *C*-factor of 130.

Pipe Information for Problem 3

Pipe	Diameter (in)	Length (ft)
P-1	8	20
P-2	8	300
P-3	8	600
P-4	6	450
P-5	6	500
P-6	6	300
P-7	8	250
P-8	6	400

Pipe	Diameter (in)	Length (ft)
P-9	6	400
P-10	6	200
P-11	6	500
P-12	8	500
P-13	6	400
P-14	6	200
P-15	10	2000

To help keep track of important system characteristics (like maximum velocity, lowest pressure, etc.), you may find it helpful to keep a table such as the following:

Results Summary for Problem 3

Variable	Average Day	Peak Hour	Minimum Hour	Fire with Sprinkler	Fire without Sprinkler
Node w/ low pressure					
Low pressure (psi)					
Node w/ high pressure					
High pressure (psi)					
Pipe w/ max. velocity					
Max. velocity (ft/s)					
Tank in/out flow (gpm)					
Pump discharge (gpm)					

Another way to quickly determine the performance of the system is to color-code the pipes according to some indicator. In hydraulic design, a good performance indicator is often the velocity in the pipes. Pipes consistently flowing below 0.5 ft/s may be oversized. Pipes with velocities over 5 ft/s are fairly heavily stressed, and those with velocities above 8 ft/s are usually bottlenecks in the system under that flow pattern. Color-code the system using the ranges in the table below. After you define the color-coding, place a legend in the drawing.

Color-Coding Range for Problem 3

Max. Velocity (ft/s)	Color
0.5	Magenta
2.5	Blue
5.0	Green
8.0	Yellow
20.0	Red

a) Fill in or reproduce the Results Summary table after each run to get a feel for some of the key indicators during various scenarios.

b) For the average day run, what is the pump discharge?

c) If the pump has a best efficiency point at 300 gpm, what can you say about its performance on an average day?

d) For the peak hour run, the velocities are fairly low. Does this mean you have oversized the pipes? Explain.

e)   For the minimum hour run, what was the highest pressure in the system? Why would you expect the highest pressure to occur during the minimum hour demand?

f)   Was the system (as currently designed) acceptable for the fire flow case with the sprinkled building? On what did you base this decision?

g)   Was the system (as currently designed) acceptable for the fire flow case with all the flow provided by hose streams (no sprinklers)? If not, how would you modify the system so that it will work?

4.   A ductile iron pipe network ($C = 130$) is shown below. Use the Hazen-Williams equation to calculate friction losses in the system. The junctions and pump are at an elevation of 5 ft and all pipes are 6 in. in diameter. (Note: Use a standard, 3-point pump curve. The data for the junctions, pipes, and pump are in the tables below.) The water surface of the reservoir is at an elevation of 30 ft.

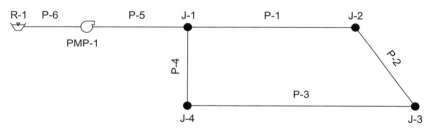

Schematic for Problem 4

Pump Information for Problem 4

Head (ft)	Flow (gpm)
200	0
175	1,000
100	2,000

Junction Information for Problem 4

Junction Label	Demand (gpm)
J-1	400
J-2	550
J-3	550
J-4	350

Pipe Information for Problem 4

Pipe Label	Length (ft)
P-1	78
P-2	40
P-3	90
P-4	39
P-5	10
P-6	10

a) What are the resulting flows and velocities in the pipes?

b) What are the resulting pressures at the junction nodes?

c) Place a check valve on pipe P-3 such that the valve only allows flow from J-3 to J-4. What happens to the flow in pipe P-3? Why does this occur?

d) When the check valve is placed on pipe P-3, what happens to the pressures throughout the system?

e) Remove the check valve on pipe P-3. Place a 6-in flow control valve node at an elevation of 5 ft on pipe P-3. The FCV should be set so that it only allows a flow of 100 gpm from J-4 to J-3 (Hint: a check valve is a pipe property). What is the resulting difference in flows in the network? How are the pressures affected?

f) Why doesn't the pressure at J-1 change when the FCV is added?

g) What happens if you increase the FCV's allowable flow to 2,000 gpm? What happens if you reduce the allowable flow to zero?

5. A local country club has hired you to design a sprinkler system that will water the greens of their nine-hole golf course. The system must be able to water all nine holes at once. The water supply has a water surface elevation of 10 ft. All pipes are PVC ($C = 150$, use the Hazen-Williams equation to determine friction losses). Use a standard, three-point pump curve for the pump, which is at an elevation of 5 ft. The flow at the sprinkler is modeled using an emitter coefficient. The data for the junctions, pipes, and pump curve are given in the tables that follow. The initial network layout is shown below.

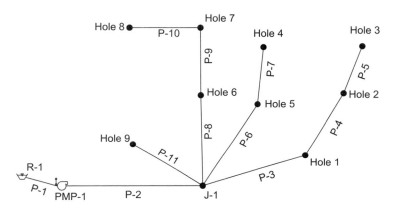

Schematic for Problem 5

Junction and Pipe Information for Problem 5

Junction Label	Emitter Coefficient (gpm/psi$^{0.5}$)	Elevation (ft)		Pipe Label	Diameter (in)	Length (ft)
J-1	-	10		P-1	4	10
Hole 1	8	7		P-2	4	1,000
Hole 2	10	7		P-3	4	800
Hole 3	15	40		P-4	3	750
Hole 4	12	5		P-5	3	500
Hole 5	8	5		P-6	3	700
Hole 6	8	15		P-7	2	400
Hole 7	10	20		P-8	4	800
Hole 8	15	10		P-9	3	500
Hole 9	8	12		P-10	2	400
				P-11	2	500

Pump Information for Problem 5

Head (ft)	Flow (gpm)
170	0
135	300
100	450

a) Determine the discharge at each hole.

b) What is the operating point of the pump?

6. A subdivision of 36 homes is being constructed in a new area of town. Each home will require 1.7 l/s during peak periods. All junction nodes are 192 m in elevation. All pipes are ductile iron ($C = 130$, use the Hazen-Williams Equation to determine the friction losses in the pipe). The current lot and network layout is shown below. (Hint: Use Auto-Prompting to lay out the system.)

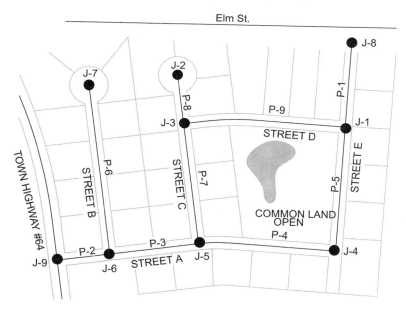

Schematic for Problem 6

Junction and Pipe Information for Problem 6

Junction Label	Number of Lots Serviced
J-1	5
J-2	4
J-3	4
J-4	5
J-5	6
J-6	6
J-7	6

Pipe Label	Length (m)	Diameter (mm)
P-1	60	150
P-2	60	150
P-3	110.5	150
P-4	164.0	150
P-5	152.5	150
P-6	204	100
P-7	148	150
P-8	61	100
P-9	194	150

Currently, a model of the entire water system does not exist. However, hydrant tests were conducted using hydrants located on two water mains, one in Town Highway #64 and the other in Elm Street. The following data were obtained:

Town Highway #64 Hydrant Test
Static Pressure 310.3 kPa
Residual Pressure 98.5 kPa at 32 l/s
Elevation of Pressure Gauge 190 m

Elm Street Hydrant Test
Static Pressure 413.7 kPa
Residual Pressure 319.3 kPa at 40 l/s
Elevation of Pressure Gauge 191.5 m

The subdivision will connect to existing system mains in these streets at nodes J-8 and J-9. (Hint: On the **Help** drop-down menu, select **How do I?** Click **Appendix A**, and then **Modeling Tips**. Select **Connection to an Existing Water Main**.)

a) What are the demands at each of the junction nodes? What is the total demand?

b) Does the present water distribution system have enough capacity to supply the new subdivision?

c) Which connection to the existing main is supplying more water to the subdivision? Why?

    d)   Are the proposed pipe sizes adequate to maintain velocities between 0.15 m/s and 2.44 m/s, and pressures of at least 140 kPa?

    e)   Would the subdivision have enough water if only one connection were used? If so, which one?

    f)   What do you think are some possible pitfalls of modeling two connections to existing mains within the same system, as opposed to modeling back to the water source?

7.   Use the pipe sizes given in the table below for the subdivision in Problem 6.

Pipe Information for Problem 7

Pipe Label	Diameter (mm)
P-1	200
P-2	150
P-3	150
P-4	150
P-5	150
P-6	150
P-7	150
P-8	150
P-9	150

City ordinances require the following:

The pressure at the fire flow discharge and at other points in the distribution system cannot fall below 125 kPa during a fire flow of 34 l/s. (Hint: The total flow at the fire flow node does not need to include the baseline demand.)

    a)   If a residential fire occurs at J-7, would the current system be able to meet the fire flow requirements set by the city?

    b)   If not, what can be done to increase the available flow to provide adequate fire flow to that hydrant?

    c)   If a fire flow is placed at J-4, does the system meet the requirements with the proposed improvements? Without the proposed improvements?

8.   A local water company is concerned with the water quality within its water distribution network. They want to determine the age and the chlorine concentration of the water as it exits the system at different junctions. The water surface at the reservoir is 70 m.

Chlorine is injected into the system at the source of flow, R-1, at a concentration of 1 mg/l. It has been determined through a series of bottle tests that the average bulk reaction rate of the chlorine in the system (including all pipes and tanks) is approximately –0.5 /day.

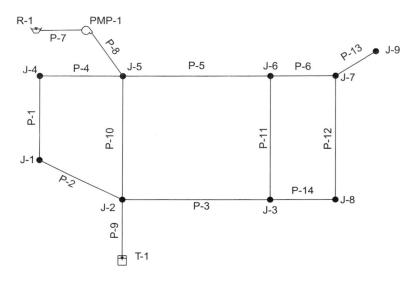

Schematic for Problem 8

The cylindrical tank has a diameter of 15 m. The base and minimum elevations are 99 m. The maximum elevation is 104 m, and the initial elevation is 103.4 m.

Pump Information for Problem 8

Head (m)	Discharge (l/min)	Controls
40	0	Off if node T-1 above 103.5 m
35	3,000	
24	6,000	On if node T-1 below 100.5 m

Stepwise Demand Pattern Data for Problem 8

Time from Start (hr)	Multiplier	Time from Start (hr)	Multiplier
0	0.80	13	1.30
1	0.60	14	1.40
2	0.50	15	1.50
3	0.50	16	1.60
4	0.55	17	1.80
5	0.60	18	1.80
6	0.80	19	1.40
7	1.10	20	1.20
8	1.50	21	1.00
9	1.40	22	0.90
10	1.30	23	0.80
11	1.40	24	0.80
12	1.40		

Junction Data for Problem 8

Junction	Elevation (m)	Demand (l/min)
J-1	73	151
J-2	67	227
J-3	81	229
J-4	56	219
J-5	67	215
J-6	73	219
J-7	55	215
J-8	84	180
J-9	88	151

Pipe Data for Problem 8

Pipe	Length (m)	Diameter (mm)	Roughness
P-1	300	200	130
P-2	305	200	130
P-3	300	200	130
P-4	200	200	130
P-5	300	300	130
P-6	200	200	130
P-7	1	300	130
P-8	5,000	300	130
P-9	300	300	130
P-10	500	200	130
P-11	500	200	130
P-12	500	200	130
P-13	150	150	130
P-14	200	200	130

a) Perform an age analysis on the system using a duration of 300 hrs and a time step of 2 hrs. Fill in the results table, indicating the maximum water age at each junction and tank after the system reaches equilibrium (a pattern of average water age vs. time becomes evident). What point in the system generally has the oldest water? Explain why the water is oldest at this location.

b) Perform a constituent analysis using the same duration and time step as in part (a). Fill in the results table, indicating the minimum chlorine concentration for each junction and tank after the system has reached equilibrium (a pattern of concentration versus time becomes evident). What point in the system has the lowest chlorine concentration? Explain why the chlorine residual is lowest at this location.

Results Table for Problem 8

Junction	J-1	J-2	J-3	J-4	J-5	J-6	J-7	J-8	J-9	T-1
Age (hours)										
Chlorine Concentration (mg/l)										

c) From the above table and graphs of demand, age, and concentration versus time generated within WaterCAD, determine the following correlations:

1) Age and chlorine concentration

2) Demand and chlorine concentration at a junction

3) Demand and water age at a junction

d) Why is it necessary to run the model for such a long time? Do you feel that 300 hours is too long or too short a time period for testing the model? Why?

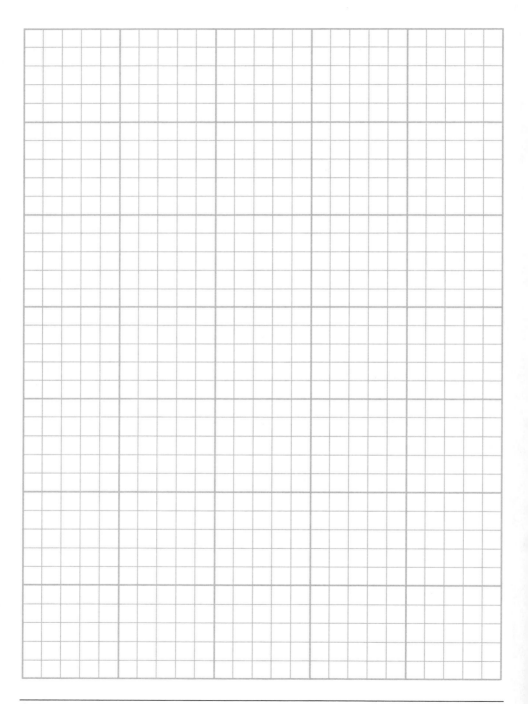

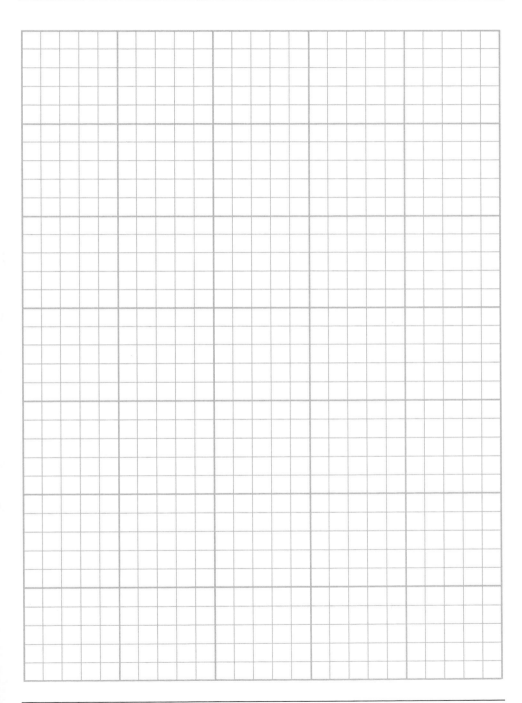

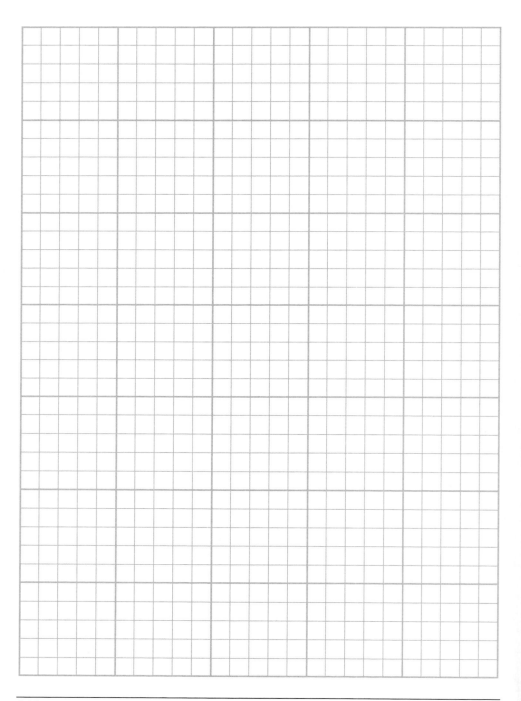

Sanitary Sewer Design

7.1 Sanitary Sewer Systems

Sanitary sewers collect wastewater from its sources and transport it to a treatment facility. Sanitary sewers are intended to convey only wastewater. However, their design must allow for the infiltration of groundwater that invariably occurs in sewers. Older systems that convey both sanitary wastes and stormwater are referred to as *combined sewers*.

Wherever practicable, sewers are gravity flow systems. When the natural slopes are not sufficient to convey flow, a combination of gravity and pressure flow systems is used. The gravity sewer transports flow to a collection point such as a wet well. The wastewater is pumped from the wet well through a force main over some obstruction or hill to another gravity sewer, or directly to a wastewater treatment facility.

The hydraulics in the gravity portion of a sanitary sewer are analyzed with the same techniques used in storm sewers hydraulics, as discussed in Section 1.6 and in Chapter 3. When the flow depth is constant, Manning's equation is used. When obstructions or changes in pipe slope exist, the gradually varied flow analysis procedure presented in Section 3.6 is applied.

The pressure portion of the sanitary sewer is analyzed in the same manner as a water distribution system, as discussed in Chapter 6. The primary difference is that flow is generally withdrawn from a water distribution network, whereas in a sewer system, flow is injected into force mains.

In this chapter, a brief introduction to sanitary sewer design is presented. The use of SewerCAD to assist in the design process is demonstrated. More comprehensive reviews of sewer design may be found elsewhere (Tchobanoglous, 1981, or WEF, 1981). Additional discussion on the development and application of hydraulic sewer models is presented in *Sanitary Sewer Modeling* (Haestad Press, 2002).

Common Sanitary Sewer Elements

Although all of the various types of sewer appurtenances and structures are too numerous to mention in this text, the most commonly modeled sanitary sewer elements include:

- **Manholes:** Manholes provide access for maintenance of a sanitary sewer. They are generally located at regular intervals (as dictated by local ordinances), at places where pipe characteristics such as diameter and slope change, and at places where several pipelines join. In sanitary sewer models, such as SewerCAD, manholes also represent points where loads enter the system.

- **Junction chambers:** Junction chambers are underground structures built at points in the sewer where multiple pipes join. Junction chambers are rarely used in sanitary sewers because their underground construction makes access and maintenance difficult.

- **Wet wells:** Wet wells are structures that collect and store wastewater until it is pumped into force mains for transport to another gravity system or to a wastewater treatment facility. Wet wells are generally designed to minimize wastewater retention time in order to prevent odors and the buildup of gases, while allowing the pumps to cycle in an efficient manner.

- **Pumps and pump stations:** Pumps, as discussed in Chapter 6, add head to flow as it passes through the sanitary sewer system.

- **Pressure junctions:** Pressure junctions represent points in the pressure system where pressure pipes are joined together. They also represent points where loads directly enter a force main, or points where the modeler wishes to know a pressure.

- **Pipes:** Pipes are conduits through which flow is transferred either by the influence of gravity or by energy supplied from pumping stations. The most common pipe section shapes in a gravity system are circular, box (rectangular), arched, elliptical, and egg-shaped. In pressure systems, pipes are usually circular. Pressurized sewer pipes are commonly referred to as *force mains*.

- **Regulators:** When stormwater loads cause flows in sewers to exceed capacity, control devices are used to divert flows. These devices are called *regulators.* They split the flow between an interceptor sewer and an overflow. Possible destinations for controlled releases include wet wells, temporary storage basins, treatment facilities, parallel relief sewers, or receiving waters.

7.2 Loading

Sanitary sewer loads are divided into two categories: sanitary loads and wet-weather loads.

- *Sanitary loads (Dry-weather loads)* result from human activity and are not weather dependent. Common sources of sanitary loads are various residential, commercial, recreational, and industrial uses.

- **Wet-weather loads** are related to rainfall activity such as groundwater infiltration (water leaking into a pipe through cracks, joints, and defects) and structure inflow (surface water entering a structure through openings around the cover, or due to a missing cover).

Time-based loads can be classified as either wet-weather or sanitary loads, and they may have hydrograph- or pattern-based formats.

Common Load Types

Two loading types can be applied as either wet-weather or sanitary loads. They are:

- Hydrographs
- Pattern loads

Hydrographs

Flow versus time data, also known as a hydrograph, can be entered as a load. The hydrograph will then be directly added to any other loads coming to that point, and then routed downstream.

In the case of wet-weather loading, the hydrograph may reflect infiltration or inflow resulting from an actual or design storm event. Sanitary load hydrographs show the variation in customer loading over time, such as over the course of a typical day. An example of a hydrograph is shown in Figure 7-1. Hydrographs may be obtained from measurements collected in a combined sewer during a rainfall event or they may be developed using the hydrologic procedures described in Chapter 2.

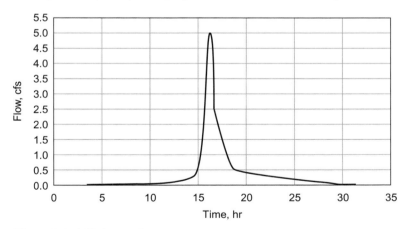

Figure 7-1: A Hydrograph

During a steady-state analysis, a hydrograph load must be converted into an instantaneous load. There are several ways of choosing an appropriate instantaneous load, and the method chosen depends on the purpose of the analysis. For instance, the hydrograph peak flow, average flow, or minimum flow may be used. If other data are used to generate steady-state loading, the hydrograph may be disregarded entirely.

Pattern Loads

A pattern load is comprised of a base load and an associated loading *pattern*. The pattern is a series of multipliers relating sanitary sewer loading to time, and it allows the user to automatically apply time-variable changes within the system.

Different categories of users, such as residential or industrial customers, may be assigned different patterns to accurately reflect their particular load variations. A *diurnal curve* is a type of pattern that describes change in loading over the course of a daily cycle. A dry-weather diurnal curve for sanitary loading often resembles the diurnal curve for water use at the same location (see Section 6.1), reflecting times when people are using more and less water than average.

Patterns are typically based on a multiplication factor versus time relationship, in which a multiplication factor of 1.0 represents the base value (usually the average value). This relationship can be expressed:

$$Q_t = A_t \times Q_{Base}$$

where Q_t = Load at time t
A_t = Multiplier for time t
Q_{Base} = Baseline load

For the residential usage, diurnal curve in Figure 7-2, we see that there is a peak in the diurnal curve in the morning, another slight peak around noon, and a third peak in the evening. During the nighttime hours, the pattern reflects the relative inactivity of the system. (Note that this curve is conceptual and should not be construed as representative of any particular network.)

As explained in Chapter 6, there are two basic forms for representing a pattern: stepwise and continuous. A *stepwise pattern* is one that assumes a constant level of usage over a period of time, and then jumps instantaneously to another level where it again remains steady until the next jump. A *continuous pattern* is one for which several points in the pattern are known and sections in between are transitional, resulting in a smoother pattern. For the continuous pattern in Figure 7-2, the magnitude and slope of the pattern at the start and end times are the same — a continuity that is recommended for patterns that repeat.

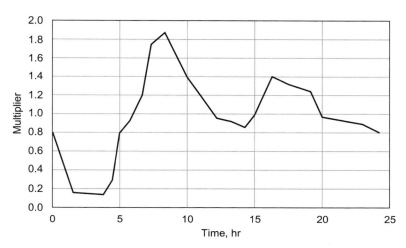

Figure 7-2: An example of a diurnal pattern for sanitary loading

Sanitary Unit Loading

Ideally, sanitary loads are based on data measured at individual loading points throughout the sewer system. In other words, the load from each source is modeled as a direct flow into the sewer system. However, data with this level of detail are not typically available. Instead, wastewater sources are grouped together, and average loads are computed based on land usage or the activities of the population generating the load.

For example, consider a small, middle-class subdivision that houses approximately 50 people. Studies have shown that, on average, a resident of middle class housing generates 280 l/day (74 gpd) of wastewater. Thus, the average load entering the sewer system at this subdivision is 14,000 l/d (3,700 gpd).

Table 7-1 Typical unit sanitary loads from different sources (Tchobanoglous, 1981)

Unit Sanitary Load	Loading Unit	Base Load (l/d per Loading Unit)
Airport	Passenger	10
Apartment	Resident	260
Automobile Service	Employee	50
Bar	Customer	8
Cabin Resort	Guest	160
Campground	Guest	120
Coffee Shop	Guest	20
Department Store	Toilet Room	2000
Dormitory	Guest	150
Home (Average)	Resident	280
Home (Better)	Resident	310
Home (Luxury)	Resident	380
Hospital (Medical)	Bed	650
Hotel	Employee	40
Prison	Inmate	450
Restaurant	Meal	10
School (Large)	Student	80
School (Medium)	Student	60
School (Small)	Student	40
Swimming Pool	Employee	40
Shopping Center	Parking Space	4

Sanitary loads are typically estimated based on a number of contributing units, with a specified average load per unit (such as 260 l/d per apartment resident). The unit is typically a measure of population such as *residents* or *employees*; however, loads can also be based on other criteria such as *contributing area* or user-defined counts of items indicative of loading behavior. See Table 7-1 for a list of standard loading sources and their associated average base loads.

Extreme Flow Factors

Sewer design and analysis generally consider a variety of loading conditions, such as minimum, average, and peak conditions. Base (average) sanitary loads are transformed into minimum or peak loads using an **Extreme Flow Factor** method (Figure 7-3).

The most common type of Extreme Flow Factor (EFF) is the Variable Peaking Factor (PF). In this method, a computed EFF is multiplied by the specified base flow.

$$Q_{peak} = Q_{base} \times EFF$$

where Q_{peak} =   transformed flow (l/d, gpd)
           Q_{base} =   base flow (l/d, gpd)
           EFF =   extreme Flow Factor (unitless)

Common Variable Peaking Factors (PF)

Some of the most common variable peaking factor calculation methods are:

- **Babbitt** (Babbitt, 1958)

$$PF = \frac{5.0}{\left(\dfrac{P}{1000}\right)^{0.2}}$$

     where P = contributing population

- **Harmon** (Harmon, 1918)

$$PF = 1.0 + \frac{14.0}{4.0 + \left(\dfrac{P}{1000}\right)^{0.5}}$$

- **Ten States Standard** (Great Lakes Upper Mississippi River Board, 1978)

$$PF = \frac{18 + \sqrt{\dfrac{P}{1000}}}{4 + \sqrt{\dfrac{P}{1000}}}$$

- **Federov** (Jakovlev, 1975)

$$PF = \frac{2.69}{Q^{0.121}}$$

     where Q = base sanitary flow (l/s)

For population-based peaking factor methods, the peaking factor decreases as the population increases. A larger population means that peak loads from different sources are likely to occur in a more staggered manner. Thus, the peak loads are likely to be less pronounced compared to the average loading rate. In systems servicing smaller populations, peak loads from different sources are more likely to coincide, causing more pronounced differences in average loading rates. The graph in Figure 7-3 shows how the extreme flow factor decreases with increasing population when applying the Ten States Standard.

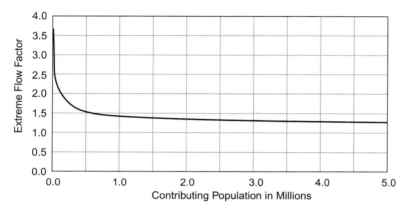

Figure 7-3: EFF versus contributing population, from the Ten States Standard

Example 7-1: Determining Peak Sanitary Loads

A shopping center and a residential subdivision of average and luxury homes load a gravity sanitary sewer. The shopping center has 100 parking spaces. 80 people live in the "average" housing, whereas 30 people live in the "luxury" housing. What is the average base load contributing to the sanitary sewer at this point? What would be an approximate peak flow applied to the system? The local ordinance dictates that the Harmon method must be applied to peak all population-based unit sanitary loads, whereas a constant peaking factor of 2 should be applied to all non-population-based loads.

Solution

First, to get the average base load, find the amount of load per unit for the three loading categories mentioned in Table 7-1. Then, multiply this unit flow by the number of units.

Shopping Center	100	Parking Spaces	×	4 l/(d-space)	=	400 l/d
Average Housing	80	Residents	×	280 l/(d-resident)	=	22,400 l/d
Luxury Housing	30	Residents	×	380 l/(d-resident)	=	11,400 l/d
				Total Base Flow	=	34,200 l/d

Apply Harmon's method to find the peaking factor for the residential population of 80 residents of "average" housing and 30 residents of "luxury" housing.

- Assuming that both population-based loads have similar peaking behavior, sum the two populations:

    80 Residents of Average Housing + 30 Residents of Luxury Housing = 110 Residents

- Apply the Harmon method using a contributing population of 110:

$$PF = 1.0 + \frac{14}{4 + \left(\frac{110}{1000}\right)^{0.5}} = 4.23$$

- Apply this peaking factor to the base loads calculated from the subdivision. Then, apply the given peaking factor of 2 to the load derived from the shopping center to compute the approximate peak flow.

$$4.23 \times (22{,}400 \text{ l/d} + 11{,}400 \text{ l/d}) + 2 \times 400 \text{ l/d} = 144{,}000 \text{ l/d}$$

Wet-Weather Loading

Wet-weather loading represents the intrusion of ground and surface water into the sewer system, and is divided into two components: infiltration and inflow. *Infiltration* represents groundwater entering into pipes through cracks, holes, and other defects. *Inflow* represents wet-weather flow that enters the sewer through manhole covers, roof drains, catch basins, sump pumps, and so forth. Collectively, these flows are referred to as *I/I*. It is important to minimize intrusion of rain water into the sewer system because of the cost of treating the added flow. Also, wet-weather loads increase the potential for overloading the system, which causes flow to back up into houses or overflow into the environment.

Infiltration causes noticeable increases in sewer flow, especially after rainstorms and subsequent rises in the groundwater table. Sewer pipes placed in low areas, such as near creek beds, are more subject to infiltration than those placed in higher ground because they are more likely to be located below the water table. Older sanitary sewers are more susceptible to infiltration than newer sewer systems because modern techniques and materials used in newer systems can generally prevent or greatly reduce infiltration.

Infiltration at an individual pipe is generally hard to quantify. Instead, infiltration is estimated for the whole system or a portion of the system. This global infiltration is then distributed to individual pipes using one of the following methods:

- Proportional to pipe length
- Proportional to pipe diameter/length
- Proportional to pipe surface area
- Proportional to some user defined count (for example, number of defects in the pipe)

Inflows are unwanted flows entering from the surface and are modeled based on estimates or requirements from local or state regulatory agencies. Like infiltration, inflows can be quite significant and can vary considerably depending on the depth of runoff, the size of the manhole cover, and the number of openings in the manhole cover.

7.3   Extended-Period Simulations

Overview

An *Extended-Period Simulation (EPS)* models how a sewer network will behave over time. This type of analysis allows the user to model how wet wells fill and drain; pumps toggle on and off; and pressures, hydraulic grades, and flow rates change in response to variable loading conditions and automatic control strategies formulated by the modeler. EPS is a useful tool for assessing the hydraulic performance of alternative pump and wet well sizes.

The SewerCAD algorithm proceeds in a general downstream direction towards the outfall, following the procedure described here:

1. The analysis begins in the gravity portion of the network. The hydrographs enter the gravity system and are successively routed and summed as the flows approach the downstream wet well or outfall. Ultimately, the total inflow hydrograph to the wet well is determined.

2. Knowing the inflow into the wet well, the pressure calculations for the force main system bounded by the wet well are performed. In addition to flow velocities and pressures, the levels in the wet well over time are determined.

3. The calculation then returns to the gravity portion of the network discussed in step 1. The hydraulics and HGL profiles are calculated throughout the gravity system for each time step using the known level of the wet well as the boundary condition for the backwater analysis.

The process repeats, continuing through the system downstream of the pressure network until an outlet is reached.

Routing Overview

As a hydrograph is routed through a conduit, it undergoes changes in shape and temporal distribution caused by translation and storage effects.

SewerCAD uses one of two methods to determine the shape and distribution of a hydrograph routed through a gravity pipe.

- Convex routing
- Weighted translation routing

Convex Routing

The underlying assumptions of the **convex routing method** are that the routed outflow for a time step is based on the inflow and outflow for the previous time step, and that the flow does not back up in the pipe (that is, no reverse flow or reduced flow due to tailwater effects exists). Each outflow ordinate is calculated as:

$$O_{t+\Delta t} = cI_t + (1-c)O_t$$

where
$O_{t+\Delta t}$ = outflow at time $t + \Delta t$
t = current time (s, min)
Δt = hydrologic time step (s, min)
c = convex routing coefficient
I_t = inflow at time t (l/s, gpm)
O_t = outflow at time t (l/s, gpm)

The convex routing coefficient is essentially a ratio of the hydrologic time step and representative flow travel time through the pipe, and is calculated as follows:

$$c = \Delta t \frac{V}{L} = \frac{\Delta t}{t_t}$$

where
Δt = hydrologic time step (s)
t_t = travel time (s)
V = velocity established for representative flow (m/s, ft/s)
L = length of pipe (m, ft)

In SewerCAD, the velocity used to calculate the coefficient is either the normal velocity or full velocity generated for a user-specified percentage of the peak of the inflow hydrograph. In other words, if the percentage of the peak flow is greater than the capacity of the pipe, the full-flow velocity is used. If the percentage of the peak flow is less than the pipe capacity, the flow velocity for normal depth is used.

The higher the percentage of flow, the faster the velocity used to calculate the convex routing coefficient, and the closer the routed hydrograph will be to a pure translation of the inflow hydrograph.

The user-specified percentage can be modified in the calculation options. A typical value is around 75 percent, but this value may be modified for oddly shaped hydrographs with sharp, uncharacteristic peaks or for calibration purposes.

Weighted Translation Routing

The convex routing method is only valid when the convex routing coefficient, c, is less than 1 or when the hydrologic time step is less than the calculated travel time. For certain cases in which the travel time exceeds the hydrologic time step, SewerCAD automatically uses an alternative method of routing called weighted translation routing.

Each ordinate of the outflow hydrograph is derived from a weighted average of the ordinates for the current and previous time steps of the inflow hydrograph. The weights are calculated based on the convex routing coefficient.

Each ordinate of the outflow hydrograph is calculated as follows:

$$O_t = \frac{1}{c}I_{t-\Delta t} + \left(1 - \frac{1}{c}\right)I_t$$

where O_t = outflow at current time step (l/s, gpm)
  c = convex Routing coefficient
  $I_{t-\Delta t}$ = inflow at previous time step (l/s, gpm)
  I_t = inflow at current time step (l/s, gpm)

Hydrologic and Hydraulic Time Steps

SewerCAD uses two distinct time steps when running an Extended Period Simulation.

- **Hydrologic Time Step:** This time step is used to calculate the routed hydrographs and represents the time increment of all hydrographs generated during the analysis. The hydrologic time step is also used as the calculation increment for the pressure calculations.

- **Hydraulic Time Step:** This time step represents how often the hydraulic calculations are performed for gravity flow. Flows are interpolated from the previously generated hydrographs using the hydraulic time step, and are then used to perform the gradually varied flow analysis for that time step.

The hydrologic time step should be less than or equal to the hydraulic time step, and the hydraulic time step should be a multiple of the hydrologic time step.

7.4 SewerCAD

What Does SewerCAD Do?

SewerCAD is a powerful, easy-to-use program for the design and analysis of wastewater collection systems. SewerCAD's intuitive graphical interface and powerful data exchange capabilities make it easy to develop and load complex models of combined gravity and pressure networks. Using SewerCAD, you can design and analyze the gravity portion of the system according to either a gradually varied flow calculation or a standard capacity analysis.

The powerful automatic design capabilities of SewerCAD allow you to design the system based on user-defined constraints for velocity, cover, and slope. You can also design for partially full pipes, multiple parallel sections, maximum section size, invert/crown-matching criteria, and the allowance of drop structures. You can disable the design feature on a pipe-by-pipe basis, to design all or only a portion of your system.

SewerCAD's powerful loading model provides complete support for all types of sanitary and wet-weather loads. The unit sanitary load library is completely user-customizable and supports population, area, discharge, and count-based sanitary loads, as well as hydrographs and load patterns. Wet-weather inflow can also be added to the model as instantaneous loads, hydrographs, or base loads with associated patterns. Infiltration can be computed based on pipe length, pipe diameter/length, pipe surface area, or unit count. Loads are peaked according to a peaking factor or extreme flow factor equations that you select from a user-customizable extreme flow factor library.

How Can You Use SewerCAD?

You can use SewerCAD to design new systems and analyze the performance of existing systems. SewerCAD's intuitive graphical editor and powerful scenario management capabilities facilitate the process of analyzing a large number of design alternatives and finding potential problems in an existing system. In summary, SewerCAD's sophisticated modeling techniques enable you to:

- Design and analyze multiple sanitary sewer networks in a single project
- Examine your system using SewerCAD's gradually varied flow algorithms or a standard capacity analysis
- Design the system using SewerCAD's automatic, constraint-based design
- Load your model based on contributing population, service area, total sanitary flow, or your own loading type
- Peak your loads using Babbitt's, Harmon's, Ten State, and Federov's equations, or use your own formulas or tables
- Calculate infiltration based on pipe length, diameter, surface area, length/diameter or user-defined data
- Generate plan and profile plots of a network
- Perform extended-period simulations that include time-variable loads and hydrologic routing
- Animate plans and profiles showing sanitary sewer system performance over time

The theory and background used in SewerCAD are presented in this chapter and in the SewerCAD online help system. Additional information on the Student and Professional versions of SewerCAD and options that are available can be found in Appendix A.

SewerCAD can analyze complex sewage collection systems under a variety of loading conditions. SewerCAD's powerful loading capabilities can be used to track system response to an unlimited range of sanitary and wet-weather loading combinations. It can be used for:

- Pipe sizing
- Pump sizing
- Master planning

- Operational studies
- Rehabilitation studies

7.5 Tutorial Examples

Tutorial 1 – Pump Size for Peak Flows

The following example provides step-by-step instructions for solving a simple problem using SewerCAD (included on the CD-ROM that accompanies this textbook).

Problem Statement

Figure 7-4 shows a skeletonized sanitary sewer system. A circular, gravity sewer main, P-1, empties into wet well WW-1. From the wet well, the wastewater is pumped over a hill to a treatment plant at 0-1 through force mains FM-2 and FM-3.

The main line runs through an area with a high water table, and it has been determined that infiltration occurs at a rate of 20 l/d per meter of pipe. It has also been determined that Babbitt's method best correlates the base loads listed below with the loading peaks in the system. The pipe, pump, wet well, and loading data are given in the following tables.

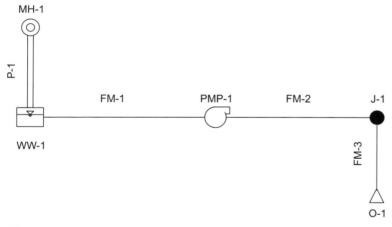

Figure 7-4: Schematic of Sewer used in the Example Problem

Node Data for Tutorial Problem

Element	Type	Element Characteristics	
MH-1	Manhole	Ground Elevation	101.0 m
		Rim Elevation	101.0 m
		Sump Elevation	99.3 m
		Structure Diameter	1.0 m
WW-1	Wet Well	Ground Elevation	100.0 m
		Section Type	Constant Area – Circular
		Maximum Elevation	100.0 m
		Alarm Elevation	99.0 m
		Initial Elevation	96.5 m
		Minimum Elevation	96.0 m
		Base Elevation	96.0 m
		Diameter	4.0 m
PMP-1	Pump	Elevation	96.25 m
		Pump Type	Standard (3-Point)
		Shutoff Head/Discharge	22.0 m 0 m³/min
		Design Head/Discharge	15.0 m 2.5 m³/min
		Max Operating Head/Discharge	9.0 m 4.0 m³/min
J-1	Pressure Junction	Elevation	105.0 m
O-1	Outlet	Ground Elevation	107.5 m
		Rim Elevation	107.5 m
		Sump Elevation	106.0 m
		Tailwater Condition	Free Outfall

Pipe Data for Tutorial Problem

Pipe	Pipe Type	Length (m)	Diameter (mm)	Material	Upstream Invert (m)	Downstream Invert (m)
P-1	Gravity	150	200	Concrete $n = 0.012$	99.35	97.50
FM-1	Force Main	1	200	PVC $C = 150$	96.00	97.25
FM-2	Force Main	215	200	PVC $C = 150$	96.25	105.00
FM-3	Force Main	200	200	PVC $C = 150$	105.00	107.00

Loading Data for Tutorial Problem

Node	Unit Sanitary Load	Loading Unit Count	Loading Unit
MH-1	Apartment	600	Resident
	Apartment Resort	500	Guest
	Home (Luxury)	200	Resident
WW-1	Home (Average)	2000	Resident

Questions

a) What is the total sanitary flow (dry weather flow) exiting the system? What is the total flow?

b) Does the pump have adequate capacity for this system? How can you tell?

c) What is the full-flow capacity of the gravity pipe P-1? By how much is this capacity being exceeded?

Solution

Project Setup Wizard

- When you start SewerCAD, you should be prompted with the Welcome to SewerCAD dialog. From this dialog, you can access the tutorials, open existing projects, and create new ones. Select **Create New Project**, provide a filename, and click **Save**.

  If the Welcome to SewerCAD dialog does not appear, SewerCAD is set to **Hide Welcome Dialog on startup**. To start a new project, select **New** from the **File** menu, enter a filename, and click **Save**. (You can change from Hide Welcome Dialog mode to Show Welcome Dialog mode in the Global Options dialog, which is accessible by selecting **Options** from the **Tools** menu.)

- When you provide a filename, the **Project Setup Wizard** appears. Add a project title and any comments, and then click **Next**.

- In the second screen of the Project Setup Wizard, select **Manning's Formula** as the Gravity Friction Method and select **Hazen-Williams Formula** as the Pressure Friction Method. Click **Next**.

- In the third screen of the Project Setup Wizard, select **Schematic** as the Drawing Scale for the project. This option allows you to define the lengths for the pipes without having to worry about scale and spatial placement on the x-y plane. Click **Next**.

  Note: If this screen does not show SI units, click **Cancel** to exit the Project Setup wizard and reset the units to SI. Select **Options** from the **Tools** menu on the main drawing screen and if necessary, change the **Unit System** field (under the **Global** tab) to **System International**. Click **OK** to exit the **Global Options** dialog. On changing the unit click Yes when prompted to confirm the change. Begin the Project Setup wizard again starting with paragraph two of the first bullet.

- Click **Finished**.

Laying Out the System

- You do not have to lay out the sanitary sewer network exactly as shown in the problem statement. For now, just roughly sketch the schematic by following the instructions below.

- Click the **Pipe Layout** ▦ button in the vertical toolbar on the left side of the screen.

- To place manhole MH-1, click the left mouse button in the workspace.

- To place the wet well WW-1, move the cursor below the manhole and click the right mouse button. Select **Wet Well** from the pop-up menu, and then click the left mouse button. Notice that the cursor has changed to the wet well icon. Position the cursor where you want to place the wet well and click the left mouse button to insert it. Gravity pipe P-1 will automatically be placed between MH-1 and WW-1.

- Place the pump PMP-1 by right-clicking, selecting **Pump** from the pop-up menu, and left-clicking to place it in the model. Note that force main FM-1 was created automatically between WW-1 and PMP-1. SewerCAD will automatically create either a gravity pipe or a force main (pressure pipe), depending on the type of end nodes that are present.

- Lay out pressure junction J-1 and outlet O-1 in exactly the same way.

- Except for the scale, your schematic should look roughly like the one given in Figure 7-4.

Data Entry

- Double-click manhole MH-1. Under the **General** tab, enter the ground elevation, sump elevation, and the structure diameter as given in the problem statement. Note that you do not have to enter the rim elevation if the box entitled **Set Rim to Ground Elevation** has been checked.

- Click the **Loading** tab at the top of the Manhole dialog. Select the **Add** button beside the Sanitary (Dry-Weather) Flow section. Select **Unit Load – Unit Type & Count** for the Load Definition and click **OK**. Select **Apartment** from the **Unit Sanitary (Dry Weather) Load** pull-down menu and enter **600** as the number of apartment residents to the Loading Unit Count. Click **OK**. Insert data for the remaining two unit loads for manhole MH-1 in the same way.

- Double-click wet well **WW-1**. Under the General tab, enter the ground elevation. Under the Section tab, select **Constant Area** from the pull-down menu in the Section field. Select **Circular** from the pull-down menu in the Cross Section field. Enter a wet well diameter of **4 m**. Finally, enter the maximum, alarm, initial, minimum, and base elevations as given in the problem statement. Enter these as elevations, not levels.

- Select the **Loading** tab at the top of the Wet Well dialog. Enter in the loading data as you did for manhole MH-1. Click **OK** to exit the dialog.

- Double-click pump PMP-1. Under the General tab, enter the pump's elevation of **96.25 m**. Next, select **Standard (3 Point)** from the pull-down menu in the Pump Type field. Then, enter in the pump curve data as given in the problem statement. Click **OK** to exit the dialog.

- Double-click pressure junction **J-1** to edit its properties. Enter the junction's elevation and click **OK** to exit the dialog.

- Double-click outlet **O-1**. Enter the ground elevation and sump elevation. Also, select **Free Outfall** from the list of available tailwater conditions. As with the manhole, if the box entitled **Set Rim to Ground Elevation** has been checked, you do not have to enter the rim elevation because it is automatically set to the ground elevation. Click **OK** to exit the dialog.

- Double-click gravity pipe P-1. Enter the upstream and downstream inverts in the appropriate fields. Enter the length in the **Length** field. Select **Circular** from the pull-down menu in the **Section Shape** field. Select **Concrete** from the pull-down menu in the **Material** field. Change the Manning's n-value from 0.013 to 0.012. Finally, select **200 mm** from the **Section Size** field.

- Select the **Infiltration** tab at the top of the Gravity Pipe dialog. Set the **Infiltration Type** to **Pipe Length**. Select an **Infiltration Loading Unit** of m. Enter the appropriate infiltration rate per unit length per day in the **Infiltration Rate per Loading Unit** field. Click **OK** to exit the dialog.

- Double-click force main **FM-1** to edit its properties. Enter the diameter and select the material type as given in the problem statement. Enter the upstream invert and the length. If the **Set Invert to Upstream Structure** box is checked, you will not have to enter the upstream invert for this problem. Also note that invert elevations are not editable if the upstream or downstream element is a pump or a pressure junction. In such cases, the invert elevation is set equal to the pump or pressure junction elevation. Click **OK**.

- Enter the data for FM-2 and FM-3 in the same way.

- To apply a peaking factor method for each of the different unit sanitary loads used in the project, select **Extreme Flow** from the **Analysis** menu at the top of the screen. Highlight the extreme flow setup labeled *Base Extreme Flow Setup* and click **Edit**. Apply the appropriate extreme flow method as dictated by the problem by selecting the method from the pull-down menu under the Extreme Flow Method column for each of the unit sanitary loads in the list. (Hint: Right-click the column heading and choose **Global Edit** to change all the rows simultaneously.) Click **OK** to exit the dialog. Click **OK** to exit the Extreme Flow Setup Manager.

- Now that all input data has been entered, save the project file to disk by choosing **Save** from the **File** menu. It is a good idea to periodically save your work in this way.

Running the Model

- Click the **GO** button in the toolbar at the top of the SewerCAD window.

- Under the Calculation tab, make sure that the Calculation Type is set to **Steady State**. Also, make sure that the **Design** box is unchecked, so that SewerCAD does not automatically design the system. Select **Base Extreme Flow Setup** from the pull-down menu in the **Extreme Flow Setup** field.

- Before running the model, click the **Check Data** button. The input data is checked for any problems that will prevent the model from running. There should not be any problems, so click **OK** to return to the dialog. If there are problems, you can view them by selecting the **Results** tab.

- Click **GO** to run the model. A dialog box displaying the results should appear with a green light displayed on the **Results** tab. The green light indicates a successful run. Yellow and red lights indicate warnings and problems, respectively.

PART (a):   *What is the total sanitary flow (dry weather flow) exiting the system? What is the total flow?*

Answer

To check the total sanitary flow exiting the system, double-click on the outlet O-1. In the **Flow Summary** section of the dialog the Total Sanitary Flow (dry weather only) equals 3,552,007 l/d. This is the peak sanitary flow. The Total Flow, which includes wet-weather flow, equals 3,555,007 l/d. The difference between the two values is caused by the infiltration along pipe P-1.

PART (b):   *Does the pump have adequate capacity for this system? How can you tell?*

Answer

Double-click **PMP-1**. At 2.78 m^3/min the pump is operating near its design point of 2.50 m^3/min, , which is greater than the total flow to the wet well of 2.47 m^3/min. The pump capacity is adequate. Note that a pump station would typically consist of redundant pumps to allow for servicing.

PART (c):   *What is the full flow capacity of the gravity pipe, P-1? How much excess capacity is there, or by how much is the capacity of the pipe being exceeded?*

Answer

Double-click gravity pipe **P-1**. In the Hydraulic Summary section, find that the pipe has a full capacity of 3,556,744 l/d. The excess full capacity is 1,931,159 l/d.

Tutorial 2 – 24-Hour Simulation of Dry Weather Flow

Problem Statement

In this example, the EPS feature of SewerCAD will be used to simulate flows through the sewer over a 24-hour period. The Scenario Manager will be used to specify different loadings to the network from Tutorial 1. The 24-hour diurnal pattern will be applied to the sanitary flows. The multiplier is used to convert average daily flows to hourly flows.

Data for Diurnal Sanitary Loads

Hour	Multiplier	Hour	Multiplier	Hour	Multiplier	Hour	Multiplier
1	0.85	7	0.87	13	1.21	19	1.05
2	0.72	8	1.08	14	1.13	20	1.11
3	0.56	9	1.32	15	1.06	21	1.19
4	0.52	10	1.42	16	0.95	22	1.05
5	0.43	11	1.61	17	0.84	23	1.06
6	0.52	12	1.49	18	0.88	24	1.00

a) During an average day, how many times does the pump turn on and off?

b) What is the maximum rate of pumping?

The same sewer system designed in Tutorial 1 will be used.

Solution

Set Pump Controls

- The user must specify how the pump operates. This is done by specifying the levels in WW-1 that trigger the pump to turn on and off. Select the pump by double-clicking **PMP-1**. Select the **Controls** tab.

- To add a pump "on" setting, click the **Add** button, set the Control Type to **Status** and the Pump Status to **On**. The Condition should be set to **node,** the Node should be set to **WW-1,** the comparison to **Above**, and the elevation to **98.0 m.** Click **OK**.

- To add a pump "off" setting, click the **Add** button, set the Control Type to **Status,** and set the Pump Status to **Off**. The Condition should be set to **node**, the Node should be set to **WW-1,** the Comparison to **Below**, and the Elevation to **96.5.** Click **OK** twice to close the pump dialog.

Set Up the EPS Scenario

- Open Scenario Manager by selecting **Scenarios** from the **Analysis** drop-down menu.

- Click the **Scenario Wizard** button and enter **24 hr Cycle** as the name of the scenario. Then click **Next**.

- Select **Base** as the scenario to serve as the basis for the 24 hr Cycle scenario. Then click **Next**.

- The Calculation Type is **Extended Period.** Use the default settings for Duration (**24 hours**), Hydrologic Time Step (**0.10 hour**), and Hydraulic Time Step (**1.0 hour**). For the Pattern Setup option, click the ellipsis button (**...**). The Pattern Setup Manager will appear. Click **Add** and enter **24 hour pattern** for the name of the pattern.

- In the Pattern Setup table, add the new diurnal pattern to each of the unit loads. On the Apartment row in the Diurnal Pattern column, click once and you will see an ellipsis button. Click this box to enter the Pattern Manager. Select **Add** to enter the pattern. The Label is **24 hour diurnal**, the Start Time is **0.0**, and the Starting Multiplier is **1.00**. On the right side of the box, enter the 24-hour pattern given in the problem statement beginning with hour 1 and continuing to hour 24. Click **OK** twice to return to the **Pattern Setup** window. For each **Unit Load**, set the diurnal pattern to **24 hour diurnal**. Click **OK** to return to the Scenario Wizard, and then click **Next**.

- Select the **Alternative** that is to be changed for this scenario. Click on the check box next to **Sanitary (Dry Weather) Loading**. Click **Next**.

- Select Create New Sanitary (Dry Weather) Loading Alternative.

- Click the **Next** button again to review the scenario. Note that all of the alternatives are inherited with the exception of the sanitary loads. Click **Finished**.

Run the Scenario

- In the Scenario Manager window, select **Go Batch Run** from the left column.

- Check the box next to **24 hr Cycle** and click **Batch**. SewerCAD will ask "Run 1 scenarios as a batch?" Select **Yes** to run the scenario. When the run is completed, click **OK**.

- Close the Scenario Manager window.

View EPS Results

- Notice that above the network view, there is a toolbar as shown here:

- This area contains the controls for displaying results of the EPS. Clicking the arrow on the left begins the display of the results at each time step. This button changes to a red square when the scenario is playing. The down arrow is used to specify the delay at each time step. The numbers in the left window indicate the time step. The left and right double arrows may be used to manually step through the simulation. The other windows indicate the time step increment and the name of the scenario.

- Double-click **O-1** to view information on the sewer outlet. Note that the EPS controls are located in the lower-right corner of the outlet window. As you step through time, the total flow (in the flow summary section) changes.

- Select the **Report** button at the bottom of the outlet window and then select the **Hydrograph**. In the Graph Setup box, select the **MH-1**, **O-1**, and **WW-1** elements. Then click **OK**. Figure 7-5 shows the 24-hour flows at the three locations.

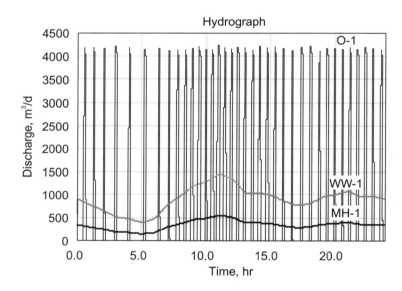

Figure 7-5: Discharge rates at MH-1, WW-1, and O-1 for 24-hour cycle

Part (a): *During an average day, how many times does the pump turn on and off?*

Answer

This graph shows the flow at MH-1, WW-1, and at the outlet. The outlet peaks correspond to pumping cycles. Note that the pump was on for 36 intervals during the 24-hour simulation period.

Part (b): *What is the maximum rate of pumping?*

Answer

At 9.4 hrs, the discharge at the outlet is 4,152,000 l/d or 2.88 m³/min.

Tutorial 3 – Constructing a Profile

Problem Statement

In the third example, a profile of a sewer is to be constructed. The same system used in the first two examples will be used. The profile is to show all structures, ground elevations, and the hydraulic profile.

a) What is the maximum hydraulic head produced by the pump?

b) Does the water in the WW-1 back up into pipe P-1?

Solution

Constructing the Profile

- The Profile Manager is located in the first row of tools. Open it by clicking its icon.
- Select **Profile Management** and then **Add**. Enter **Example Profile** as the profile name and click **OK**.
- The **Profile Wizard** walks the user through the profile construction process. Click the **Select From Drawing** button. Select the pipe elements you wish to profile by clicking once on each pipe (the solid lines will turn to dashed lines). Then right-click and select **Done** to indicate that the selection is complete. Click the **Next** button.
- Select the **Standard template** and click the **Next** button.
- Set the **Horizontal Increment** to 0+50 and the **Vertical Increment** to 2 m. Exit the Profile Wizard by clicking **Finished**. The profile will appear on-screen.

Customizing the Profile

- Annotations can be moved by left-clicking on them, holding the button down, and dragging the annotation to the desired location.
- Annotation text or properties can be changed by moving the mouse over them and right-clicking. Annotation can also be rotated.
- Use the **Options** button in the profile window to change the range and the increments of the horizontal and vertical axes and the text height, as well as to define the annotation for each element type.
- When the annotation is complete, select **Print Preview** to preview a hard copy of the profile. Select **Print** to send the file to your printer.

Using the Hydraulic Grade Line

- In order to view the changes in the hydraulic grade line, the animation must be set to **0.1 hours**. While in the profile view, click the **Scenario Manager** button. Highlight the 24-hour EPS scenario, right-click, and select **Edit**. Click the **Calculation** tab and set the Hydraulic and Hydrologic time steps to **0.05 hr**. Click **Go Batch Run** to recalculate the scenario, and then close out of Scenario Manager.
- In the profile view, set the Increment to **0.05 hr** and click the **Play** button to animate.

Part (a): *What is the maximum hydraulic head produced by the pump?*

Answer

Note that when the pump is not running, the hydraulic grade line in the force main is level with the crown of the outlet (107.2 m). When the pump is running the hydraulic grade line rises at the pump, and then declines as flow approaches the outlet.

Part (b): *Does the water in the WW-1 back up into the pipe P-1?*

Answer

Note that the level in the wet well varies over the course of the simulation. The profile in Figure 7.6 shows the simulation at 10.9 hr. The level in the wet well is at 98 m, which causes pipe P-1 to be full at the downstream end. The zone of full flow in P-1 extends upstream approximately 25 m.

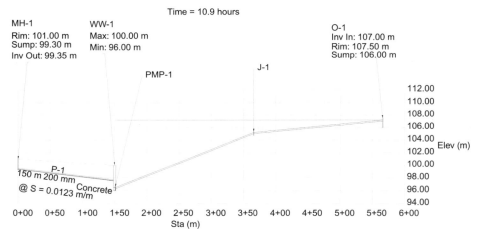

Figure 7-6 Profile of Sewer Network at 10.9 hour

Tutorial 4 – Capital Cost Estimating

SewerCAD has many tools for preparing project cost estimates. See Appendix C for a detailed discussion of capital cost analysis with Haestad Methods software. In this exercise, the Unit Cost function and the Cost Table features will be demonstrated.

Problem Statement

Prepare a cost estimate for materials and installation portion of the project in Tutorial #2. Use the following cost data in the following table. The coefficients a, b, c, and d will be applied to the cost function formulas: unit cost $= d + a(x{-}c)^b$

Cost Functions for Pipes and Gravity Sewer

Structure	Unit Cost Unit	Unit Cost Function Attribute	a	b	c	d
Force Main	$/m	Diameter (mm)	0.15	1.3	150	60
Gravity Sewer	$/m	Rise (mm)	0.15	1.1	175	55
Sewer Manhole	$	Depth (m)	200	1.8	0	1,000

Fixed Costs for Other System Components

Pipe Junction	$1,000
Pump Station	
Pump	$15,000
Installation	$4,000
Valves and piping	$750
Wet well	$50,000
Outlet	$2,500

Solution

- From the **Analysis** pull-down menu, select **Compute Costs,** and then select **Unit Cost Functions**.

- Select the **Pressure Pipe** tab and click the **Add** button. Select **Formula Unit Cost Function** as the Unit Cost Function Type and **Diameter** in the Unit Cost Attribute. Click **OK.** Enter the data for force main pipe from the preceding table. To view a plot of the function, click the **Initialize Range** button and choose **Plot.** Close the Plot viewer. Click **OK** to close the Cost Function dialog box and return to the Unit Cost Functions dialog.

- Select the **Gravity Pipe** tab and click the **Add** button. Select **Formula Unit Cost Function** as the Unit Cost Function Type and **Rise** in the Unit Cost Attribute field. Click **OK.** Enter the data for gravity sewer pipe from the table above. Click **OK** to close the Cost Function dialog and return to the unit cost functions dialog.

- Select the **Manhole** tab and click the **Add** button. Select **Formula Unit Cost Function** as the Unit Cost Function Type and **Structure Depth** in the Unit Cost Attribute. Click **OK.** Enter the data for manholes from the table above. Click **OK** to close the Cost Function dialog and return to the Unit Cost Functions dialog. Click OK to close the dialog to exit the Cost Manager.

- Click the **Tabular Reports** button [≣] in the toolbar at the top of the screen. Select **Pipe Cost Report** from the Available Tables list and click **OK.**

- Check the box next to **Include in Capital Cost Calculation?** for FM-1, FM-2, and FM-3.

- Right-click the header of the **Cost ($)** column. Select the **Global Edit** option. Enter **Materials and Installation** in the first line of the label column. Click the **Advanced** button. Check the box next to **Set Quantity Equal to Pipe Length,** and then select **Force Main Cost Function** for the Unit Cost Function. Click **OK** twice and close the pipe cost report.

- Double left-click **MH-1** and select the **Cost** tab. Enter **Materials and Installation** in the first line of the label column. Click the **Advanced** button. Select **Manhole Cost Function** for the Unit Cost Function. Click **OK** to close the MH-1 window.

- Double left-click **WW-1** and select the **Cost** tab. Enter **Materials and Installation** in the first line of the label column. Enter **50,000** in the **Unit Cost ($)** column. Click on **OK** twice to close the WW-1 window.

- Double left-click **PMP-1** and select the **Cost** tab. Enter **Pump** in the first line of the label column. Enter **15,000** in the **Unit Cost ($)** column. Add the remaining cost data on the next two lines. Click **OK** to close the PMP-1 window.

- Double-click **O-1** and select the **Cost** tab. Enter **Materials and Installation** in the first line of the label column. Enter **25,000** in the Unit Cost ($) column. Add the remaining cost data on the next two lines. Click **OK** to close the O-1 window.

- You are now ready to calculate the total project costs. On the Analysis drop-down menu, select **Compute Costs** to open Cost Manager. The cost will be calculated for the base scenario. Click the **Cost Reports** button and select **Detailed Report** from the drop-down menu. The Detailed Cost Report table will be activated. To obtain a hard copy, select **Print Review** and then **Print**.

Answer

- From the **Analysis** drop-down menu, select **Capital Costs**. Note that costs may be calculated for any scenario. In this example, the physical layout is identical for all three scenarios. Click the **Report** button next to "Scenario Costs." A report with the flowing table is produced.

Base			
Label	Construction Costs ($)	Non-Construction Costs ($)	Total Cost ($)
Wet Well	50,000	0	50,000
Manhole	1,720	0	1,720
Pressure Pipe	35,049	0	35,049
Outlet	2,500	0	2,500
Gravity Pipe	9,136	0	9,136
Pump	19,750	0	19,750
Pressure Junction	1,000	0	1,000
Total			119,155

7.6 Problems

1. In the sanitary sewer represented by the following diagram, a load from a development of high-rise apartments (at wet well WW-1) with 10,000 residents is pumped to the top of a hill, where it is then transported via a circular gravity line to a treatment plant (represented by O-1). At manhole MH-1 is a resort apartment with 300 guests. The load generated here flows down a circular gravity pipe to the same gravity line mentioned above. A bar that serves, on average, 50 people per day and 2 large cafeterias with 20 employees each are located near manhole MH-2.

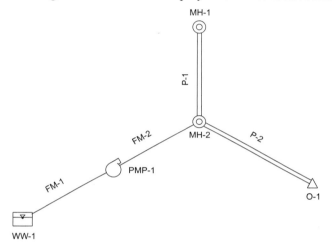

Schematic for Problem 1

Pipe Data for Problem 1

Pipe	Pipe Type	Material	Diameter (mm)	Length (m)	Upstream Invert (m)	Downstream Invert (m)
P-1	Gravity	PVC $n = 0.010$	200	100	98.90	97.62
P-2	Gravity	PVC $n = 0.010$	375	200	97.62	96.62
FM-1	Pressure	Ductile Iron $C = 130$	300	1	70.00	70.00
FM-2	Pressure	Ductile Iron $C = 130$	350	1,000	70.00	97.62

Node Data for Problem 1

Node	Ground Elevation (m)	Rim Elevation (m)	Sump Elevation (m)	Structure Diameter (m)
MH-1	100.30	100.30	98.90	1.00
MH-2	99.10	99.10	97.62	1.00
O-1	100.00	100.00	96.62	N/A
WW-1	74.00	--	--	--

The base and minimum elevations for the wet well are both 70 m. The initial elevation is 73 m, and the maximum elevation is 73.5 m. The diameter of the circular wet well is 3 m.

The tailwater elevation at outlet O-1 is 98 m.

The three defining points of the pump curve are 0 m^3/min at 33.33 m; 5.00 m^3/min at 25.00 m; and 10 m^3/min at 0 m. The pump's elevation is 70 m.

a) What is the total peak sanitary outflow if no peaking factor method is applied to the four unit sanitary loads mentioned above? If Babbitt's peaking factor method is applied? If Harmon is applied? Which peaking factor method is the most conservative?

b) With the Harmon peaking factor applied to each of the four unit dry loads, what is the hydraulic grade at MH-2? How does this peaking factor change the hydraulic load and the flow velocity of pipe P-1 from when no peaking factor was applied?

c) Identify and describe any problems for each of the three scenarios from part (a).

2. The estimated infiltration rate for each of the concrete gravity pipes in the proposed sanitary sewer system represented below is 20 l/d per mm-km. The estimated inflow into each of the manholes during a 5-yr storm event is approximately 75 l/d. The ground elevations for MH-1, MH-2, MH-3, JC-1, and O-1 are 12.10 m, 12.10 m, 11.20 m, 11.80 m, and 10.25 m, respectively. The top of junction chamber JC-1 is 11.8 m. The tailwater condition is a free outfall.

Use SewerCAD's Automatic Design feature to design the inverts and sizes of concrete pipes in the proposed sanitary sewer. The design constraints and pipe lengths are given in the tables below. Apply both the wet-weather (given above) and dry-weather sanitary loads (given in the table below). Use Federov's equation to calculate the peaking factor for each of the unit sanitary loads.

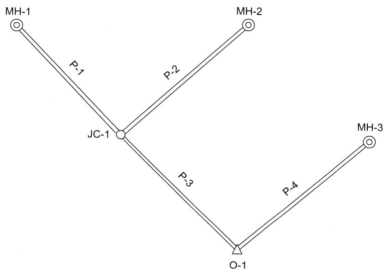

Schematic for Problem 2

Pipe and Constraint Data for Problem 2

Pipe	Length (m)
P-1	200
P-2	150
P-3	200
P-4	300

Constraint	Minimum	Maximum
Velocity (m/s)	0.5	3
Cover (m)	1	3
Slope (m/m)	0.005	0.1

Node Data for Problem 2

Node	Unit Sanitary Load	Loading Unit	Loading Unit Count
MH-1	Hospital (Medical) per Bed	Bed	400
	Cafeteria per Employee	Employee	20
	Apartment Resort	Guest	100
MH-2	Apartment	Resident	400
	Shopping Center per Employee	Employee	100
	Laundromat per Wash	Wash	200
MH-3	School (Boarding)	Student	500

a) List the diameter and slope for each newly designed pipe. Are there any problems with the designed system?

b) What percentage of the total flow is wet-weather flow? Which pipe has the most infiltration?

c) For a larger magnitude storm, the inflow rate into each manhole is estimated at 100 l/d. Analyze the model using the previously designed system and apply the larger wet-weather loading. What percentage of the total flow is wet-weather loading?

d) Do you consider the amount of wet-weather flow into the system significant? What are some methods for alleviating infiltration?

3. The following network is an initial design for a system of force mains in a sanitary sewer. All pipes are ductile iron (Hazen-Williams' $C = 130$). The pump, PMP-1, is at an elevation of 691 m. Enter the system data given in the tables below and answer the following questions. The ground elevation at the outlet is 715 m and the sump elevation is 712 m.

Hints: Make sure that the **Fixed Level in Steady State** box is checked under the Section tab of the Wet Well dialog. In addition, before running the model, make the following modification to the calculation options: within the GO dialog, click the **Options** button, scroll to the right, and in the **Pressure Hydraulics** tab check the **Use Pump Loads** box.

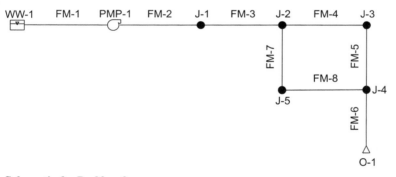

Schematic for Problem 3

Pump and Wet Well Data for Problem 3

Pump Curve Point	Head (m)	Flow (m³/min)
Shut-Off	30	0
Design	20	4
Max Operating	5	6

Ground Elevation (m)	694.7
Maximum Elevation (m)	694.0
Initial Elevation (m)	691.5.
Minimum Elevation (m)	688.5
Base Elevation (m)	687.0
Diameter (m)	3.0

Junction Data for Problem 3

Pressure Junction	Elevation (m)
J-1	698
J-2	701
J-3	703
J-4	705
J-5	703

Pipe Data for Problem 3

Pipe	Diameter (mm)	Length (m)	Upstream Invert (m)	Downstream Invert (m)
FM-1	400	2	687.00	691.00
FM-2	250	58	691.00	698.00
FM-3	350	45	698.00	701.00
FM-4	350	88	701.00	703.00
FM-5	350	71	703.00	705.00
FM-6	450	67	705.00	712.00
FM-7	450	39	701.00	703.00
FM-8	450	68	703.00	705.00

a) What is the head loss across the entire system?

b) Why is there more flow in FM-7 than FM-4?

c) Fill in the following table.

Answer Table for Part (c) of Problem 3

Pipe	Flow (m³/s)	Velocity (m/s)	Head Loss (m)
FM-2			
FM-3			
FM-4			
FM-5			
FM-6			
FM-7			
FM-8			

d) If the minimum velocity required in the force main to keep particles from settling is 0.6 m/s, which areas are going to have problems?

e) What are some possible changes to the design to fix the problem portions of the system?

f) Implement a solution suggested in part (e). Describe the fix(es) and fill in the following chart.

Answer Table for Part (f) of Problem 3

Pipe	Diameter (mm)	Flow (m³/s)	Velocity (m/s)	Head Loss (m)
FM-2				
FM-3				
FM-4				
FM-5				
FM-6				
FM-7				
FM-8				

4. A major interceptor along a river collects laterals from subdivisions. The lower residential area loads are collected in a wet well and pumped to the major interceptor on the other side of a hill. The layout of the system is shown below. All pipes shown as double lines are circular, concrete, gravity-flow pipes ($n = 0.013$). The two pressure pipes (FM-1 and FM-2) are ductile iron (Hazen-Williams' $C = 130$). There is an overflow diversion at MH-5. All input data is given below.

To determine the performance of the system, set up and run three scenarios:

1. A steady-state analysis of the average (base) sanitary loading only

2. An extended-period analysis of the sanitary loading only

3. An extended-period analysis of both the sanitary and wet-weather loading.

For the extended-period analyses, use a 24-hour duration with a 1-hour hydraulic time step and a 0.1-hour hydrologic time step.

Hint: For this problem, it is only necessary to create one Sanitary Loading Alternative that will contain the base and pattern loads. During a steady-state analysis, SewerCAD will ignore the time-based pattern. However, it will be necessary to create two infiltration & inflow loading alternatives (one without the wet-weather loads and the other with the wet-weather loads) because Scenario 2 should not consider the wet-weather loads. Define the wet-weather loading pattern in the manhole prototype before laying out the network.

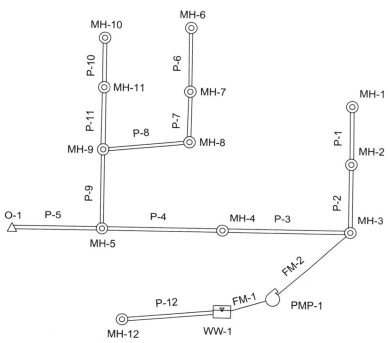

Schematic for Problem 4

Pipe Data for Problem 4

Pipe	Section Size (in)	Upstream Invert Elevation (ft)	Downstream Invert Elevation (ft)	Length (ft)
P-1	18	146.50	141.50	400
P-2	18	141.50	136.00	400
P-3	24	136.00	119.00	400
P-4	36	119.00	114.00	400
P-5	36	114.00	94.00	400
P-6	12	157.00	146.50	400
P-7	18	146.50	136.50	400
P-8	18	136.50	126.00	400
P-9	24	126.00	114.00	400
P-10	12	147.00	136.50	400
P-11	18	136.50	126.00	400
P-12	18	74.50	45.00	400
FM-1	24	45.00	45.00	2
FM-2	24	45.00	136.00	60

Node Data for Problem 4

Node	Ground Elevation (ft)	Sump Elevation (ft)
MH-1	150.00	146.50
MH-2	145.00	141.50
MH-3	140.00	136.00
MH-4	129.00	119.00
MH-5	124.00	114.00
MH-6	160.00	157.00
MH-7	150.00	146.50
MH-8	140.00	136.50
MH-9	130.00	126.00
MH-10	150.00	147.00
MH-11	140.00	136.50
MH-12	80.00	74.50
Outlet	100.00	94.00
PMP-1	45.00	N/A
WW-1	60.00	N/A

Overflow Data for MH-5 in Problem 4

System Flow (gpm)	Diverted Flow (gpm)
0	0
20,000	0
30,000	10,000

All manholes have a sanitary base load of 100 gpm and a continuous diurnal pattern applied to them as defined below. Each manhole also has wet-weather loading given by the following hydrograph.

Domestic Pattern Data for Problem 4

Time (hr)	Multiplier
Starting	0.4
3	1.0
6	1.4
9	1.2
12	1.4
15	0.9
21	0.6
24	0.4

Wet-Weather Loading Data for Problem 4

Time (hr)	Flow (gpm)
0.00	0
3.00	0
4.00	100
5.00	300
6.00	900
7.00	1,500
8.00	1,800
9.00	1,600
10.00	1,000
11.00	600
12.00	300
13.00	100
14.00	0

Wet Well Data for Problem 4

Wet Well	Ground Elevation (ft)	Base Elevation (ft)	Minimum Elevation (ft)	Initial Elevation (ft)	Alarm Elevation (ft)	Maximum Elevation (ft)	Wet Well Diameter (ft)
WW-1	60.00	45.00	45.00	55.00	59.00	60.00	20.00

Pump Data for Problem 4

Pump Curve Point	Head (ft)	Flow (gpm)
Shutoff	100	0
Design	80	4,000
Max Operating	40	8,000

The pump turns on when the elevation in the wet well rises to 57.0 ft, and shuts off when the elevation drops to 45.0 ft.

To verify important information such as minimum and maximum velocities, it will be helpful to keep a table like the following.

Variable	Steady State	EPS Sanitary Only	EPS Dry and Wet
Maximum flow at outlet (gpm)			
Time of max. flow at outlet (hr)	N/A		
Maximum velocity in system at this time (ft/s)			
Pipe with max. velocity at this time			
Minimum flow at outlet (gpm)	N/A		
Time of min. flow at outlet (hr)	N/A		
Min. velocity in system at this time (ft/s)			
Pipe with min. velocity at this time			
Maximum diverted flow (gpm)			
At what hour?			

a) Fill in the table for each scenario.

b) Is there surcharging or flooding in the system? Explain the difference between surcharging and flooding.

c) Does the diversion divert any flow? If so, for which scenario?

d) If the pump has a best efficiency point at 4,000 gpm, what can you say about its performance for the dry- and wet-weather scenarios?

e) Plot profiles from MH-1 to the outlet for all three scenarios and compare the HGLs.

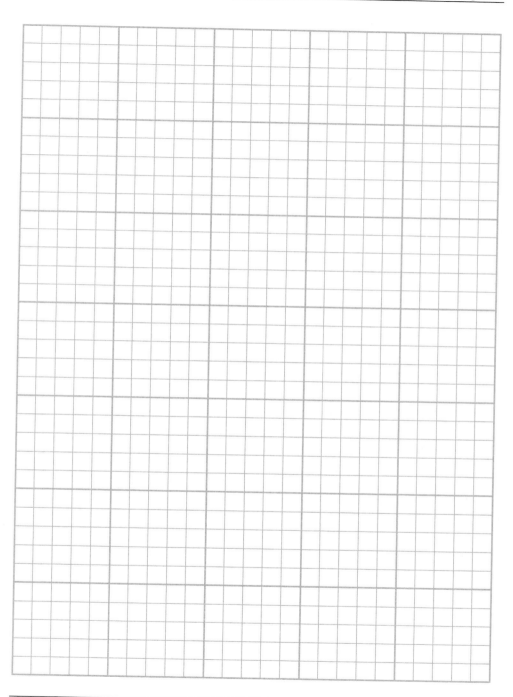

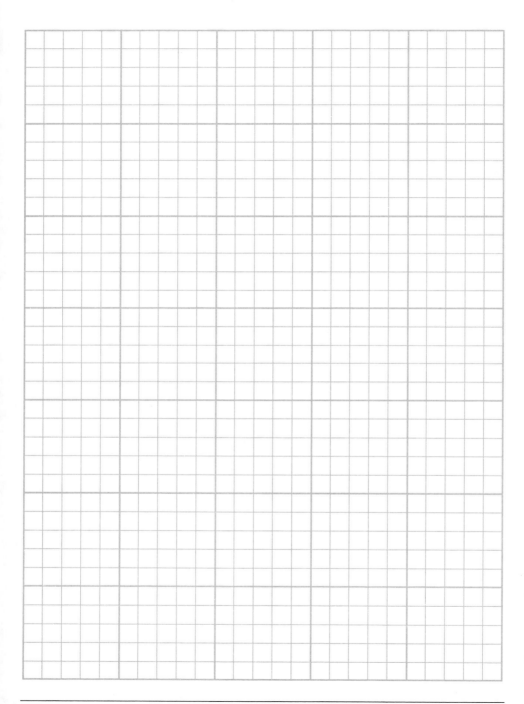

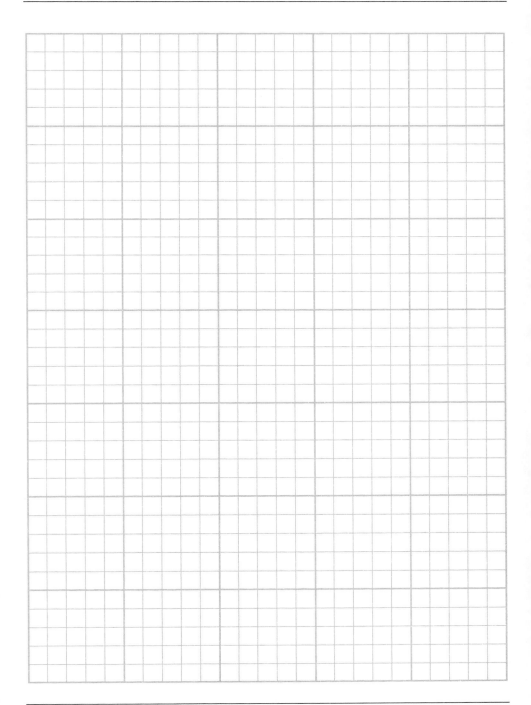

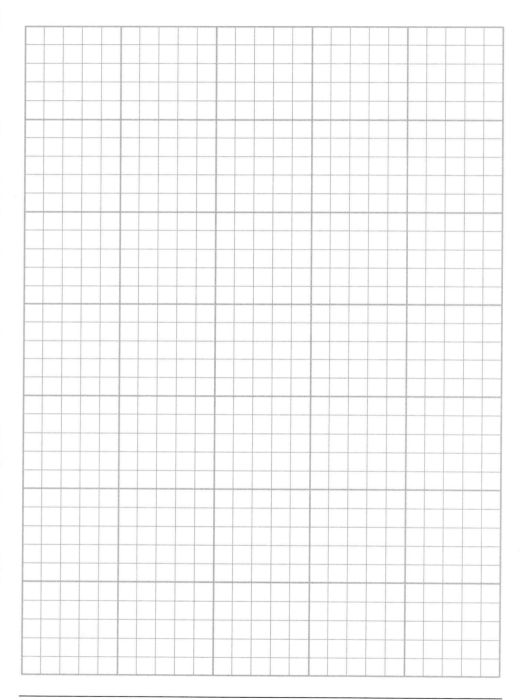

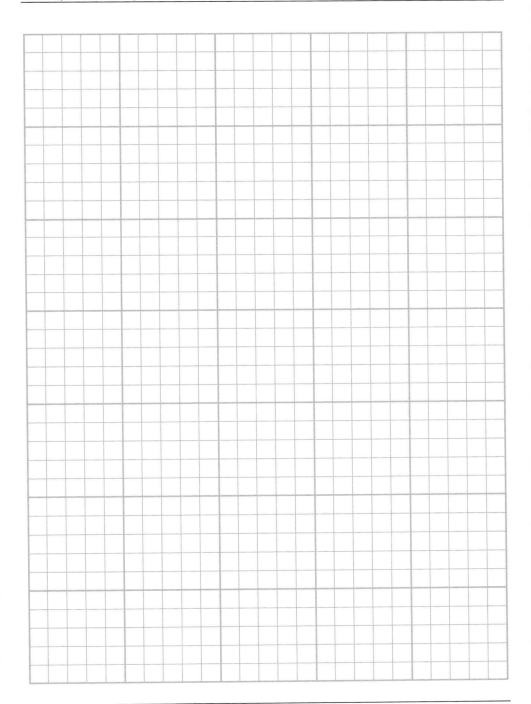

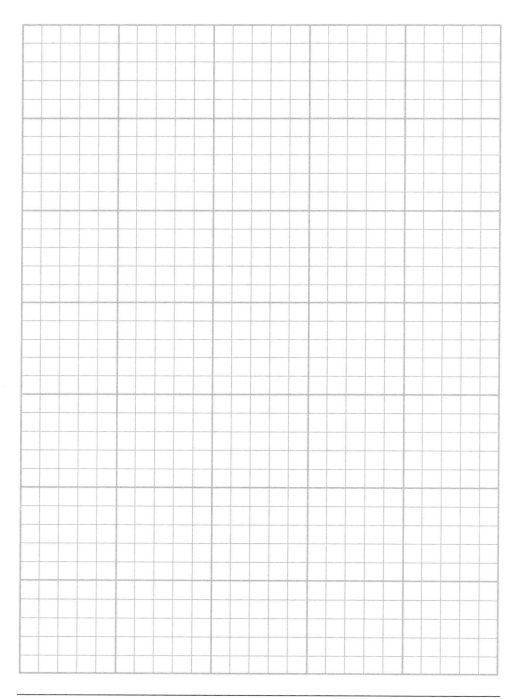

Haestad Methods Software

A.1 Software Packages

The CD-ROM that accompanies this book includes six Haestad Methods software programs with academic licenses. These licenses (with the exception of CulvertMaster) provide all software features available in the professional version. However, the licenses for programs incorporating networked hydraulic systems (that is, StormCAD, WaterCAD, SewerCAD, and PondPack) limit the number of network elements that may be included in a single project. Further, programs with academic licenses may be used only for academic purposes such as completing the exercises in this book—professional or commercial use is prohibited.

Table A-1 describes the capabilities of the included academic licenses, as well as the additional options that are available with the purchase of a professional license or upgraded academic license. (Academic license upgrades are available only to academic institutions.) For more information on these packages, visit **www.haestad.com**.

Table A-1: Software Packages on the CD-ROM

Program	Description	Academic License	Professional License Options
FlowMaster	Hydraulic solver for pressure pipes, open channels, weirs, orifices and inlet structures	All features present	Same features as academic version but licensed for professional use
CulvertMaster	Design and analysis tool for culvert hydraulics	Quick Culvert Calculator features only	Full version includes Quick Culvert Calculator; Culvert Designer; and Culvert Analyzer
StormCAD	Storm sewer design and modeling package	10 inlets; Stand-Alone interface	Additional inlets; AutoCAD integration
WaterCAD	Water distribution design and modeling package	25 pipe segments; Stand-Alone interface	Additional pipe segments; AutoCAD integration; Darwin Calibrator
SewerCAD	Sanitary sewer design and modeling package	25 pipe segments; Stand-Alone interface	Additional pipe segments; AutoCAD integration
PondPack	Stormwater detention design package	Limited to 1 detention basin and 250-ac watershed	Additional detention basins; interconnected pond modeling; unlimited watershed area

A.2 General Tips and Common Tools

Haestad Methods software programs share many common features and interface tools. This section summarizes the basic characteristics of some of these shared features. You are encouraged to "play" with the software to become more familiar with them. These features are quite intuitive and can help to increase the efficiency of your water resources modeling activities.

Online Help

Electronic documentation can be kept up-to-date more easily than paper documentation. It is accessible from within the program, and it is environmentally friendly. For these reasons, Haestad Methods' programs have extensive online Help systems to guide the user through the analysis and design process. The Help system is used most often to:

- Obtain context-sensitive information about an area of the program
- Search for topics such as background theory and equations
- Use "How Do I" to get detailed step-by-step instructions for completing a task

Context-Sensitive Help

The quickest way to access the Help topic related to your current task (that is, ***context-sensitive help***) is to press the **F1** key, click a **Help** button, or right-click the mouse and select **Help** from the pop-up menu. Context-sensitive help provides instant access to the help topics related to the current dialog.

How Do I?

The **How Do I?** section of the Help system has step-by-step instructions for common applications of the model. You may find it beneficial to read over these topics before using the software, or at least to familiarize yourself with them. When a related question arises, you can quickly find the answer.

Pop-ups and Jumps

Certain words within many Help topics are underlined and displayed in a different color. These words are known as ***pop-ups*** and ***jumps.*** When you select a pop-up (dotted underline), a definition of the word or phrase appears on the screen. To close the pop-up window, click anywhere outside the pop-up dialog. When you select a ***jump*** (solid underline), a related Help topic is displayed.

Graphical Editor

Network models such as StormCAD, WaterCAD, SewerCAD, and PondPack have a graphical editor to aid the engineer in laying out the system. The Haestad Methods graphical editor is an "intelligent" drafting environment, meaning that it recognizes the characteristics and behavior of different modeling elements and maintains connectivity when the user drags and drops elements on-screen.

This intelligent graphical editor prevents problems such as incorrect pipe connections and "hanging" pipes (pipes with a node defined at only one end). Models that do not have this type of behavior can be easily "broken," and it may take hours (or days) to locate the source of the problem.

DXF Files

A drawing exchange file (DXF) is the standard format used for translating from one CAD system, such as AutoCAD®, to another, such as MicroStation™. DXF files can also be imported into StormCAD, WaterCAD, and SewerCAD for use as background drawings. For example, a roadway network plan can be imported and used as a background map for laying out and designing a proposed storm sewer system, sanitary sewer system, or water distribution network.

If desired, drawing elements from DXF files can be automatically converted to network components using the Polyline-to-Pipe import feature. DXF lines and polylines can be converted to pipes, and DXF blocks can be converted to node elements.

To learn more about importing and using DXF backgrounds, look in the online help system of StormCAD, WaterCAD, or SewerCAD. You can find topics in the **How Do I?** section or perform a search with a keyword such as "DXF" or "import."

Scaled or Schematic?

In StormCAD, WaterCAD, and SewerCAD, you may choose to either create a schematic drawing or define the horizontal and vertical distance scale. The scaled mode is typically used when a DXF or CAD background file is present. The scale is set so that one drawing unit is equal to a unit of measure (for example, 1 DXF unit equals 1 foot). In a scaled plan, you can also set the drawing scale that you want to use when printing or plotting.

A schematic plan is not drawn at any defined scale, so there is no connection between dimensions shown on the plan and real-world dimensions. There may not even be a correlation between individual dimensions shown on a schematic plan. For example, in a schematic plan, the length representing a pipe with a length of 50 meters may be less than, equal to, or greater than, the line representing a pipe with a length of 20 meters.

To get to the drawing scale options, choose **Options** from the **Tools** menu and go to the **Drawing** tab. The available options are as follows:

- **Schematic** – You enter the pipe length in the **Pipe Properties** dialog for each pipe. Absolute positioning in the drawing editor is not used.

- **Scaled** – You enter the drawing unit scale to be used to determine the length of the drawn pipes. The pipe length will be calculated based on the starting and ending coordinates. The length in the drawing editor corresponds to a real-world length. You can also enter the horizontal and vertical drawing scales at which output should be plotted.

Color Coding

One way to determine the performance of a system is to color code the system according to some indicator. For hydraulic design work, pipeline velocity is often a useful indicator. For example, pipes consistently flowing below 0.15 m/s may be oversized. Pipes with velocities over 1.5 m/s are fairly heavily stressed, and those above 2.4 m/s are often bottlenecks in the system.

Table Manager and Table Customization

StormCAD, WaterCAD, SewerCAD, and FlowMaster have tabular data sheets called FlexTables. These tables aid the modeler in entering and editing data, as well as in organizing and presenting the results of the model. FlexTables have several built-in features that are discussed in detail in the online help system. For information about customizing FlexTables, search the online help for topics such as "table" or "customize." The following are a few of the topics related to table preferences.

- **Changing the Table Title** — When you choose to print a table, the table name is used as the title in the printed report. You can change the report title by using the **Table Manager** to rename the table.

- **Adding and Removing Columns** — You can add and remove column headings by using the table setup options from the table manager.

- **Drag-and-Drop Column and Row Placement** — Select the column or row that you would like to move by holding down the left mouse button on its heading and simply dragging it to the desired location.

- **Resizing Columns** — In the column heading section of the table, place your mouse over the vertical separator between columns. The cursor shape changes to indicate that you are over the separator. Hold down the left mouse button and drag the mouse to the left or right to set the new column width.

- **Changing Column Properties** — The display units for various data types can be changed in the tables. To view or edit the properties of any numeric column, right-click the heading area of the column and choose **Properties** from the pop-up menu. The unit properties will be displayed in the **Set Field Options** dialog.

- **Changing Column Labels** — To change the label of any column, right-click the column heading and choose **Edit Column Label** from the context menu.

- **Using Local Units** — Local units allow data columns to have fixed units and display precision, regardless of the current unit settings of the model. This option can be used to create standardized reports or to present the same data side-by-side in different units (especially handy for projects that use both English and SI units).

In addition to changing the previous table properties, you can also perform data management operations such as sorting, filtering, and global editing.

- **Sorting** — A table can be sorted in ascending or descending order according to any variable. Right-click on the column heading, select Sort, and then select Ascending or Descending. In this way, the elements can be quickly reorganized based on the alphanumeric labels, pipe flow rates, pipe diameters, hydraulic grade lines, and so on.

- **Filtering** — Occasions often arise when a modeler wants to view only a subset of the entire system. For example, the modeler may be concerned with all pipes carrying more than 3 m^3/s in a storm or sanitary sewer, or there may be problems with junction nodes having a pressure below 150 kPa in a water distribution network. The ability to show only some of a system's elements is called *filtering*, and it is accomplished by specifying the desired filter criteria in the table's **Filter** dialog box. Each element in the filter list requires three items:

  - **Column** — The table column containing the element property by which to filter.

  - **Operator** — The operator used to compare the specified filter value to the values in the specified column. Operators include: $=$, $>$, $\geq$, $<$, $\leq$, and $\neq$.

  - **Value** — The comparison value for the filter.

  Any number of criteria can be added to a filter. Multiple criteria are implicitly joined with a logical AND statement. So, when multiple criteria are defined, only rows that meet all of the specified criteria will be displayed.

  The status pane at the bottom of the **Tabular** window shows the number of elements displayed and the total number of rows available (for example, 10 of 20 elements displayed). When a filter is active, the element labels will turn blue. Table filtering allows you to perform global editing (see next bullet) on a subset of elements that you want to change.

- **Global Editing** — Factors and constants can be applied to every value of any editable variable within a FlexTable. Global editing operations include multiplication, division, addition, subtraction, or directly setting all values, depending on the modeler's needs. Only the elements displayed in the table will be changed, so global editing is often used in conjunction with filtering to obtain the desired results. To access global editing, right-click the column heading of the column that you want to edit and select the **Global Edit** option from the pop-up menu.

FlexUnits

You can set field options — the properties of a numeric value — from almost any field in any of Haestad Methods' programs. These properties include the units, decimal precision, scientific notation display option, and the allowable range of values. This feature is referred to as **FlexUnits**.

To set these options for a particular field type, simply right-click the field and select **Properties** from the context menu. This action opens the **Set Field Properties** dialog where you can select the options that you want.

If you would like to set up the units for many data types from the same location in the program, choose **FlexUnits** from the **Tools** pull-down menu to open the FlexUnits dialog.

Units

FlexUnit offers a wide variety of possible units for any field. In the **Set Field Options** dialog, click the **Units** drop-down menu and select the desired unit from the list. The value in the field will be automatically converted to the new unit using the appropriate conversion factor. The FlexUnit feature allows you to mix and match any units, even if you are using a combination of English and SI units.

Once you begin changing units, you will probably notice that some units have multiple representations (for example, psi and lbs/in^2, cfs and ft^3/s). Computationally, these units are the same; however, the additional choices allow you to control the way the units are presented on-screen and in program output.

Display Precision

Display precision can be used to control the number of digits displayed after a decimal point or the rounding of a numeric value. When the precision is greater than or equal to zero, it specifies the number of digits that are displayed after the decimal point. For example, π (3.14159265…) with a decimal precision of 4 would be presented as 3.1416.

Specifying a negative number for display precision results in a displayed value that is rounded to the nearest power of 10. –1 rounds to 10, –2 rounds to 100, –3 rounds to 1000, and so on. For example, the number 1,234 with a display precision of –2 would be displayed as 1,200.

Note: The display precision affects only the way the numbers are displayed, not their actual values. The internal values stored by the software are still carried out to their maximum decimal precision — they are just displayed differently. This concept is important concept to keep in mind, especially when checking calculations by hand or working with values that are lower than the usual decimal precision. For example, be aware that a 0.75-inch diameter pipe with a display precision of 0 will result in a displayed value of 1 inch, even though the calculations will be performed based on the true 0.75-inch diameter.

Scientific Notation

Scientific notation displays a value as a real number multiplied by some power of 10. It is displayed as an integer or real value followed by the letter "e" and a positive or negative integer. For example, 12,345 could be written in scientific notation as 1.2345 e4, and 0.12345 could be written as 1.2345 e–1.

Scientific notation follows the same display precision rules outlined previously. To turn scientific notation on or off, just check or uncheck the box labeled **Scientific notation**.

Minimum and Maximum Allowable Values

These options are available for selected input data and control the range of input values that the program will accept. For example, the user may want to set minimum or maximum values for roughness coefficients, slope, and so forth in order to limit these values to a realistic range, thus helping to prevent typographic errors during data entry.

Scenario Management

B.1 Overview

Haestad Methods' Scenario Manager is included in StormCAD, WaterCAD, and SewerCAD. This feature can dramatically increase your productivity in the "What If?" areas of modeling, including calibration, operations analysis, and planning. By investing a little time to understand scenario management, you can avoid unnecessary editing and data duplication.

In contrast to the old methods of scenario management (editing or copying data), automated scenario management using inheritance gives you these advantages:

- A single project file makes it possible to generate an unlimited number of "What If?" conditions without becoming overwhelmed with numerous modeling files and separate results.

- Because the software maintains the data for all the scenarios in a single project, it can provide you with powerful automated tools for directly comparing scenario results. Any set of results is immediately available at any time.

- The Scenario/Alternative relationship empowers you to mix and match groups of data from existing scenarios without having to declare any data again.

- With inheritance, you do not have to re-enter data if it remains unchanged in a new alternative or scenario, avoiding redundant copies of the same data. Inheritance also enables you to correct a data input error in a parent scenario and automatically update the corrected attribute in all child scenarios.

These advantages, while obvious, may not seem compelling for small projects. It is as projects grow to hundreds or thousands of network elements that the advantages of true scenario inheritance become clear. On a large project, being able to maintain a collection of base and modified alternatives accurately and efficiently can be the difference between evaluating optional improvements and being forced to ignore them.

B.2 About This Appendix

The depth of scenario management as implemented by Haestad Methods is probably far beyond what you have ever seen before. With that in mind, this appendix is intended as an introduction to the philosophy and terminology upon which scenario management is based.

This appendix is not intended as a step-by-step guide to using the software. If you are a moderately experienced Windows software user, you should have no difficulty learning and exploring the scenario management interface.

In addition to the tutorials in this book, excellent tutorials and context-sensitive online help are also available within the software itself. These learning tools will help you with all aspects of the software, and should certainly not be ignored if you are having difficulty. For more information, just click the **Help** button, which is available from anywhere within the program. In addition, you can contact Haestad Methods or visit **www.haestad.com** for the schedule of training seminars held around the world.

B.3 Before Haestad Methods: Distributed Scenarios

Let us begin by understanding the approaches that have historically been used to attempt "What If?" analyses. Traditionally, there have only been two possible ways of analyzing the effects of change on a software model:

- Change the model, recalculate, and review the results
- Create a copy of the model, edit that copy, calculate, and review the results

Although either of these methods may be adequate for a relatively small system, the data duplication, editing, and re-editing becomes very time-consuming and error-prone as the size of the system — and the number of possible conditions — increase. Additionally, comparing conditions requires manual data manipulation, because all output must be stored in physically separate data files.

B.4 With Haestad Methods: Self-Contained Scenarios

The scenario-management feature developed by Haestad Methods successfully meets the following objectives:

- Minimize the number of project files the modeler needs to maintain (one, ideally).

- Maximize the usefulness of scenarios through easy access to things such as input and output data, and direct comparisons.

- Maximize the number of scenarios you can simulate by mixing and matching data from existing scenarios (data reuse).

- Minimize the amount of data that needs to be duplicated to consider conditions that have a lot in common.

A single project file enables you to generate an unlimited number of "What If?" conditions, edit only the data that needs to be changed, and quickly generate direct comparisons of input and results for desired scenarios.

B.5 The Scenario Cycle

The process of working with scenarios is similar to the process of manually copying and editing data, but without the disadvantages of data duplication and troublesome file management. This process allows you to cycle through any number of changes to the model, without fear of overwriting critical data or duplicating important information (see Figure B-1). Of course, it is possible to directly change data for any scenario, but an "audit trail" of scenarios can be useful for retracing the steps of a calibration series or for understanding a group of master plan updates.

Scenario Anatomy: Attributes and Alternatives

Before exploring scenario management further, a few key terms should be defined:

- An *attribute* is a fundamental property of an object, often a single numeric quantity. For example, the attributes of a pipe include diameter, length, and roughness.

- An *alternative* holds a family of related attributes so pieces of data that you are most likely to change together are grouped for easy referencing and editing. For example, a physical properties alternative groups physical data for the network's elements, such as elevations, sizes, and roughness coefficients.

- A *scenario* has a list of referenced alternatives (which hold the attributes), and combines these alternatives to form an overall set of system conditions that can be analyzed. This referencing of alternatives enables you to easily generate system conditions that mix and match groups of data that have been previously created. Note that scenarios do not actually hold any attribute data — the referenced alternatives do.

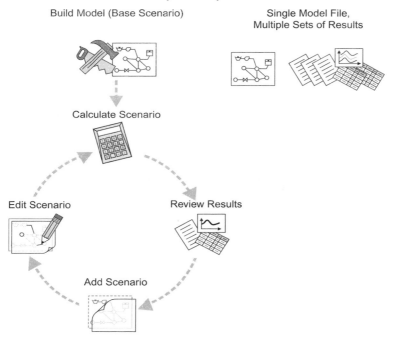

Figure B-1: With Haestad Methods: Self-Contained Scenarios

A Familiar Parallel

Although the structure of scenarios may seem a bit difficult at first, anyone who has eaten at a restaurant should be able to relate fairly easily. A meal (scenario) is comprised of several courses (alternatives), which might include a salad, an entrée, and a dessert. Each course has its own attributes. For example, the entrée may have a meat, a vegetable, and a starch. Examining the choices, we could present a menu as in Figure B-2.

The restaurant does not have to create a new recipe for every possible meal (combination of courses) that could be ordered. They can just assemble any meal based on what the customer orders for each alternative course. Salad 1, Entrée 1, and Dessert 2 might then be combined to define a complete meal.

Generalizing this concept, we see in Figure B-3 that any scenario simply references one alternative from each category to create a "big picture" that can be analyzed. Note that different types of alternatives may have different numbers and types of attributes, and any category can have an unlimited number of alternatives to choose from.

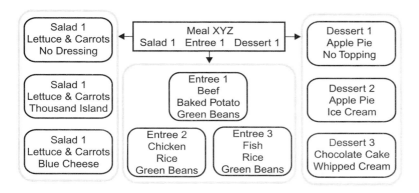

Figure B-2: A Restaurant Meal "Scenario"

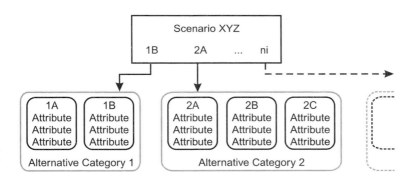

Figure B-3: Generic Scenario Anatomy

B.6 Scenario Behavior: Inheritance

The separation of scenarios into distinct alternatives (groups of data) meets one of the basic goals of scenario management: maximizing the number of scenarios you can develop by mixing and matching existing alternatives. Two other primary goals have also been addressed: a single project file is used, and easy access to input data and calculated results is provided in numerous formats through the intuitive graphical interface.

But what about the other objective: minimizing the amount of data that needs to be duplicated to consider conditions that have a lot of common input? Surely an entire set of pipe diameters should not be re-entered if only one or two change?

The solution is a familiar concept to most people: ***inheritance***.

In the natural world, a child inherits characteristics from a parent. This may include such traits as eye color, hair color, and bone structure. There are two significant differences between the genetic inheritance that most of us know and the way inheritance is implemented in software:

- Overriding inheritance
- Dynamic inheritance

Overriding Inheritance

Overriding inheritance is the software equivalent of cosmetics. A child can override inherited characteristics at any time by specifying a new value for that characteristic. These overriding values do not affect the parent, and are therefore considered "local" to the child. Local values can also be removed at any time, reverting the characteristic to its inherited state. The child has no choice in the value of his inherited attributes, only in local attributes.

For example, suppose a child has inherited the attribute of blue eyes from his parent. Now the child puts on a pair of green-tinted contact lenses to hide his natural eye color. When the contact lenses are on, we say his natural eye color is "overridden" locally, and his eye color is green. When the child removes the tinted lenses, his eye color instantly reverts to blue, as inherited from his parent.

Dynamic Inheritance

Dynamic inheritance does not have a parallel in the genetic world. When a parent's characteristic is changed, existing children also reflect the change. Using the eye-color example, this would be the equivalent of the parent changing eye color from blue to brown, and the children's eyes instantly inheriting the brown color also. Of course, if the child has already overridden a characteristic locally, as with the green lenses, his eyes will remain green until the lenses are removed. At this point, his eye color will revert to the inherited color, now brown.

This dynamic inheritance has remarkable benefits for applying wide-scale changes to a model, fixing an error, and so on. If rippling changes are *not* desired, the child can override all of the parent's values, or a copy of the parent can be made instead of a child.

When Are Values Local, and When Are They Inherited?

Any changes that are made to the model belong to the currently active scenario and the alternatives that it references. If the alternatives happen to have children, those children will also inherit the changes unless they have specifically overridden that attribute. Figure B-4 demonstrates the effects of a change to a mid-level alternative. Inherited values are shown as gray text, local values are shown as black text.

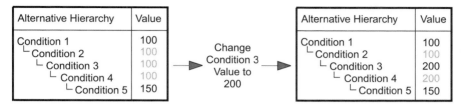

Figure B-4: A Mid-level Hierarchy Alternative Change

Minimizing Effort through Attribute Inheritance

Inheritance has an application every time you hear the phrase "just like *x* except for *y*". Rather than specifying all of the data from *x* again to form this new condition, we can simply create a child from *x* and change *y* appropriately. Now we have both conditions, with no duplicated effort.

We can even apply this inheritance to our restaurant analogy as follows. Inherited values are shown as gray text, local values are shown as black text.

Salad Alternative Hierarchy	Attribute: Vegetables	Attribute: Dressing
Salad 1	Lettuce & Carrots	No Dressing
├─Salad 2	Lettuce & Carrots	Thousand Island
└─Salad 3	Lettuce & Carrots	Blue Cheese

- "Salad 2 is just like Salad 1, except for the dressing."
- "Salad 3 is just like Salad 1, except for the dressing."

Note: Salad 3 could inherit from Salad 2, if we prefer: "Salad 3 is just like Salad 2, except for the dressing."

Meal Scenario Hierarchy	Attribute: Meat	Attribute: Starch	Attribute: Vegetable
Entree 1	Beef	Baked Potato	Green Beans
└─Entree 2	Chicken	Rice	Green Beans
└─Entree 3	Fish	Rice	Green Beans

- "Entrée 2 is just like Entrée 1, except for the meat and the starch."
- "Entrée 3 is just like Entrée 2, except for the meat."

Note: If the vegetable of the day changes (say from green beans to peas), only Entrée 1 needs to be updated, and the other entrées will automatically inherit the vegetable attribute of "Peas" instead of "Green Beans."

Dessert Alternative Hierarchy	Attribute: Bakery Item	Attribute: Topping
Dessert 1	Apple Pie	No Topping
└─ Dessert 2	Apple Pie	Ice Cream
Dessert 3	Chocolate Cake	Whipped Cream

- "Dessert 2 is just like Dessert 1, except for the topping."

Note: Dessert 3 is a parent alternative and has nothing in common with the other desserts, so it can be created as a "root" or "base" alternative. It does not inherit its attribute data from any other alternative.

Minimizing Effort through Scenario Inheritance

Just as a child alternative can inherit attributes from its parent, a child scenario can inherit which alternatives it references from its parent. This is essentially still the phrase "just like x except for y", but on a larger scale.

Carrying through on the meal example, consider a situation where you go out to dinner with three friends. The first friend places his order, and the second friend orders the same thing except for the dessert. The third friend orders something totally different, and you order the same meal as hers except for the salad.

The four meal "scenarios" could then be presented as follows (inherited values are shown as gray text, local values are shown as black text):

Meal Scenario Hierarchy	Salad Alternative	Entree Alternative	Dessert Alternative
Meal 1	Salad 1	Entree 2	Dessert 3
└─ Meal 2	Salad 1	Entree 2	Dessert 1
Meal 3	Salad 3	Entree 3	Dessert 2
└─ Meal 2	Salad 2	Entree 3	Dessert 2

- "Meal 2 is just like Meal 1, except for the dessert." The salad and entrée alternatives are inherited from Meal 1.
- "Meal 3 is nothing like Meal 1 or Meal 2." A totally new "base" or "root" is created.
- "Meal 4 is just like Meal 3, except for the salad." The entrée and dessert alternatives are inherited from Meal 3.

B.7 A Water Distribution Example

This section presents a fairly simple water distribution system: a single reservoir supplies water by gravity to three junction nodes (see Figure B-5).

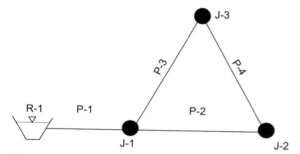

Figure B-5: Example Water Distribution System

Although true water distribution scenarios include such alternative categories as initial settings, operational controls, water quality, and fire flow, we are going to focus on the two most commonly changed sets of alternatives: demands and physical properties. Within these alternatives, we are going to concentrate on junction baseline demands and pipe diameters.

Building the Model (Average Day Conditions)

During model construction, probably only one alternative from each category is going to be considered. This model is built with average demand calculations and preliminary pipe diameter estimates. At this point we can name our scenario and alternatives, and the hierarchies look like the following (showing only the items of interest):

Demand Alternative Hierarchy	J-1	J-2	J-3
Average Day	100 gpm	500 gpm	100 gpm

Physical Alternative Hierarchy	P-1	P-2	P-3
Preliminary Pipes	8 inches	6 inches	6 inches

Scenario Hierarchy	Demand Alternative	Physical Alternative
Avg. Day	Average Day	Preliminary Pipes

Analyzing Different Demands (Maximum Day Conditions)

In our example, the local planning board also requires analysis of maximum day demands, so a new demand alternative is required. No variation in demand is expected at J-2, which is an industrial site. As a result, the new demand alternative can inherit J-2's demand from "Average Day" while the other two demands are overridden.

Demand Alternative Hierarchy	J-1	J-2	J-3
Average Day	100 gpm	500 gpm	100 gpm
└—Maximum Day	200 gpm	500 gpm	200 gpm

Now we can create a child scenario from "Average Day" that inherits the physical alternative, but overrides the selected demand alternative. As a result, we get the following scenario hierarchy:

Scenario Hierarchy	Demand Alternative	Physical Alternative
Avg. Day	Average Day	Preliminary Pipes
└—Max. Day	Maximum Day	Preliminary Pipes

Because no physical data (pipe diameters) have been changed, the physical alternative hierarchy remains the same as before.

Another Set of Demands (Peak Hour Conditions)

Based on pressure requirements, the system is adequate to supply maximum day demands. Another local regulation requires analysis of peak hour demands, with slightly lower allowable pressures. Because the peak hour demands also share the industrial load from the "Average Day" condition, "Peak Hour" can be inherited from "Average Day." In this instance, "Peak Hour" could inherit just as easily from "Maximum Day."

Demand Alternative Hierarchy	J-1	J-2	J-3
Average Day	100 gpm	500 gpm	100 gpm
├—Maximum Day	200 gpm	500 gpm	200 gpm
└—Peak Hour	250 gpm	500 gpm	250 gpm

Another scenario is also created to reference these new demands, as shown here:

Scenario Hierarchy	Demand Alternative	Physical Alternative
Avg. Day	Average Day	Preliminary Pipes
├— Max. Day	Maximum Day	Preliminary Pipes
└— Peak	Peak Hour	Preliminary Pipes

Note again that the physical data was not changed, so the physical alternatives remain the same.

Correcting an Error

This analysis results in acceptable pressures, until it is discovered that the industrial demand is not actually 500 gpm — it is 1,500 gpm! Because of the inheritance within the demand alternatives, however, only the "Average Day" demand for J-2 needs to be updated. The changes will ripple through to the children. After the single change is made, the demand hierarchy is as follows:

Demand Alternative Hierarchy	J-1	J-2	J-3
Average Day	100 gpm	1500 gpm	100 gpm
├─Maximum Day	200 gpm	1500 gpm	200 gpm
└─Peak Hour	250 gpm	1500 gpm	250 gpm

Notice that no changes need to be made to the scenarios to reflect these corrections. The three scenarios can now be calculated as a batch to update the results.

When these results are reviewed, it is determined that the system does *not* have the ability to adequately supply the system as it was originally thought. The pressure at J-2 is too low under peak hour demand conditions.

Analyzing Improvement Suggestions

To counter the head loss from the increased demand load, two possible improvements are suggested:

- A much larger diameter is proposed for P-1 (the pipe from the reservoir). This physical alternative is created as a child of the "Preliminary Pipes" alternative, inheriting all the diameters except P-1's, which is overridden.
- Slightly larger diameters are proposed for all pipes. Because there are no commonalities between this recommendation and either of the other physical alternatives, this can be created as a base (root) alternative.

These changes are then incorporated to arrive at the following hierarchies:

Demand Alternative Hierarchy	J-1	J-2	J-3
Average Day	100 gpm	1500 gpm	100 gpm
├─Maximum Day	200 gpm	1500 gpm	200 gpm
└─Peak Hour	250 gpm	1500 gpm	250 gpm

Physical Alternative Hierarchy	P-1	P-2	P-3	P-4
Preliminary Pipes	8 inches	6 inches	6 inches	6 inches
└Larger P-1	18 inches	6 inches	6 inches	6 inches
Preliminary Pipes	12 inches	12 inches	12 inches	12 inches

This time, the demand alternative hierarchy remains the same since no demands were changed. The two new scenarios ("Peak, Big P-1," "Peak, All Big Pipes") can be batch run to provide results for these proposed improvements.

Next, features like Scenario Comparison Annotation (from the Scenario Manager) and comparison Graphs (for extended period simulations, from the element editor dialogs) can be used to directly determine which proposal results in the most improved pressures.

Finalizing the Project

It is decided that enlarging P-1 is the optimum solution, so new scenarios are created to check the results for average day and maximum day demands. Notice that this step does not require handling any new data. All of the information we want to model is present in the alternatives we already have!

Scenario Hierarchy	Demand Alternative	Physical Alternative
Avg. Day	Average Day	Preliminary Pipes
├ Max. Day	Maximum Day	Preliminary Pipes
└ Max. Day, Big P-1	Maximum Day	Larger P-1
├ Peak	Peak Hour	Preliminary Pipes
├ Peak, Big P-1	Peak Hour	Larger P-1
└ Peak, All Big Pipes	Peak Hour	Larger All Pipes
└ Avg. Day, Big P-1	Average Day	Larger P-1

Also note that it would be equally effective in this case to inherit the "Avg. Day, Big P-1" scenario from "Avg. Day" (changing the physical alternative) or to inherit from "Peak, Big P-1" (changing the demand alternative). Likewise, "Max. Day, Big P-1" could inherit from either "Max. Day" or "Peak, Big P-1."

Neither the demand nor physical alternative hierarchies were changed in order to run the last set of scenarios, so they remain as they were.

Demand Alternative Hierarchy	J-1	J-2	J-3
Average Day	100 gpm	1500 gpm	100 gpm
├Maximum Day	200 gpm	1500 gpm	200 gpm
└Peak Hour	250 gpm	1500 gpm	250 gpm

Physical Alternative Hierarchy	P-1	P-2	P-3	P-4
Preliminary Pipes	8 inches	6 inches	6 inches	6 inches
└─Larger P-1	18 inches	6 inches	6 inches	6 inches
Larger All Pipes	12 inches	12 inches	12 inches	12 inches

Cost Management

C.1 Overview

Cost Manager, a tool available in WaterCAD, StormCAD, and SewerCAD, enables you to track the costs associated with a water distribution, storm sewer, or sanitary sewer construction project. It is set up to mimic the way that a typical engineer would track the costs of a capital improvement project during a planning study. In order to compute the cost of a particular scenario, you must supply the model with the following information:

- **Elements included in costing.** The first step is to select the elements from the model that you want to include in a given cost scenario. This set of elements may include all the elements in the model if, for instance, you are modeling a new subdivision, or a subset of the elements if you are simply expanding an existing system.

- **Unit costs.** The second level of data is the costs associated with each element. The costs for each element are broken into two types, construction and non-construction. Construction costs are specified on a per unit basis where the unit can be either an item (for example, $/hydrant) or a length unit (for example, $/ft or $/m). Most unit costs are constants, but unit costs for pipe elements and gravity structures can also be specified as a function of diameter or some other property of the element using a unit cost function. A unit cost function defines the relationship between the unit cost for an element and some attribute of that element. Non-construction costs can be specified as either a percentage of the total construction costs or as a lump sum amount.

- **Quantities.** The third level of information is the quantity of each item (for example, number of service lines, length of pipe, number of valves) associated with a given element. In the case of pipes, the user need not specify the length, because the default value for the quantity is the length of the pipe segment.

- **Adjustments.** Finally, the user can enter the adjustments that should be made to the total costs computed for the elements in a scenario (that is, project). You can specify these project-level cost adjustments as a lump sum or as a percentage of the total cost.

Element Cost Data versus Cost Manager

The early sections of this appendix describe how to handle cost data for each element. Entering the cost data for individual elements does not involve the use of the Cost Manager portion of the program. Cost Manager is used to sum the costs of the elements and prepare project cost reports. **Cost Manager** is accessed by clicking the **Cost**

Manager button or by selecting **Analysis\Compute Costs** from the pull-down menu. Costs for individual elements can be calculated without entering Cost Manager.

Navigating Within Cost Manager

You can choose from five selections within Cost Manager.

- **Unit Cost Functions:** Enables you to construct unit cost functions.

- **Cost Alternatives:** Opens the Cost Alternative dialog, where you can edit the element cost data defined in the project.

- **Cost Adjustments:** Enables you to enter cost adjustments that pertain to the overall scenario, not just individual elements.

- **Active Scenarios:** Enables you to specify which scenarios will appear in Cost Manager.

- **Cost Reports:** Enables you to view cost reports with varying levels of detail.

Cost Manager also provides a way of viewing the calculated costs at user-selected levels of detail.

Level of Detail

The cost analysis feature is extremely flexible with regard to the level of detail in which you can develop cost estimates. At the simplest level, you may want to capture all the costs of a pipe in a single $/ft or $/m unit cost. At the other extreme, you may break down the cost of a pipe into numerous cost items, including materials, installation, repaving, hydrants, services, valves, land, engineering, inspection, legal, permits, and contribution to a capital clearing account, plus an explicit allowance for omissions and contingencies. Either approach can be easily accommodated using Cost Manager.

Construction versus Overall Project Cost

It is important to understand which costs you are calculating — construction costs or overall capital costs. For example, you must decide if the costs calculated are pure construction costs, or if they include items such as inspection, design, land, easements, and so on. There is no single correct way to compute costs, but it is important to realize which costs are included or not included in the totals, and to perform cost evaluations in a consistent manner.

Indirect Costs by Element or by Project

Indirect costs such as design and inspection may be assigned to each element individually or to the project as a whole, depending on how you want to account for the costs in your estimate. For instance, if a pipeline project is made up of five pipe elements, the inspection cost may be added into each element, or calculated after summing the individual costs and added to the overall project cost.

Cost Functions versus Fixed Unit Cost

For pipes and gravity node structures, it is possible to specify unit costs as a function of an attribute of the element. For instance, the unit cost of a pipe might be a function of the diameter, or the cost per unit for a gravity structure could be a function of the structure depth. By using a cost function, the unit cost for an element will be automatically updated as the physical characteristics of the element change.

Scenarios versus Cost Alternatives

Although cost data are stored in the cost alternatives, costs are calculated for individual scenarios. This distinction is necessary because element properties such as pipe diameter and manhole depth are not stored with cost data, but rather with the system's physical data. The cost must be based on a scenario, which includes both a Cost Alternative and a Physical Properties Alternative.

Multiple Scenarios

The cost data that you enter is stored in a Cost Alternative, so you can easily change the cost data that is used from scenario to scenario. For instance, you may have several phases of construction for which you want to separately compute the associated costs. You can do this by creating two Cost Alternatives, one containing the cost data for the elements in phase one, and another containing the costs for the elements in phase two. By creating the appropriate scenarios to reference these alternatives, you can quickly compute and compare the costs associated with each phase.

C.2   Assigning Costs to Model Elements

The costs for each type of element are divided into two types, construction and non-construction. The definition of each type of cost depends to a certain extent on the user. However, in general, the difference between the two types of costs is that construction costs are based on a unit cost multiplied by a quantity, whereas non-construction costs are specified as either a lump sum or as a percentage of the total construction costs. The method of specifying non-construction costs is identical for every element. There are slightly different options for specifying construction costs, depending on the type of element to which you are assigning the cost. The sections that follow explain these nuances in greater detail.

Although cost management for the various elements shares most features, different types of elements have some special behaviors. The four distinct categories are pipes, nodes with cost functions, nodes without cost functions, and pump stations. Each type is described in more detail in the following sections.

Pipe Costs

Cost Per Item versus Cost Per Length

The construction costs for pipes are entered into the construction cost table portion of the **Cost** tab for the element. The table can contain any number of construction cost items. You can specify each pipe construction cost item as either a cost per item or a cost per length. If you specify the cost on a per item basis, the total construction cost is simply the cost per item multiplied by the quantity or number of objects. The user indicates the type of cost in the **Unit** column by selecting:

- Each if the costs are calculated per item, or
- Any length unit if the costs are calculated per length.

Items with Cost Per Length

If a length unit (for example, ft or m) is selected in the **Unit** column, the number in the **Quantity** column is the length by which the unit cost is to be multiplied. The default value in the **Quantity** field is the length of the pipe used in the hydraulic calculations. However, if that particular unit cost only applies to a portion of the pipe, you can enter another value by deselecting **Set Quantity Equal to Pipe Length** in the **Advanced Options** dialog for each cost item.

Unit Cost Functions for Pipes

Cost Manager allows you to specify the unit cost as a function of a pipe attribute using a unit cost function. The unit cost function relates the cost per unit length to a pipe property such as diameter. If you specify a unit cost function for a construction cost item, the program will calculate the unit cost for that item. Creating unit cost functions is described later.

Example

Consider 650 ft of a 10-in. diameter pipe with the cost data shown in Table C-1.

Table C-1: Unit Cost as a Function of Diameter

Diameter (in)	Unit Cost ($/ft)
8	45
10	55
12	60

As well as with the following unit costs and quantities:

- Material and installation $55/ft (calculated based on Table C-1)
- Seven service connections at $650 each
- Omission and contingency at 15 percent of construction cost
- Inspection services at 5 percent of construction cost
- Utility easement at $350

The Cost tab for this pipe would appear as shown in Figure C-1.

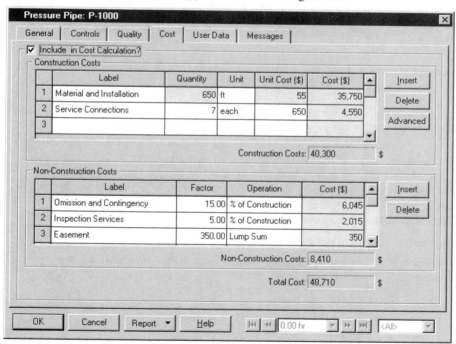

Figure C-1: Cost Tab of the Pipe Editor Dialog

Each pipe can have as many construction cost items as you want, which means that any number of unit cost functions can be used for a single pipe. For instance, you could have unit cost functions for materials, excavation, or resurfacing. The advantage of specifying the costs in terms of unit cost functions is that, as the physical characteristics of the pipe change, the cost for the element is automatically updated.

Node Costs

Types of Nodes by Cost

In terms of assigning construction costs, nodal elements can be broken down into two categories: those that support unit cost functions and those that do not support unit cost functions. For the most part, the construction cost items for these two categories of nodal elements are specified in a very similar fashion. The first category includes the gravity structures: manholes, inlets, and junctions. The second category consists of the remaining nodal elements: outlets, pressure junctions, pumps, valves, tanks, and reservoirs.

Cost Items for Nodes

The construction cost items for nodal elements consist of a label, quantity, unit, and unit cost. The unit field contains a user-defined string and is primarily used for bookkeeping, because it does not affect the total cost of the item. The total cost for the construction cost item is simply the quantity multiplied by the unit cost, which are parameters defined by the user.

For node elements that support unit cost functions (manholes, inlets, and junctions), the function can be defined in Cost Manager and assigned to the construction cost item. As with pipes, if a unit cost function is assigned to a construction cost item, the unit cost is computed based on some attribute. The difference is that for pipes the unit cost function computes a cost per length (for example, ft or m), whereas for nodal elements the unit cost function computes a cost for the item (for example, structure). So if a unit cost function is assigned to a construction cost item, the quantity defaults to 1, and the unit will default to *each*. A quick way to determine whether an element supports cost functions is to look at the element dialog. If it is possible to select the **Advanced** button, you can assign a cost function to that element. Cost functions can be assigned to items by using the **Advanced Options** dialog, as described later in this document.

Example for a Node without a Cost Function

The construction cost of a tank, a type of element that does not support unit cost functions, may consist of the following items:

- 1 steel tank at $250,000
- 600 ft of fencing at $15/ft
- Site clearing and grading at $20,000
- 1 SCADA system and radio transmitter at $20,000

The Cost tab for this item is shown in Figure C-2.

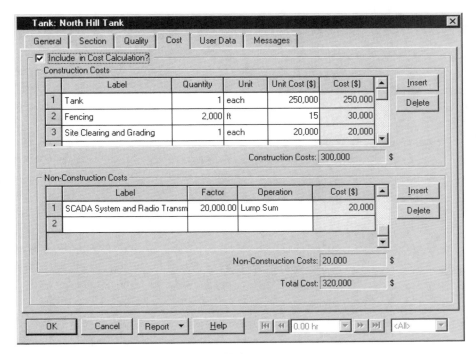

Figure C-2: Cost Tab of the Tank Editor Dialog

Example of a Node with a Cost Function

For an inlet, you could use a unit cost function so that the construction costs for the element are updated as the design changes. Consider an inlet with the cost data shown in Table C-2.

Table C-2: Unit Cost Function of Structure Depth

Depth (ft)	Cost of Subsurface Structure ($)
6	3,000
8	3,500
10	4,000

As well as with the following characteristics:

- 1 subsurface structure 8 ft deep at $3,500 (calculated from the unit cost function)
- 1 surface inlet at $2,000

The Cost tab for this item appears as shown in Figure C-3.

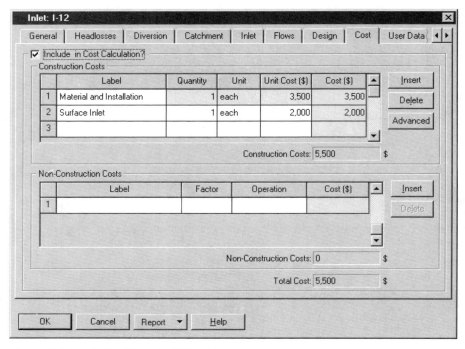

Figure C-3 Cost Tab of the Inlet Editor Dialog

Pump Station Costs

Pump stations are a special case of nodal elements. In terms of the hydraulic model, a pump station with three pumps makes up three hydraulic elements. However, in terms of cost estimating, a pump station is a single entity. There are two ways to address this situation. You can either apportion the costs evenly between the three elements or aggregate the cost for the entire pump station on a single pump. From a reporting and management perspective, it often makes the most sense to assign all the costs to a single pump, as illustrated here:

- 3 pumps at $12,000 each
- 3 pump installations at $4,000 each
- 9 gate valves installed at $2,500 each
- 3 check valves at $690 each
- 1 pump station structure at $80,000
- 1 SCADA system with sensors and radio at $25,000

- Engineering and inspection at 15 percent of construction
- Allowance for contingencies at 5 percent of construction
- Land for pumping station at $20,000

The sum of all these costs is the total cost for the element and would show up only in the selected pump. The other two pumps at the station would have zero cost. In Figure C-4, note that only three items are shown in the table, but the table can be scrolled to show the remaining items.

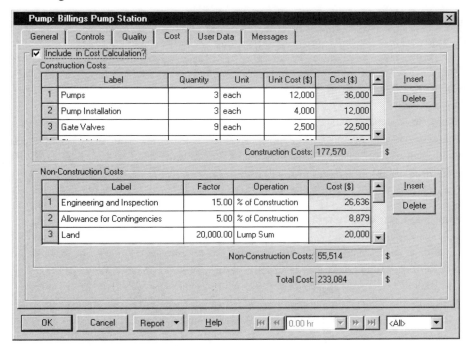

Figure C-4: Cost Tab of the Pump Editor Dialog

Non-Construction Costs

There are numerous indirect costs that are applied to construction projects. The terminology describing these costs varies depending on local conventions, whether a public or private utility is involved, and whether construction is being done with force account labor or outside contractors. There are numerous items that can be included in these indirect costs, such as:

- Design and bidding
- Construction phase engineering services

- Inspection
- Utility overhead
- Capital clearing account
- Administration
- Legal
- Permits
- Allowance for interest on funds used during construction
- Insurance

You are able to include these costs in the following ways:

- With each element as a lump sum
- With each element as a percentage
- For the overall scenario as a lump sum
- For the overall scenario as a percentage of construction costs
- For the overall scenario as a percentage of both construction and non-construction costs (percent of total cost)
- As a factor applied to the overall project (multiplier)

A few of these costs are described in more detail in the following sections.

Omissions and Contingencies

Usually, cost estimators make an allowance for unforeseen items that come up during projects, sometimes referred to as "Omissions and Contingencies" (O&C). These costs are usually high when the project is being formulated initially (25 percent) and get smaller (5 percent) as the scope and details of the project are worked out.

It is important not to count the allowance for O&C twice by including an allowance on an element-by-element basis, and then another allowance for the project as a whole.

Land, Easement, and Right-of-Way Costs

Many projects involve procurement of land, easements, or rights-of-way. These costs are usually not a function of element size, and so can be handled on an element-by-element basis as a lump sum or as a cost per foot or acre multiplied by the number of feet or acres. If the land costs are not going to be accounted for element-by-element, but rather by a single land purchase for the entire project, a lump sum cost adjustment should be made to the appropriate scenario.

Specifying Non-Construction Costs

Non-construction cost items for all types of elements are computed in the same manner, and can be specified as either a lump sum or as a percentage of the total construction costs. For instance, you may want to make allowances for omissions and contingencies on an element-by-element basis. You can do this by assigning a non-construction cost item to every element that is 15 percent of the total construction cost of the element.

The dialogs and reports that follow illustrate how the construction and non-construction costs for the following elements will appear in **Cost** tab of the **Element Editor** dialog and in the cost report for each element.

Pipe (using values from a previous example), shown in Figures C-1 and C-5:

- 650 feet of 10-inch diameter pipe at $55/ft
- 7 service connections at $650 each
- Omission and contingency at 15 percent of construction
- Inspection services at 5 percent of construction
- Utility easement at $350

Label	Quantity	Unit	Unit Cost ($)	Cost ($)	Subtotal ($)	Element Total ($)
Material and Installation	650	ft	55	35,750		
Service Connections	7	each	650	4,550		
Total Construction Cost					40,300	
Omission and Contingency	15	% of Construction		6,045		
Inspection Services	5	% of Construction		2,015		
Easement	350	Lump Sum		350		
Total Non-Construction Cost					8,410	
P-1000						48,710

Figure C-5: Pressure Pipe Cost Report

Tank (shown in Figures C-2 and C-6):

- 1 steel tank at $250,000
- 1 ft of fencing at $15/ft
- Site clearing and grading at $20,000
- 1 SCADA system and radio transmitter at $20,000
- Engineering and inspection at 12 percent of construction
- 2 acres of land at $50,000/acre

Label	Quantity	Unit	Unit Cost ($)	Cost ($)	Subtotal ($)	Element Total ($)
Tank	1	each	250,000	250,000		
Fencing	600	ft	15	9000		
Site Clearing and Grading	1	each	20,000	20,000		
SCADA System and Radio Transmitter	1	each	20,000	20,000		
Total Construction Cost					299000	
Engineering and Inspection	12	% of Construction		35,880		
Land	100,000	Lump Sum		100,000		
Total Non-Construction Cost					135,880	
Prospect Tank						434,880

Figure C-6: Tank Cost Report

Inlet (using values from a previous example), shown in Figures C-3 and C-7:

- 1 surface inlet at $2,000
- 1 subsurface structure 8 ft deep at $3,500
- Engineering and inspection at 25 percent of construction cost

Label	Quantity	Unit	Unit Cost ($)	Cost ($)	Subtotal ($)	Element Total ($)
Material and Installation	1	each	3,500	3,500		
Surface Inlet	1	each	2,000	2,000		
Total Construction Cost					5,500	
Engineering and Inspection	25	% of Construction		1,375		
Total Non-Construction Cost					1,375	
I-223						6,875

Figure C-7: Inlet Cost Report

Entering Data for Multiple Elements

Thus far, data entry has been described for individual elements. However, in most cases, unit costs are the same for a given type of item regardless of the element with which it is associated. For example, a service line may cost $1,200, and you want to use that same unit price for all elements. You can define these costs by either using: prototypes, globally editing the costs, or using unit cost functions. Each method is explained in the next sections.

Prototypes

If you know that you will be using Cost Manager before you begin your project, the Prototype feature allows you to easily establish default cost data by using the **Cost** tab, as shown in Figure C-8. For instance, if you know that all your pipes are going to have construction cost items for material and installation, valves, and service connections, you can enter these items into the construction cost table, along with their unit costs. Then, when you have finished laying out your system, you can select the Pipe Editor and update the appropriate quantity for each of these items.

For example, the pipe prototype may have an item labeled *Service Connection* with a quantity of 0 and a unit cost of 750. Then, for each element, the labels and unit costs appear with the default values from the prototype, and you only need to specify the quantity of each item.

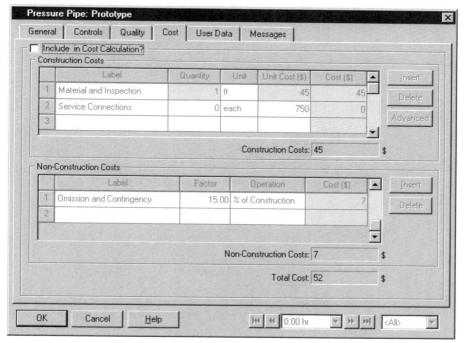

Figure C-8: Pipe Cost Prototype Dialog

Setting the Include in Cost Calculation Box

In the prototype shown in Figure C-8, cost data has been entered, but the box labeled **Include in Cost Calculation?** has not been checked. When new pipes are created in the graphical editor, their cost data will default to the values shown here, but they will not be selected for inclusion in the cost analysis. If you select **Include in Cost Calculation** in the prototype, the program will calculate costs for every element subsequently entered into the model. It may be necessary to use the Table Manager or Alternative Manager to ensure that the model is only calculating costs for the elements that the user wants included in the costing. For example, costs should not be calculated for existing pipes. The **Pressure Pipe** tab in the **Cost Alternative Editor** (shown in Figure C-9) shows how you can specify that only certain pipes are included in the cost calculation.

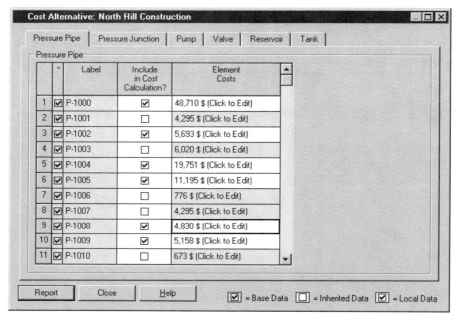

Figure C-9: Cost Alterative Editor for Pressure Pipe

Global Edit

Entering Cost Items and Unit Prices Globally

If you have already entered a system for which you would like to compute the cost, you can globally edit the cost data either through a FlexTable or the **Cost Alternative Editor**. From the **Cost Alternative Editor,** select the alternative to be edited, and choose the tab corresponding to the type of element to be edited. Then right-click the **Element Costs** column heading and select **Global Edit**. In this way, it is possible to add a global unit cost for hydrants or service lines. Then, within each element, you need only enter the quantity of these items. If necessary, you can still override the unit cost in an individual Element Editor or delete an item entirely.

Using Filters to Edit Only Some Elements

If you use FlexTables, you can easily select subsets of elements for applying different default cost data. For instance, you might want to apply a different unit cost function to a material item and an installation item for pipes having different materials. In the FlexTables, you can filter a table to view only the pipes that are made of ductile iron, and then globally edit the cost data for these pipes. You can then repeat the process for your PVC pipes. Combining element prototypes and the global editing capabilities enables you to quickly and easily enter large amounts of cost data and develop a planning-level estimate of the cost of your system.

C.3 Unit Cost Functions

Unit cost functions define a relationship between a unit cost and a certain property of an element. For pipe elements, the unit cost would be in units of $/length and might be related to the diameter of the pipe. In WaterCAD, pipes are the only elements for which unit cost functions can be defined. However, in StormCAD and SewerCAD, you can also define unit cost functions for gravity structures like inlets, junctions, and manholes. Unit cost functions for gravity structures relate the cost of the element to some property, such as structure depth. As with any function, unit cost functions can give the relationship between cost ($/length or $/structure) and an element property (diameter or structure depth) in either a tabular form or an equation.

Form of Cost Functions

Cost functions can be specified in formula (equation) or tabular (table) format as illustrated in Figures C-10 and C-11:

1. Formula unit cost function:

$$\$/\text{ft} = 0.4\,D^{1.5}$$

where D = diameter (in)

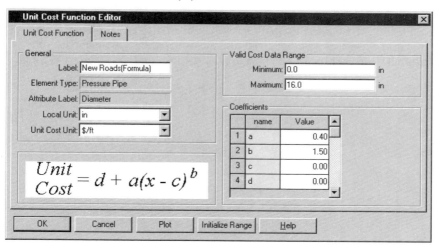

Figure C-10: Unit Cost Function Formula Editor

-OR-

2. Tabular unit cost function

D (in)	6	8	10	12	14	16
$/ft	5.90	9.00	12.60	16.60	20.90	25.60

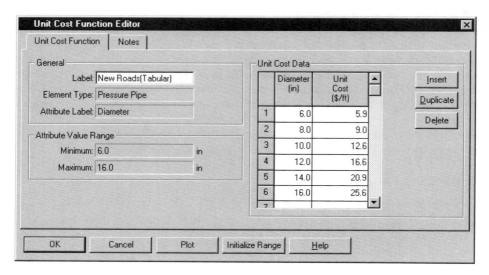

Figure C-11: Unit Cost Function Tabular Editor

The two cost functions are essentially the same at the actual discrete diameters. The format that the user chooses is strictly a matter of individual preference. Graphs of the formula and tabular unit cost functions given previously are shown in Figures C-12 and C-13.

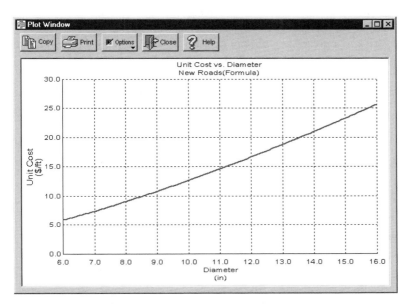

Figure C-12: Graph of Formula Unit Cost Function

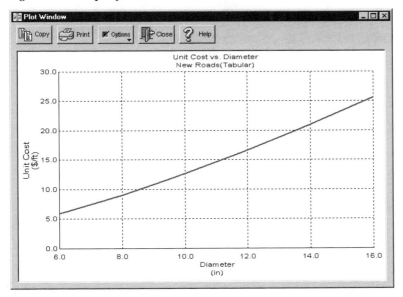

Figure C-13: Graph of Tabular Unit Cost Function

Multiple Cost Functions

Of course, not every pipe of a given size is going to have the same unit cost. Pipes laid in new subdivisions in soil generally have lower costs than pipes laid in congested downtown areas with a great deal of rock and extensive repaving. The user may therefore want to define several different cost functions corresponding to different pipes and different conditions. Each of these cost functions should be given its own unique name or label.

Some typical unit cost functions may be:

- New roads
- Cross country with rock
- Downtown urban area
- Old neighborhood
- Boring under highway

A typical list of cost functions (in this case for pipes) is shown in Figure C-14. Note that you can build a new cost function by adding it or by duplicating and editing an existing function.

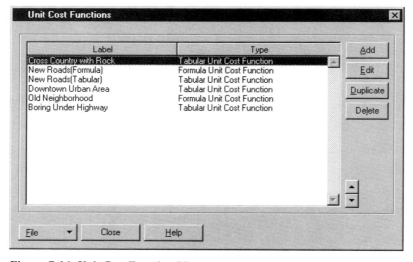

Figure C-14: Unit Cost Function Manager

Assigning Cost Functions to Elements

Once the cost functions have been named and defined, you can assign them to any number of construction cost items for each pipe being included in the cost calculations. This assignment can be made using the Pipe Editor, FlexTables, or the Cost Alternative Editor.

Entering Cost Function Data

You can enter data to construct the cost functions by selecting **Unit Cost Functions** from **Cost Manager**, or by clicking the **ellipsis (...)** button in the **Advanced Options** dialog located under the **Cost** tab of any element that supports cost functions. The units of the independent variable will be the units of that variable elsewhere in the model, whereas the units of the unit cost are $/ft or $/m for pipe and $/unit for non-pipes.

Formula Cost Functions

Defining Cost Formulas

When you decide to use a formula rather than a table to describe unit costs, you need to enter only four coefficients to describe the cost function, rather than an entire table of values. With this method, adjusting the costs for a different cost function involves changing only one or two of the coefficients of the equation rather than an entire table. The general form of the cost function is:

$$\$/ft = d + a\,(x\text{-}c)^b$$

where x = the value of an element attribute such as diameter, rise, or span (in length units

   such as inches and millimeters for diameter and feet or meters for depth)
   $a, b, c,$ and d = coefficients of the cost equation

In general, typical ranges for the coefficients for pipe cost functions in $/ft, where diameter (span) is expressed in inches, are:

   $0.4 < a < 1.0$

   $1.2 < b < 1.8$

   $0.0 < c < 20$

   $0.0 < d < 6$

The following section describes these coefficients in more detail.

Coefficients in Cost Formulas

Costs are most dependent on b because it is an exponent. It indicates how sensitive costs are to size. If costs are relatively independent of size, b is small, whereas if they vary dramatically with size, b is larger. The coefficient d represents a minimal cost for something like pavement restoration, which is independent of the size of the pipe. The coefficient a is the best parameter to adjust when converting cost from one laying/excavation condition to another.

If a user has a few data points, it is best to set c and d to zero, b to 1.6, and determine which value of the a coefficient best fits the cost data. Try using a spreadsheet graph for this. Then, adjust b to get the curvature of the cost curve, and c and d to get the correct x- and y-axis intercepts.

Tabular Cost Functions

Defining Cost Tables

Setting up a cost table simply involves typing in pairs of values in the **Unit Cost Function Editor** dialog. Although the independent variables for the formula cost functions must be numbers, the independent variables for tabular functions can be numeric or text values, as shown in Table C-3.

Table C-3: Variables for Tabular Cost Functions

Numeric Variables	Text Variables
Rise	Section Size
Structure Depth	Material Type
Structure Diameter	
Pipe Diameter	
Minor Loss Coefficient	

Note: In a circular gravity pipe, the rise and span both equal the diameter.

Complex Pipe Elements

Sometimes a single pipe may actually have different unit costs along its length. Consider a 500-ft pipe that has an 80-ft stream crossing partway along the pipe, 320 ft of cross country pipe, and 100 ft of pipe laid in an old neighborhood. There are two ways to approach costing this kind of pipe element:

- Set up three separate model elements (pipes), each with its own cost function. This method is the most straightforward way, even though it increases the number of pipes the hydraulic model must solve.

-OR-

- Set up one 500-ft pipe with the cost function for cross country pipe and add the following: a cost item for the additional cost of the stream crossing with a quantity of 80 ft and a unit price of, say, $30/ft, and a cost item for the additional cost of laying pipe in the old neighborhood with a quantity of 100 ft and a unit price of $20/ft, where the $30 and $20 represents the incremental costs for the more expensive pipe laying. The difficulty with this approach is that the add-on cost is independent of pipe size. If the add-on costs are a function of pipe size, new cost functions for those items can be defined. See Figure C-15.

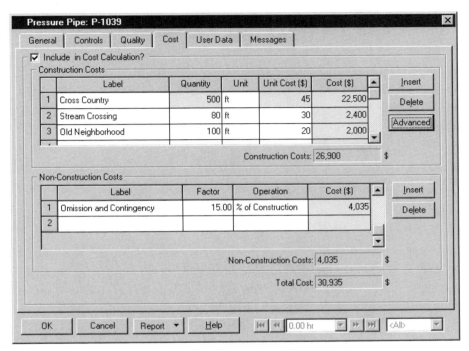

Figure C-15: Costs for a Complex Pipe Element

C.4 Building Cost Scenarios

Costs are calculated for scenarios, which are made up of physical data, demands or loads, initial settings, costs, and other alternatives. The data used in the cost calculations is primarily found in the Cost Alternative, but pipe and manhole sizes are taken from the Physical Alternative and system adjustment data is entered in **Cost Manager** under **Cost Adjustments** on a scenario basis. Values in the other alternatives, such as demands and water quality, have no impact on the cost calculations. Figure C-16 illustrates the relationship between sources of data for cost calculations.

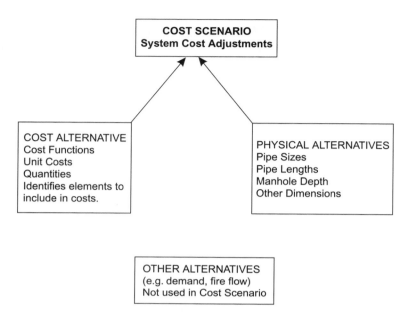

Figure C-16: Cost Scenario Diagram

Associating Costs with Scenarios

Although cost data is entered in the Element Editors, FlexTables, and Cost Alternatives, these costs must be associated with a scenario. This is done in **Scenario Manager** by selecting the **Cost Alternative** to be used with a scenario. Each scenario has a cost associated with it, which means that there may be many scenarios with the same cost. This occurs when the Cost and Physical Alternatives are the same for a particular scenario even though the scenarios may have a different demand alterative or initial condition. However, you can control which scenarios will appear in Cost Manager.

Application

Consider a pipe on Jones Street that is assigned a cost function in a Cost Alternative that is based on the diameter of the pipe. In Physical Properties Alternative 1, the pipe is given a diameter of 12 inches, and in Physical Properties Alternative 2, it is given a diameter of 16 inches. When Physical Properties Alternative 1 is combined in a scenario with the Cost Alternative, it will generate a cost for the 12-inch Jones Street pipe, and when Physical Properties Alternative 2 is combined with the Cost Alternative, it will generate a cost for the 16-inch pipe.

Using Cost Alternatives to Segregate Multiple Projects in a Plan

Cost Alternatives can also be used to separate costs into distinct projects. A Cost Alternative identifies which elements are included in the cost calculation and summary. For example, you may have ten elements, such as nine pipes and a pump station, that have costs calculated for them in the model. Seven of the pipes will be installed on the north side of town in a single project, whereas two pipes and a pump station will be installed in the south side under a different project. When defining the Cost Alternative, you set up one Cost Alternative with the seven north side pipes, and another Cost Alternative with the two south side pipes and the pump station. Checking the **Include in Cost Calculation** box in the **Cost Alternative Editor** under **Cost Manager** determines which elements are part of the cost analysis for each scenario.

C.5 Viewing Cost Results

You can view cost results on the screen, export them to spreadsheets and other software, and print them for use in reports. These reported costs can be given on an element-by-element basis in the element dialogs, aggregated by pipes and nodes in FlexTables, and on a project basis in Cost Manager. The default display units on cost are dollars ($) with no decimal places, although they can be changed to thousands of dollars (k$), and the display precision can be adjusted.

Active Scenarios

Cost Manager can calculate costs for every scenario created in Scenario Manager. However, some scenarios may share the same Cost Alternative and Physical Alternative, and differ only in the loading (demand) or initial conditions. In these cases, the costs will be the same for the different scenarios. You may therefore want to view the costs for only a few of the available scenarios. This can be done by selecting **Active Scenarios** in **Cost Manager** and checking the appropriate boxes. Only those scenarios that are selected as active in Cost Manager will have costs calculated for them.

Use of Cost FlexTables

The cost reports are formatted as FlexTables, so the columns can be adjusted and display properties changed. The tables can also be exported to a tab-delimited or comma-delimited file, or copied to the Windows Clipboard and pasted into other software. The actual values displayed in the cells — not the formulas — are copied, so the numerical values should not be adjusted once they are exported. That is, if the unit cost or quantity changes, the totals will not automatically be updated in the spreadsheet. See Figure C-17.

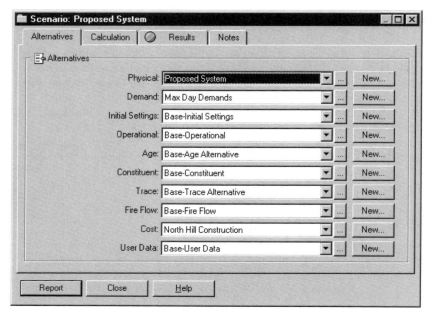

Figure C-17: Cost Report Dialog

Individual Element Costs

For any element, costs can be viewed under the **Cost** tab of the **Element** dialog. If there are more than three construction or non-construction costs, not all will be visible at once. The costs can be viewed in a report like the one shown in Figure C-18 by selecting **Report** followed by **Cost Report** from the pull-down menus. To obtain a printout, select **Print Preview** and **Print**.

Label	Quantity	Unit	Unit Cost ($)	Cost ($)	Subtotal ($)	Element Total ($)
Tank	1	each	250,000	250,000		
Fencing	600	ft	15	9,000		
Site Clearing and Grading	1	each	20,000	20,000		
SCADA System and Radio Transmitter	1	each	20,000	20,000		
Total Construction Cost					299,000	
Engineering and Inspection	12	% of Construction		35,880		
Land	100,000	Lump Sum		100,000		
Total Non-Construction Cost					135,880	
Prospect Tank						434,880

Figure C-18: Sample Cost Report

Node and Pipe Cost Tables

Just as models contain some standard pipe and node tables, they also contain standard cost tables. These can be viewed from the Tabular Reports dialog by selecting **Node Cost Report** or **Pipe Cost Report.** In this view, it is possible to sort or filter elements and use all the functionality of FlexTables to customize the look of the table. The table can also be exported, copied, and printed. You can filter out elements not included in the cost calculation by selecting **Options, Filter,** and then **Custom.**

Cost Scenario Tables

The costs can be viewed for an entire scenario (project) in Cost Manager itself. The costs are presented in a tree structure such that the user can expand or collapse various branches of the tree to suit the level of detail desired.

More attractive tables are available by selecting **Cost Reports**. There are four levels of detail available, as shown in the following examples:

Detailed tables show all unit costs and quantities, as illustrated in the following figure.

Label	Quantity	Unit	Unit Cost ($)	Cost ($)	Element Total ($)	Subtotal ($)	Project Total ($)
Manhole							
MH-17							
Material and Installation	1	each	5,800	5,800			
Total Construction Cost				5,800			
Engineering	12	% of Construction		696			
Total Non-Construction Cost				696			
Total Cost: MH-17					6,496		
Total Cost: Manhole						6,496	
Pressure Junction							
J-1							
Material and Installation	1	each	3,600	3,600			
Total Construction Cost				3,600			
Engineering	12	% of Construction		432			
Total Non-Construction Cost				432			
Total Cost: J-1					4,032		
Total Cost: Pressure Junction						4,032	
Gravity Pipe							
P-01							
Material and Installation	20	m	200	3,920			
Total Construction Cost				3,920			
Engineering	12	% of Construction		470			
Total Non-Construction Cost				470			
Total Cost: P-01					4,390		
Total Cost: Gravity Pipe						4,390	
Pressure Pipe							
FM-03							
Material and Installation	153	m	100	15,300			
Total Construction Cost				15,300			
Engineering	12	% of Construction		1,836			
Total Non-Construction Cost				1,836			
Total Cost: FM-03					17,136		
FM-04							

Label	Quantity	Unit	Unit Cost ($)	Cost ($)	Element Total ($)	Subtotal ($)	Project Total ($)
Material and Installation	50	m	100	5,000			
Total Construction Cost				5,000			
Engineering	12	% of Construction		600			
Total Non-Construction Cost				600			
Total Cost: FM-04					5,600		
FM-02							
Material and Installation	70	m	100	7,000			
Total Construction Cost				7,000			
Engineering	12	% of Construction		840			
Total Non-Construction Cost				840			
Total Cost: FM-02					7,840		
FM-01							
Material and Installation	123	m	100	12,300			
Total Construction Cost				12,300			
Engineering	12	% of Construction		1,476			
Total Non-Construction Cost				1,476			
Total Cost: FM-01					13,776		
FM-05							
Material and Installation	526	m	120	63,120			
Total Construction Cost				63,120			
Engineering	12	% of Construction		7,574			
Total Non-Construction Cost				7,574			
Total Cost: FM-05					70,694		
Total Cost: Pressure Pipe						115,046	
Total Cost: Proposed, Large Pipes							129,964

Figure C-19: Detailed Cost Report

Element Summary tables give construction and non-construction costs for each element, as illustrated in Figure C-20.

Label	Construction Costs ($)	Non-Construction Costs ($)	Element Total ($)	Subtotal ($)	Project Total ($)
Manhole					
MH-17	5,800	696	6,496		
Total Cost: Manhole				6,496	
Pressure Junction					
J-1	3,600	432	4,032		
Total Cost: Pressure Junction				4,032	
Gravity Pipe					
P-01	3,920	470	4,390		
Total Cost: Gravity Pipe				4,390	
Pressure Pipe					
FM-03	15,300	1,836	17,136		
FM-04	5,000	600	5,600		
FM-02	7,000	840	7,840		
FM-01	12,300	1,476	13,776		
FM-05	63,120	7,574	70,694		
Total Cost: Pressure Pipe				115,046	
Total Cost: Proposed, Large Pipes					129,964

Figure C-20: Element Summary Cost Report

Project Summary tables give totals for each type of element (pipes, tanks, etc.), as illustrated in Figure C-21.

Label	Construction Costs ($)	Non-Construction Costs ($)	Total Cost ($)
Manhole	5,800	696	6,496
Pressure Junction	3,600	432	4,032
Gravity Pipe	3,920	470	4,390
Pressure Pipe	102,720	12,326	115,046
Total Cost: Proposed, Large Pipes			129,964

Figure C-21: Project Summary Cost Report

Pipe Costs tables give the total length and cost for the pipes included in the cost analysis, as illustrated in Figure C-22.

Pressure Pipe-Ductile Iron			
Material	Section Size	Length (m)	Total Cost ($)
Ductile Iron	300.0 mm	526.00	70,694
Ductile Iron	150.0 mm	396.00	44,352

Circular-Concrete			
Material	Section Size	Length (m)	Total Cost ($)
Concrete	450 mm	72.10	16,150
Concrete	200 mm	537.50	60,200
Concrete	300 mm	559.00	93,912

Figure C-22: Pipe Cost Report

Gravity Flow Diversions

D.1 What Are Diversions?

Most system structures (manholes and wet wells, for example) have only a single outlet pipe, because of the treelike structure of gravity storm and sanitary sewer systems. However, in certain situations, there can be more than one way for water to leave a node or to leave the sewer system altogether. A node with more than one outflow pipe is called a *diversion node.*

Some examples of diversions are combined sewer overflows, flow out of a manhole due to a hydraulic restriction downstream, multi-barrel sewers, relief sewers, pump station flooding, diversion of flow into a holding tank or tunnel, and basement flooding.

Both SewerCAD and StormCAD have the ability to estimate the diversion rate and to designate a pathway for the redirected flow. The diverted flows are fully accounted for in the network. This feature is extremely useful for simulating combined sewer overflows (CSOs). This appendix presents the fundamentals of modeling diversions.

What Happens to the Flow at a Diversion Node?

All of the flows from upstream pipes, incoming flows diverted from other nodes in the system, and local loads are summed to give the total upstream flow for the diversion node. The total upstream flow is then split between the downstream pipe and the diversion target (that is, another node or out of the system), as shown in Figure D-1.

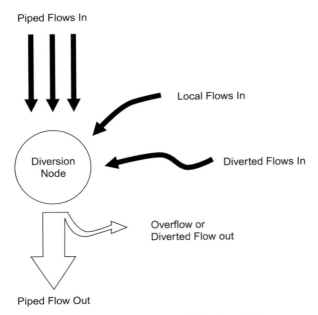

Piped Flows In

Local Flows In

Diversion Node

Diverted Flows In

Overflow or
Diverted Flow out

Piped Flow Out

Figure D-1: Definition of Flows at Diversion Node

Why Do Diversions Only Exist in Gravity Systems?

Pressure flow systems can have multiple loops. Thus, the flow split at any pressure node can be calculated directly from the continuity and energy equations. However, in gravity systems, the calculation of the quantity of water going in each direction is considerably more complicated, necessitating a special diversion node.

Is a Surcharged Gravity Pipe Considered a Pressure Pipe?

A gravity pipe can flow less than full, but a pressure pipe must always be full. In terms of diversions, a gravity pipe that is full, or surcharged, is still treated as a gravity pipe.

How Can a User Model a Node as a Diversion?

You can indicate that a node is a diversion by checking the **Has Diversion?** box on the **Diversion** tab of the node's element editor. This check mark indicates that flow is diverted out of that diversion node. The flow can then be diverted to a downstream node that is specified in the **Diversion Target** field, as shown in Figure D-2, or it can simply overflow out of the system, as shown in Figure D-3.

Figure D-2: Diversion Tab for Diversion Node with Target Node

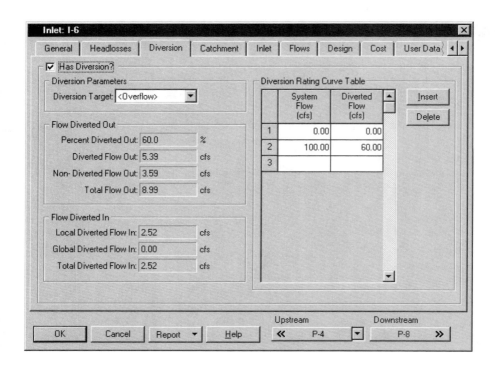

Figure D-3: Diversion Tab for Diversion Node with Overflow

When flow is diverted to a target node, the target node will have a non-zero value in the **Total Diverted Flow In** field for that scenario, as shown in Figure D-4. For example, if node M-17 diverts flow to node M-37, node M-17 is the diversion node and it will identify node M-37 as the diversion target. Node M-37 will have non-zero values for **Local Diverted Flow In** and **Total Diverted Flow In.**

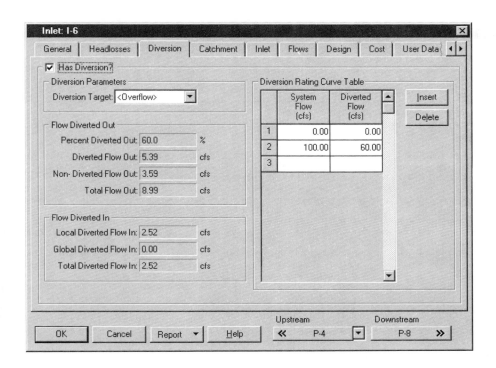

Figure D-4: Diversion Tab for Target Node

What Happens to the Diverted Flow?

The diverted flow can either leave the system completely, as in an overflow, or return to the system at a downstream node, as in the case of a parallel relief sewer. In the latter instance, the downstream node, referred to as the *diversion target,* can be located either in the same network (tree-shaped layout) or in another subnetwork altogether (see Figures D-5 and D-6).

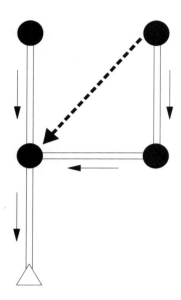

Figure D-5: Diversion to Lower Point in Network

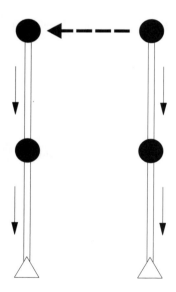

Figure D-6: Diversion to Another Subnetwork

Are There Any Rules for the Diversion Target?

If the diversion target is not an overflow, it must be located downstream of the diversion node or in a separate subnetwork, such that water cannot be circulated back to the upstream side of the diversion through a loop. Looping flow back upstream of the diversion node creates a mathematical anomaly that prevents the model from solving properly.

You do not need to ensure that diversion targets are valid. The program will automatically determine the valid diversion targets and offer them as options.

In validating diversion targets, downstream nodes are defined as the nodes between the diversion node and the outlet, as well as all nodes in branches that merge into downstream nodes. The most important thing is that the diversion does not create a loop in the system (see Figures D-7 and D-8).

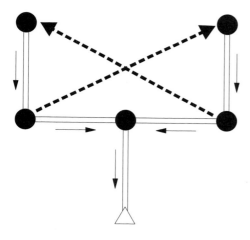

Figure D-7: Looped Diversion Not Allowed

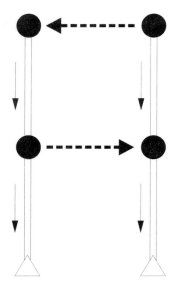

Figure D-8: Looped Network Not Allowed

If there are two diversions in series, the target node for the upstream diversion must be upstream of the target node for the downstream diversion.

A diversion can divert flow to any node in another network, as long as the target network is downstream from the diversion network. A diversion network is considered to be upstream from a target network if any node in the diversion network is diverting flow to a node in the target network (see Figure D-9).

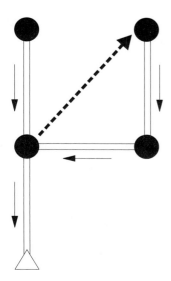

Figure D-9: Diversion to Upstream Node Not Allowed

What Does a Diversion Look Like in the Drawing?

When a diversion is applied to a node, the node is automatically annotated with one of the symbols shown in the following figures. Figure D-10 represents an overflow diversion, and Figure D-11 is a regular diversion with a specified diversion target.

Figure D-10: Symbol for Diversion to Overflow

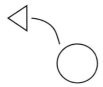

Figure D-11: Symbol for Diversion to Target Node

Additionally, the Diversion Network window provides a graphical view of the diversion network. The links in the diversion network indicate the directions of diverted flow. The diversion network is displayed with the existing sewer network as the background.

What Is the Diversion Network View?

The Diversion Network view shows a plot of the network that allows you to see where the flows are diverted in the system. Clicking the **Diversion Network** button or selecting **Tools\Diversion Network** opens the Diversion Network view. In this view, overflow diversions appear as single nodes, and the association between a diversion and its diversion target is represented with a straight bold line, as shown in Figure D-12. The arrow on the line indicates the direction of diverted flow.

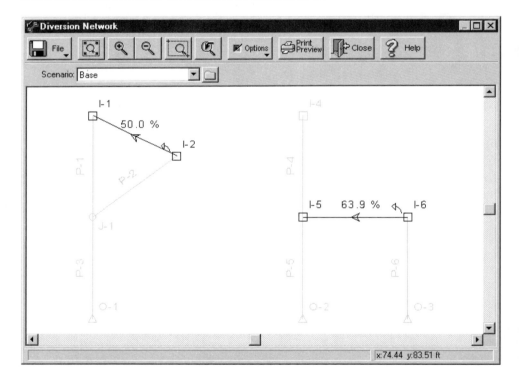

Figure D-12: Diversion Network View

What Happens to Flow that Is Not Diverted?

Flow that is not diverted is specified in the **Non-diverted Flow Out** field in the node's element editor. It is the difference between the total upstream flow and the diverted flow, and it is passed to the downstream pipe.

What Is the Difference Between Local and Global Diversions in the Model?

The terms *Local* and *Global* in relation to diverted flow refer to the node receiving the diverted flow, and indicate whether the flow came from another point in the same network or from a different pipe network. Therefore, a local diversion is a node that is receiving diverted flow from within the same network, whereas a global diversion receives flow from outside the network, as illustrated in Figures D-13 and D-14.

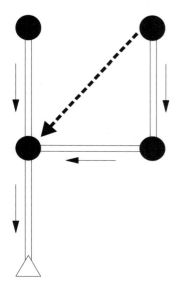

Figure D-13: Local Diversions

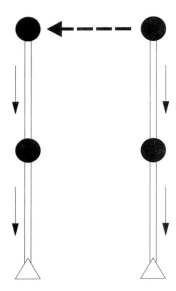

Figure D-14: Global Diversions

How Does a Diversion Node Split the Flow between Flow Being Piped Downstream and Flow Being Diverted?

Although in theory it is possible to hydraulically determine the flow split given tailwater conditions and detailed descriptions of the hydraulic characteristics of the diversion, most users do not have that kind of data available. Instead, users enter "rating curves" describing how the diversion structure splits the flow.

D.2 Rating Curves

A *rating curve* for a diversion determines the amount of flow that is diverted given the total flow into the diversion node. A rating curve is a function, shown as a table or a graph, such that for any inflow value there is only one value for diverted flow. The diverted flow must always be nonnegative and less than or equal to the total upstream flow.

How Many Data Points Do I Need to Describe a Rating Curve?

The model uses linear interpolation and extrapolation to calculate diversions. If the flow is diverted proportionately over the entire range of flows, only two points are needed to describe the rating curve. If the rating curve has a great deal of curvature, significantly more points are needed to adequately represent the curve to the model. Some typical rating curves are described next and shown in Figure D-15.

- Proportional split (for example, parallel relief sewer)

- All flow diverted (for example, downstream blockage, power outage at pump station)

- Threshold flow with excess diverted (for example, weir, regulator)

- Initial throttling of flow (for example, vortex regulator)

Figure D-16- shows a rating curve as displayed in the model.

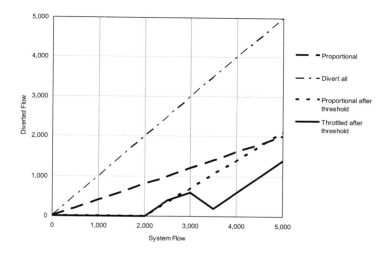

Figure D-15: Typical Rating Curves

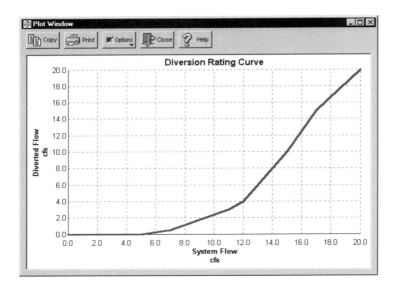

Figure D-16: Rating Curve as Displayed in the Model

How Can the Values for the Rating Curve Be Determined?

The most accurate way to determine the values for the rating curve is to take field measurements of two of the three possible flows (upstream, direct, and diverted flow) at the diversion node for a range of upstream flows. Because it is best to make these measurements for as wide a range of flows as possible, it is recommended to conduct the testing during wet weather periods.

What If Flow Measurements Cannot Be Obtained?

In the absence of flow measurements, the manufacturers of some diversion structures may be able to provide a table of flow capacity, or minor loss k-values, for various sizes and settings of the control device (for example, valve, regulator, weir, orifice, or vortex controller). Otherwise, some reasonable estimates must be made and possibly adjusted during calibration.

D.3 Special Cases

What Can Be Done for Overflows Caused By a Hydraulic Restriction Downstream?

If the overflow (diversion) is due to limited flow capacity downstream, steady-state model runs may be used to determine the downstream flow capacity. The model can be run for a range of flows in the pipe downstream of the diversion. There will be some flow above which the hydraulic grade line exceeds the manhole rim elevation. Any flow beyond that rate will be diverted. Although this value is an approximation, it may be adequate for preliminary modeling. A typical curve showing HGL vs. flow rate for several runs is shown in Figure D-17. In this example, if the rim elevation is 826 ft, the threshold flow is 3200 gpm, and any flow over that is likely to be diverted.

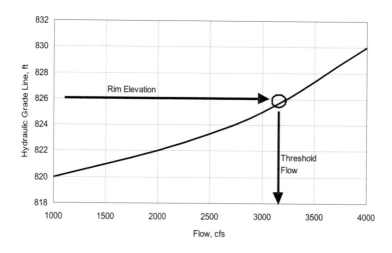

Figure D-17: Threshold Flow Graph

If a Hydraulic Restriction Causes an Overflow Upstream, Should the Diversion Node Be at the Location of the Restriction or the Overflow?

The diversion node should be located at the point of overflow, or where the flow actually leaves the collection system.

How Can Parallel Relief Sewers Be Modeled?

There are several ways to model such situations:

Identical pipes. This case is modeled explicitly in Haestad Methods software. In this case, you do not need to use diversions. To model a sewer reach with multiple equivalent pipes, set the **Number of Sections** field to the number of parallel equivalent pipe barrels.

Equivalent pipes. If the sections of the parallel pipes do not have the same diameter, you can determine the diameter of the equivalent pipe using Manning's equation, as follows:

$$D_e = (D_1^{8/3} + D_2^{8/3})^{3/8}$$

where D_e = diameter of equivalent pipe
          D_1 = diameter of first parallel pipe
          D_2 = diameter of second parallel pipe

For example, to determine the equivalent diameter of a 12-in. and 16-in. pipe in parallel, the equation becomes:

$$D_e = (12^{8/3} + 16^{8/3})^{3/8} = 18.4 \text{ in}$$

Diversion. The two pipes can also be modeled as a pipe in the system with a second pipe diverting flow to a downstream node. In this case, you will generally use the larger pipe as the direct flow pipe and the smaller one as the diversion. The flow split should be proportional to the diameters to the 8/3 power. This relationship is given by the following equation:

$$\frac{Q_2}{Q_t} = \left(\frac{D_2^{8/3}}{D_1^{8/3} + D_2^{8/3}} \right)$$

where Q_2 = diverted flow
          Q_t = total upstream flow
          D_1 = diameter of direct flow pipe
          D_2 = diameter of diversion pipe

For example, if the parallel pipes have diameters of 16 in. and 12 in., and the diversion is the 12-inch pipe, the fraction of flow split into the 12-inch pipe is:

$$\frac{Q_2}{Q_t} = \frac{12^{8/3}}{16^{8/3} + 12^{8/3}} = 0.37$$

and the rating curve is given by Table D-1.

Table D-1: Sample Rating Curve

Upstream Flow (gpm)	Diverted Flow (gpm)
0	0
1000	370

How Can Diversions Be Used to Model Off-Line Storage?

Steady-state methodologies (such as the Rational Method for hydrology or Extreme Flow Factor loading for a sanitary sewer) are based solely on rates of flow, not volumes of flow. In order to determine volume of storage, you need to multiply flow rate by the duration of the flow rate. If sizing of storage is the primary purpose for using the analysis, Haestad Methods' PondPack may be a more appropriate model.

How Should the Models Be Used to Handle Basement Flooding?

To the extent that basement flooding can be represented by a rating curve, the gravity flow models can predict the rate of flooding. However, in most cases, the volume of water flowing into a basement is small compared with the total flow in the pipe, and you are only interested in knowing whether or not basement flooding is occurring. Therefore, it may be more useful to simply monitor the hydraulic grade line (HGL) in the vicinity of the suspected basement flooding. If the HGL exceeds a threshold value, basement flooding is likely to occur. This threshold value needs to be determined based on experience with the system.

In Some Cases, the Tailwater Depth in the Receiving Stream Can Affect the Rating Curve. Can This Be Modeled?

There is only a single rating curve for any diversion in a given run. If there are different rating curves for different tailwater depths, you can utilize Scenario Manager (covered in Appendix B) to set up multiple rating curves based on the range of tailwater depths, run the different scenarios simultaneously, and compare the results.

Can I Divert Water Uphill?

The model allows you to divert flow uphill, such as in the case of flow that is diverted via a pump. If uphill diversions are not desired, you need to check that the invert, or sump, of the diversion target node is at a lower elevation than the invert of the diversion node. It is your responsibility to determine whether such a diversion is physically possible, as in the case of a pumped diversion or one that activates only when a manhole or wet well is surcharged.

Where Can I Enter and View Data on Diversions in Scenario Manager?

Data on diversions is considered to be physical data, and is therefore stored within a scenario under the current Physical Alternative on the **Manhole** or **Junction Chamber** tab.

How Can I Divert Flows Out of a Wet Well in SewerCAD?

If the overflow occurs at a wet well, you should place a fictitious manhole immediately upstream of the wet well and define the diversion there.

D.4 Model Loading

Which Program, StormCAD or SewerCAD, Should I Use to Model My Diversions?

Both models have essentially the same logic for handling diversions. The decision on which model to use depends on the way that flow will be loaded into the model. If most of the inflow is rainfall (or snowmelt) in a combined sewer system, StormCAD has better capability for determining flows. If most of the flow results from normal municipal and industrial sanitary loads, SewerCAD is more suitable for determining flows. If the collection system is a mixture of sanitary and combined sewers, the wet weather events are usually of the greatest interest, and StormCAD is the preferred model.

SewerCAD Has the Ability to Calculate Extreme Flow Factors. How Do Diversions Affect This?

The calculations in the model at the diversion node are not made in flow units but in terms of loads (catchment area and population). It is these loads that are diverted. If peaking factors are not used, the results will be the same whether the calculations are done in loading or flow units. However, if peaking factors are used, fewer loading units are passed downstream and the peaking factor is increased. In terms of flow units, it will appear that the sum of the flows out of the diversion is larger than the sum of the flows in.

Bibliography

AASHTO Task Force on Hydrology and Hydraulics. (1991). *Model Drainage Manual*, American Association of Highway and Transportation Officials, Washington, DC.

American Society of Civil Engineers. (1982). *Design and Construction of Urban Stormwater Management Systems,* American Society of Civil Engineers, New York.

American Society of Civil Engineers. (1982). *Gravity Sanitary Sewer Design and Construction,* American Society of Civil Engineers, New York.

Babbitt, H.E. and Baumann, E.R. (1958). *Sewerage and Sewage Treatment*, John Wiley & Sons, New York.

Benedict, R. P. (1980). *Fundamentals of Pipe Flow,* John Wiley & Sons, New York.

Brater, E. F. and King, H.W. (1976). *Handbook of Hydraulics,* McGraw-Hill, New York.

Brown, S.A., Stein, S.M. and Warner, J.C. (1996). *Urban Drainage Design Manual, Hydraulic Engineering Circular No. 22*, U.S. Department of Transportation, Federal Highway Administration, Washington, DC.

Cesario, A. L. (1995). *Modeling, Analysis, and Design of Water Distribution Systems*, American Water Works Association, Denver, Colorado.

Chow, V. T. (1959). *Open-Channel Hydraulics,* McGraw-Hill Book Company, New York.

Clark, R. M., Grayman, W.M., Males, R.M. and Hess, A.F. (1993). "Modeling Contaminant propagation in Drinking Water Distribution Systems", *Journal of Environmental Engineering*, ASCE, 119(2), 349.

Joint Committee of the American Society of Civil Engineers and the Water Pollution Control Federation. (1969). *Design and Construction of Sanitary and Storm Sewers,* ASCE Manual of Practice, No. 37. New York.

Debo, T. N. and Reese, A.J. (1995). *Municipal Storm Water Management,* CRC Press, Boca Raton, Florida.

Durrans, Rocky (2002). *Stormwater Conveyance Modeling and Design.* Haestad Press, Waterbury, Connecticut.

Featherstone, R.E. and C. Nalluri, C. (1982). *Civil Engineering Hydraulics,* Granada, New York.

Federal Aviation Agency (FAA), Advisory Circular on Airport Drainage, (1970). "Report A/C 150-5320-58," U.S. Department of Transportation, Washington, DC.

Frederick, R.H., Meyers, V.A., Auciello, E.P. (1977). "Five to 60-minute Precipitation Frequency for the Eastern and Central Unites States, NOAA Technical Memorandum NEW Hydro-35", www.nws.noaa.gov/oh/hdsc/studies/prcpfreq.html

French, R.H. (1985). *Open-Channel Hydraulics,* McGraw-Hill, New York.

Great Lakes-Upper Mississippi River Board of Sanitary Engineers. (1978). *Recommended Standards for Sewage Works*, Health Education Service, Albany, New York.

Hathaway, 1945 Hathaway, G.A. (1945). "Design of Drainage Facilities," *Transactions, American Society of Civil Engineers,* 110, 697.

Harmon, W.G. (1918). "Forecasting Sewage at Toledo under Dry Weather Conditions," *Engineering News-Record,* 80.

Haestad Methods. (2001). *SewerCAD v5 for Windows,* Haestad Methods, Waterbury, Connecticut.

Haestad Methods. (2000). *CulvertMaster V 2.0 for Windows*, Haestad Methods, Waterbury, Connecticut.

Haestad Methods. (2000). *FlowMaster PE v6.1 User's Guide for Windows*, Haestad Methods, Waterbury, Connecticut.

Haestad Methods. (2000). *StormCAD v4.1 for Windows,* Haestad Methods, Waterbury, Connecticut.

Haestad Methods. (2000). *WaterCAD for Windows*, Haestad Methods, Waterbury, Connecticut.

Haestad Methods. (1999). *PondPack V 7 for Windows*, Haestad Methods, Waterbury, Connecticut.

HEC No. 19, Hydrology, Federal Highway Administration, 1984.

Henderson, F.M. (1966). *Open Channel Flow*, Macmillan Publishing Co. Inc., New York.

Henderson, F.M., and Wooding, R.A. (1964). Overland Flow and Groundwater Flow from a Steady Rain of Finite Duration, *Journal of Geophysical Research,* 69(8), 1531.

Hersfield, D.M. (1961). "Rainfall Frequency Atlas of the United States for Durations from 30 Minutes to 24 Hours and Return Periods from 1 to 100 Years," Tech. Paper 40, U.S. Department of Commerce, Weather Bureau, www.nws.noaa.gov/oh/hdsc/studies/prcpfreq.html.

Horton, R.E. (1939). "Analysis of Runoff Experiments with Varying Infiltration Capacity," *Transactions of the American Geophysical Union*, 20.

Huff, F.A. and Angle, J.R. (1992). "Rainfall Frequency Atlas of the Midwest," Illinois State Water Survey, Champaign IL, Bulletin 71.

Hwang, N. H. C. and Hita, C.E. (1987). *Hydraulic Engineering Systems,* Prentice-Hall, Englewood Cliffs, New Jersey.

Hydraulics Research Station. (1951). "Velocity Equations for Hydraulic Design of Pipes", Metric edition, HMSO, London.

Izzard, C.F. (1946). "Hydraulics of Runoff from Developed Surfaces," *Proceedings, Highway Research Board,* 26, 129.

Jakovlev, S.V., Karelm J.A.A., Zukov A.I., Kolobanov Siki. (1975). *Kanalizacja*, Stroizdat, Moscow.

Johnstone, D., and Cross, W.P. (1949). *Elements of Applied Hydrology,* Ronald Press, New York.

Kerby, W.S. (1959). "Time of Concentration Studies," *Civil Engineering,* March.

Kirpich, Z.P. (1940). "Time of Concentration of Small Agricultural Watersheds, Civil Engineering, 10(6).

Males R. M., Grayman, W.M., and Lark, R.M. (1988)."Modeling Water Quality in Distribution System," *Journal of Water Resources Planning and Management*, ASCE, 114, 197-209.

Mays, L.W. (2001). *Stormwater Collection Systems Design Handbook.* McGraw-Hill, New York.

Measurement of Peak Discharge at Culverts by Indirect Methods, U. S. Department of the Interior, 1982.

McKay, M. and Wilkes, D.S. (1995). *Atlas of Short-Duration Precipitation Extremes for the Northeastern United States and Canada.* Northeast Regional Climate Center Research Series Publication No. RR95-1, Ithaca, New York.

Metcalf & Eddy. (1981). *Wastewater Engineering: Collection and Pumping of Wastewater.* McGraw-Hill, Inc., New York.

Miller, J.F., Frederick, R.H. and R.J. Tracey, R.J. (1973). "Precipitation-Frequency Atlas of the Coterminous Western United States, NOAA Atlas 2, 11 vols." National Weather Service, Silver Spring, MD.

National Resources Conservation Service, (2001). National Engineering Handbook Part 630 – Hydrology, U.S. Department of Agriculture, Washington, DC, http://www.wcc.nrcs.usda.gov/water/ quality/common/neh630/4content.html

Normann, J. M., Houghtalen, R.J. and Johnson, W.J. (2001). *Hydraulic Design Of Highway Culverts, Hydraulic Design Series No. 5, Second Edition.* Federal Highway Administration; Washington, D.C.

Pilgrim, D.H. (1987). *Australian Rainfall and Runoff.* The Institute of Engineers, Barton, Australia, 1987.

Rawls, W., Yates, P. and Asmussen, L. (1976). "Calibration of Selected Infiltration Equations for the Georgia Coastal Plain," Technical Report ARS-S-113, U.S. Dept. of Agriculture, Agricultural Research Service, Washington, DC.

Roberson, J.A. and Crowe, C.T. (1990). *Engineering Fluid Mechanics (4th Edition).* Houghton Mifflin Company, Boston, Massachusetts.

Roberson, J.A., Cassidy, J.J. and Chaudhry, H.M. (1988). *Hydraulic Engineering.* Houghton Mifflin Company, Boston, Massachusetts.

Rossman, L.A. and Boulos, P.F. (1996). "Numerical Methods for Modeling Water Quality in Distribution Systems: A Comparison." *Journal of Water Resources Planning and Management*, ASCE, 122(2), 137.

Rossman, L. A. (1993). *EPANet User's Manual (AWWA Workshop Edition).* Risk Reduction Engineering Laboratory, Office of Research and Development, USEPA, Cincinnati, Ohio.

Rossman, L. A., Clark, R.M. and Grayman, W.M. (1994)."Modeling Chlorine Residuals in Drinking-water Distribution Systems," *Journal of Environmental Engineering*, ASCE, 120(4), 803.

Sanks, R. L. (1989). *Pumping Station Design*, Butterworth-Heinemann, Inc, Stoneham, Massachusetts.

Schaake, J.C. Jr., Geyer, J.C. and Knapp, J.W. (1967). "Experimental Examination of the Rational Method," *Journal of the Hydraulics Division,* ASCE, 93(HY6).

Simon, A.L. (1976). *Practical Hydraulics.* New York: John Wiley & Sons, Inc.

Singh, V.P., (1988). *Hydrologic systems, Volume I.- Rainfall-runoff Modeling.* Prentice Hall, Englewood Cliffs, New Jersey.

Singh, V.P. (1992). *Elementary Hydrology.* Prentice Hall, Englewood Cliffs, New Jersey.

Soil Conservation Service. (1969). National Engineering Handbook, Section 4, Chapter 16, National Resources Conservation Service, www.wcc.nrcs.usda.gov/water/quality/common/neh630/4content.html

Soil Conservation Service. (1986). *TR-55, Urban Hydrology for Small Watersheds*, U.S. Department of Agriculture, Natural Resources Conservation Service, Engineering Division, http://www.wcc.nrcs.usda.gov/water /quality/common/tr55/tr55.pdf

Strafraci, A.M. (1998). *Essential Hydraulics and Hydrology*, Haestad Press, Waterbury, Connecticut.

Streeter, V. L., Wylie, E.B. (1985). *Fluid Mechanics,* McGraw-Hill, New York, 1985.

Urban Water Resources Research Council of the ASCE and the WEF. (1992). *Design and Construction of Urban Stormwater Management Systems ASCE Manuals and Reports of Engineering Practice No. 77 and WEF Manual of Practice FD-20*, ASCE Reston, Virginia.

Van Havern, B.P. (1986). *Water Resources Measurements*, American Water Works Association, Denver, Colorado.

Walski, Thomas M. (2002). *Advanced Water Distribution Modeling and Management.* Haestad Methods, Waterbury, Connecticut.

Walski, Thomas M. (2002). *Sanitary Sewer Modeling.* Haestad Methods, Waterbury, Connecticut.

Walski, Thomas M. (1993). *Water System Modeling Using CYBERNET®*, Haestad Methods, Waterbury, Connecticut.

Williams, G.B. (1922). "Flood Discharges and the Dimensions of Spillways in India," *Engineering* (London), 134, 321.

Wanielista, M. P. (1990). *Hydrology and Water Quantity Control.* John Wiley & Sons, New York, 1990.

Zipparro, V. J. and Hasen, H. (1993). *Davis' Handbook of Applied Hydraulics.* McGraw-Hill, New York, 1993.

Index

Notes

Notes

Notes

Notes

Notes

Notes

Notes

✒ Notes

Notes

Computer Applications in Hydraulic Engineering

DATE	ISSUED TO
~~due~~	name/student #/ph #
Mar 4/05	Quak lee 24Sept03

DATE	ISSUED TO
due	name/student #/ph #

TC 157.8 C653 2002

Computer Applications in Hydraulic Engineering

Date Due

END-USER LICENSE AGREEMENT

IMPORTANT, PLEASE READ CAREFULLY: This Haestad Methods, Inc. (HMI) End-User License Agreement (Agreement) is a legal agreement between HMI and you (either an individual or a single entity, such as a partnership, corporation, LLC, or other entity) for the HMI software product contained in this package (SOFTWARE). The SOFTWARE includes computer software on associated media and printed materials, and may include on-line or electronic documentation. By installing, copying, or otherwise using the SOFTWARE, you agree to be bound by the terms of this Agreement. If you do not agree with the terms of this Agreement, do not install, copy or use the SOFTWARE, but promptly return the package and unused SOFTWARE to HMI.

GRANT OF LICENSE: The SOFTWARE is licensed, not sold, from HMI to you. HMI retains ownership of the software and any and all copies that you make of it. This SOFTWARE is licensed for the sole use of the original licensee, at the original location, on a single computer. You may install one copy of the SOFTWARE on a single computer at a single location for use by one person at a time. You may not install the SOFTWARE on a server or networked computer unless you first obtain from HMI a license for each computer or station connected to that server or networked computer that has access to the SOFTWARE. A license for the SOFTWARE may not be shared or used concurrently.

ACADEMIC EDITION LICENSE: The SOFTWARE is licensed for academic purposes only. Professional or commercial use is strictly prohibited under the terms of this agreement.

SOFTWARE TRANSFER: This Software License is not transferable. This SOFTWARE is licensed for the sole use of the original licensee, at the original location, on a single computer.

RENTAL: You may not rent or lease the SOFTWARE.

TERMINATION: Without prejudice to any other rights, HMI may terminate this Agreement if you fail to comply with its terms and conditions. If HMI notifies you that it has terminated this Agreement, you agree to immediately destroy all copies of the SOFTWARE and all of its component parts.

UPGRADES: If the SOFTWARE is an upgrade of an older HMI software product, you agree to destroy or return to HMI all copies of the older HMI software product within thirty (30) days of installing the upgrade.

COPYRIGHT: The SOFTWARE is protected by copyright and other intellectual property law in the United States of America and in other countries by international treaties. Therefore, you may not make or sell copies of the SOFTWARE, except that you may either (a) make one copy of the SOFTWARE solely for backup or archival purposes, or (b) install the SOFTWARE on a single computer and keep the original copy solely for backup or archival purposes. You may not make or sell copies of the printed or on-line materials accompanying the SOFTWARE.

WARRANTY: For a period of one (1) year after you receive this SOFTWARE (regardless of whether you use the SOFTWARE during the one year period), HMI warrants that the media on which it is contained will not be defective. In the event that during this warranty period the media containing the SOFTWARE is defective, your sole remedy is to contact HMI and HMI in its sole discretion will (a) replace or repair the defective media or (b) refund your money upon your returning to HMI the original and all copies of the SOFTWARE.

DISCLAIMER OF WARRANTIES: EXCEPT FOR THE EXPRESS WARRANTY STATED ABOVE, THE SOFTWARE IS PROVIDED 'AS IS' AND WITHOUT WARRANTY OF ANY KIND, EXPRESSED OR IMPLIED, INCLUDING BUT NOT LIMITED TO ANY IMPLIED WARRANTIES OF MERCHANTABILITY OR FITNESS FOR A PARTICULAR PURPOSE. THE ENTIRE RISK AS TO THE QUALITY AND PERFORMANCE OF THE SOFTWARE LIES WITH YOU.

LIMITATIONS OF LIABILITY: HMI SHALL NOT BE LIABLE FOR ANY DAMAGES TO YOU OR ANY OTHER PERSON OR ENTITY IN CONNECTION WITH THE USE OF THIS SOFT-WARE. UNDER NO CIRCUMSTANCES WILL HMI BE LIABLE FOR INCIDENTAL, CONSEQUENTIAL OR OTHER DAMAGES, EVEN IF HMI HAS BEEN ADVISED OF THE POSSIBILITY OF SUCH DAMAGES. DO NOT USE THIS SOFTWARE IN ANY WAY OR FOR ANY PURPOSE IF YOU DESIRE HMI TO TAKE ANY LIABILITY FOR ITS USE.

LAW OF THE LAND: Your rights may vary from state to state, and from country to country. Some of the provisions of this Agreement may not apply.

CONTACT US: If you have any questions or comments, please contact HMI at the address listed in or on this or the accompanying material.